Chemical Infrared Spectroscopy

VOLUME I, TECHNIQUES

Chemical Infrared Spectroscopy

W . J . POTTS , JR .

Chemical Physics Research Laboratory, The Dow Chemical Company

VOLUME I, TECHNIQUES

John Wiley & Sons, Inc., New York · London · Sydney

544.6
P 871
v.1

To Norman Wright

Preface

My original intention in this work was to provide in one reasonably convenient place a good share of the material with which a practicing chemical infrared spectroscopist would wish to be familiar. While its preparation was in progress, however, it became obvious that it would require far longer to complete than originally estimated and that the field of infrared spectroscopy was changing rapidly enough to make the earlier sections obsolete before the whole work was finished. Accordingly, the decision was made to present the work in two volumes, into which it naturally divides: Volume I on experimental techniques and background theory and Volume II on spectral interpretation.

This volume is essentially a synthesis of the experience of the infra-red section of the Chemical Physics Research Laboratory of The Dow Chemical Company. It is not primarily intended as a textbook but rather as a practical guide to the techniques by which infrared spectroscopy is applied to the problems of chemistry. An extensive bibliography has been omitted, for references have already been supplied in other works (see, especially, Lecomte's treatise on infrared spectroscopy in *Handbuch der Physik);* selected references have been given solely for the purpose of guiding the reader to discussions on particular points more extensive than those that fall within the scope of this work. I have avoided discussion of commercial spectroscopic equipment and concentrated instead on general principles. This was possible because nearly all of the equipment in our laboratory was constructed there; all spectra and data presented in this volume have been obtained with spectrometers designed and built by L. W. Herscher and his associates in our laboratory.

This work can only be properly described as multiauthored, for nearly all of its chapters have been influenced both generally and specifically by several people. It is a real pleasure to acknowledge their contributions:

The advice of H. D. Ruhl, A. M. Bartz, and especially L. W. Herscher has been most helpful in the preparation of Chapters 3 and 4 on infrared instrumentation.

Chapter 5, dealing with sample preparation techniques, is to a large extent the synthesis of the experience in our laboratory over many years and is the product of its many workers, both past and present. The list of contributors here is far too long to be meaningful, but to each sincere thanks are due nonetheless.

Association with N. Wright over several years provided much of the stimulation for Chapter 6 on the aspects of quantitative analysis. His pioneer work in this field is well known. My thanks are also extended to J. R. Scherer and J. Overend for discussions on the subject of integrated intensities.

The techniques of difference spectroscopy and aqueous solutions covered in Chapter 7 were originally conceived by N. Wright and have been developed and expanded by D. S. Erley.

It would not have been possible for me to prepare Chapter 8, a condensed theory of polyatomic vibrational spectra, without the patient instruction in these subjects by J. Overend and J. R. Scherer. However, full responsibility for any errors or misleading impressions belongs to me alone.

The permission of The Dow Chemical Company to prepare this work for publication and the extensive use made of their facilities are gratefully acknowledged.

The encouragement and stimulation of Professors B. L. Crawford and S. W. Fenton had much to do with the initial decision to prepare this work, and I am indebted to them for many helpful discussions and suggestions in its preparation. Continued association with them in teaching the summer infrared courses at the University of Minnesota is a rewarding and pleasant experience. The pedagogical nature of the material included herein and its order of presentation is close to the lecture material presented in this course.

I take great pleasure in thanking R. M. Hexter of the Mellon Institute for his conscientious critical review of this work while in preparation. Few authors, I think, have been so fortunate as a result of their publisher's choice of reviewer.

This work owes its principal inspiration to N. Wright, director of the Chemical Physics Research Laboratory of The Dow Chemical Company. Although he will deny it, he could and should have prepared it himself many years ago. It is a rare privilege to work in his laboratory.

The unfailing cooperation and understanding of Mrs. Joyce B. Potts during the preparation of this book has made it not only possible but a pleasant task as well.

Midland, Michigan   W. J. POTTS, JR.
July 1963

Contents

1. The Nature and Properties of Infrared Radiation, 1

   I. Fundamental Properties of Electromagnetic Radiation, 1

      A. Wave Nature of Light
      B. Wavelength
      C. Frequency
      D. Velocity and the Relation between Wavelength
         and Frequency
      E. Quantum Nature of Light
      F. Units Used in Spectroscopy

   II. The Electromagnetic Spectrum, 7

  III. Blackbody Radiation, 7

  IV. Optical Materials in the Infrared Region, 9

      A. Transmission: Windows
      B. Focus: Lenses and Mirrors

**2. Elementary Theory. The Absorption of
Infrared Radiation by Molecules, 12**

   I. The Classical Harmonic Oscillator, 12

II. The Quantum-Mechanical Harmonic Oscillator, 14

    A. An Outline of Quantum Mechanics
    B. Energy Levels of the Quantum-Mechanical
       Harmonic Oscillator

III. The Diatomic Molecule, 17

IV. Absorption of Radiation by Molecular Vibration:
Selection Rules, 18

    A. Dipole-Moment Change: Symmetry Selection Rule
    B. The Absorption Process: Energy Relations
    C. The Harmonic Oscillator Selection Rule
    D. "Hot" Bands
    E. Fundamental Absorptions

V. Anharmonicity and Overtones, 22

VI. Polyatomic Molecules, 24

    A. The Number of Fundamentals
    B. Energy Levels and Spectral Transitions
    C. Degeneracy
    D. A Typical Infrared Absorption Spectrum: Assignments

3. *Spectrometer Optics: The Basic Infrared
Monochromator, 29*

    I. Design and Discussion of the Basic Monochromator, 29

        A. The Source and Source Optics
        B. The Collimating Mirror
        C. The Dispersing Element
        D. The Entrance and Exit Slits
        E. The Detector and Detector Mirror
        F. Operation of the Monochromator as a Whole

    II. Prism Properties and Materials, 39

        A. The Prism as a Disperser of Radiation Frequencies
        B. Comparison of Prism Materials

    III. The Use of Plane Gratings in Infrared Spectrometers, 41

        A. The Properties of Plane Gratings
        B. The Problem of Order Separation

IV. Monochromator Quality and Performance, 46

    A. Factors Affecting Resolution
    B. Factors Affecting Transmitted Energy
    C. The Blackbody Curve and the Necessity
       for Programmed Slits
    D. Scattered Light

**4. The Performance and Operation of
Infrared Spectrometers, 56**

    I. Infrared Radiation Detection and Signal Amplification, 56

        A. Detector Types
         . *The thermocouple*
         . *The bolometer*
         . *The pneumatic detector*
        B. Amplification of the Detector Signal for Recording
        C. Detector Theory and Performance

    II. Photometry: Single- and Double-Beam Spectrometers, 63

        A. The Single-Beam Spectrometer
        B. The Double-Beam Optical-Null Spectrometer
        C. The Double-Beam Ratio-Recording Spectrometer
        D. Double Monochromators

    III. The Limitations in Practical Operation of a Double-Beam
       Optical-Null Spectrometer, 75

        A. Spectrometer Block Diagram
        B. Noise
        C. Signal and Signal-to-Noise Ratio
        D. Recording Time
        E. Some Additional Considerations of Servo Response
        F. Practical Spectrometer Operation and Testing

    IV. Special Devices for Improving Spectrometer
       Performance, 77

        A. Scale Expansion
        B. Single-, Double-Beam Interchange
        C. Automatic Speed Suppression
        D. Automatic Servo-Energy Control

5. Sample Preparation Techniques, 92

I. Solution Techniques, 92

   A. The Case for Solution Spectroscopy
   B. The CCl_4-CS_2 Solution Technique
   C. Use of Solvents Other Than CCl_4-CS_2
   D. Compensation of Solvent Absorptions

II. Preparation and Use of Infrared Absorption Cells, 107

   A. Techniques for Polishing Alkali Halide Plates
   B. Cell Construction and Repair
   C. Use and Care of Absorption Cells
   D. Measurement of Cell Length

III. Vapor Phase Techniques, 122

   A. Uses and Limitations of the Vapor Phase
   B. Gas Absorption Cells and Their Use

IV. Liquid and Solid Films, 130

   A. Liquid Capillary Films
   B. Polymer Films

V. Crystalline State Techniques, 135

   A. Light Transmission by Small Crystalline Particles
   B. The Oil-Mull Technique
   C. The Pressed Disk Technique

6. Quantitative Analysis, 155

I. The Beer-Lambert Law and Its Application
to Quantitative Analysis, 156

   A. The Beer-Lambert Law
   B. The Absorbance

II. Elements of Quantitative Analysis, 160

   A. "Cell-In—Cell-Out" Method
   B. "Base-Line" Method
   C. Accuracy of Quantitative Analysis

III. Deviations from Beer's Law, 174

   A. Beer's Law Deviations: Chemical Effects
   B. Beer's Law Deviations: Spectrometer Effects

IV. Multicomponent Analyses, 181

    A. Simple Absorption Coincidences
    B. Multicomponent Analyses: General Case
    C. .Limitations in Multicomponent Analysis

V. Quantitative Analysis without Use of Reference Spectra, 188

VI. Ratio Methods of Analysis, 191

    A. The Method of the Indeterminant Optical Path
    B. Internal Standards

VII. The Use of Integrated Intensities, 196

    A. Brief Theory of Measurement of Integrated Intensity
    B. Application of Integrated Intensities to Quantitative
       Analysis in Condensed Phases

VIII. The Best Method of Quantitative Analysis: An Opinion, 202

7. *Auxiliary Devices and Special Techniques, 204*

    I. Compensated Spectra, 204

        A. Compensation of a Low I_0
        B. Compensation of Solvent Absorption
        C. Detection and Analysis of Minor Constituents
        D. Sensitivity Limits
        E. Difference Spectra

    II. Water Solutions, 225

    III. Techniques for Obtaining Spectra of Samples
        of Limited Size, 230

        A. Long-Path Gas Cells
        B. Microsampling Devices

    IV. Attenuated Total Reflection, 238

    V. Spectra of Molecules Adsorbed on Surfaces, 242

    VI. The Construction and Use of an Infrared Polarizer, 245

    VII. Special Cells for Obtaining Spectra at Low
         and High Temperatures, 248

        A. Precise Measurement of Solution Temperature
        B. Absorption Spectra at Low Temperatures
        C. Absorption Spectra at Elevated Temperatures

8. An Outline of the Theory of Infrared Spectra of Polyatomic Molecules, 258

I. Theory of Polyatomic Molecular Vibrations, 258

    A. The Secular Equation
    B. The Normal Coordinates and Their Significance
    C. Determination of Force Constants

II. Symmetry Considerations, 275

    A. An outline of the Results of Group Theory
    B. Application of Group Theory to Characterization of Infrared Spectral Transitions
    . *Classification of normal modes*
    . *Prediction of the number of modes belonging to each representation*
    . *Selection rules*
    . *Symmetry reduction*

III. Rotation-Vibration Bands, 297

    A. Diatomic Molecules
    B. Linear Molecules
    C. "Symmetric Top" Molecules
    D. "Asymmetric Top" Molecules

Index, 313

1

The nature and properties
of infrared radiation

Infrared radiation is usually defined as that electromagnetic radiation whose wavelength is between the limits of 0.7 and $\sim$500 μ. Radiation shorter than 0.7 μ falls in the visible region, whereas radiation of wavelengths greater than $\sim$500 μ begins to fall within the purview of those concerned with microwave radiation and can be generated by strictly electronic apparatus. Later we shall subdivide this larger region of the electromagnetic spectrum into smaller regions, and we shall see which are of most interest for chemical analysis and structure determination and why.

I. Fundamental properties of electromagnetic radiation

Since infrared light is a form of electromagnetic radiation, let us first review some of the simple fundamental properties of such radiation. An elementary understanding of it is necessary before we can proceed to describe its interaction with matter. Here, and in subsequent chapters, the results of quantum theory and other advanced concepts of physics are presented without proof; the reader is referred to appropriate texts for this material.

A. Wave nature of light

Before the quantum theory was expounded, physicists were able to explain most of the properties of light by postulating it to be an *alternating electric* field of very high frequency, which moves in the direction of the light propagation. A moving electric field implies a moving magnetic field perpendicular to it (see any text on electromagnetic radiation); hence light radiation was pictured as a combination of an alternating electric field and magnetic field:

where $\overset{+}{\underset{-}{\uparrow}}$ represents the instantaneous electric vector, S → N represents the instantaneous magnetic vector, the direction of light propagation being toward the reader. Further, this electric field motion was visualized as a wave motion (sine function). The maximum points

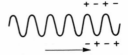

on this curve of wave motion represent the electric vector pointing upward; the minimum points represent the electric vector pointing downward. (As already mentioned, specification of the electric component of radiation implies the magnetic component; hence we shall ignore it in our discussion. It is the electric component that concerns us.)

B. Wavelength

The linear distance between two successive maxima (or minima) of the wave motion is termed the *wavelength*, usually abbreviated λ.

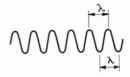

This property explained well the diffraction effects of light (see any elementary physics text) and was assumed to be a fundamental property of light radiation. The specification of wavelength was found sufficient to describe completely any type of monochromatic radiation, and the properties of a given sort of radiation could all be deduced from the statement of wavelength alone.

2   *The nature and properties of infrared radiation*

C. Frequency

Another property of light radiation, which is *not* independent of wavelength, but related to it, as we shall see, is the *frequency*. The frequency of monochromatic radiation is the number of times per second that the electric vector goes through a complete cycle of direction change (from plus to zero to minus to zero to plus). The classical wave-motion concept of light defines frequency as the value of ν in the equation

$$\mathbf{E} = \mathbf{A} \sin 2\pi\nu t, \tag{1-1}$$

where $\mathbf{E}$ is the instantaneous electric vector, $\mathbf{A}$ is a vector whose length is proportional to the square root of light intensity, t is time.

D. Velocity and the relation between wavelength and frequency

All electromagnetic radiation, no matter what its wavelength or direction of propagation, moves (in a vacuum) with a constant velocity. This universal constant of nature is abbreviated c, has the value 3×10^{10} cm/sec, and is the basis for the relation between wavelength and frequency. Consider a fixed point past which radiation is moving (as a wave motion). The number of maxima passing the fixed point

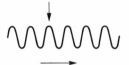

per second is the frequency, the distance between crests is the wavelength. Hence the velocity of propagation is

$$\lambda\nu = c = 3 \times 10^{10} \text{ cm/sec} \tag{1-2}$$

(λ in centimeters, ν in cycles per second). Wavelength and frequency are therefore not independent; specification of one implies the value of the other.

E. Quantum nature of light

The foregoing classical concept visualizes light radiation as a *continuous* wave motion. This postulate explained satisfactorily the properties of light radiation, except for what was known in blackbody radiation theory as the "ultraviolet catastrophy": the Rayleigh-Jeans

Fundamental properties of electromagnetic radiation   3

equation describing blackbody radiation energy, deduced from the continuous wave picture just described, predicted that the energy emitted by a body at finite temperature became large without bounds as the wavelength approached zero, clearly not in accord with experimental facts. This difficulty was overcome by Planck, who assumed that electromagnetic radiation was *not* continuous but was emitted by its source in discrete units, called quanta. Modern quantum theory predicts, and various physical experiments have consistently shown, that the *energy* of a single light quantum is given by

$$E = h\nu, \tag{1-3}$$

where E is energy in ergs, ν is frequency of the radiation in cycles per second, and h, Planck's constant, a universal constant of nature, which has the value 6.62×10^{-27} erg-sec.

The earlier results of classical physics demand a wave nature to light; quantum theory demands that light exist in discrete units, or quanta, of energy. One way to visualize radiation endowed with both these properties simultaneously is to picture a light quantum as a "wave packet," where λ, the wavelength, is the distance

between successive maxima, as before, and the frequency ν is the number of complete cycles of electric field change per second or the number of maxima passing a fixed point per second. These "wave packets," or light quanta, move in space with constant velocity, $c = 3 \times 10^{10}$ cm/sec $= \lambda\nu$, as before.

The result of the quantum theory that we must bear in mind is that the *energy* of a quantum of light is completely specified by and is directly proportional to the frequency (equation 1-3). As we shall see, this most important relation forms the basis of interpretive spectroscopy. Had quantum theory come into being *before* light diffraction studies, it is quite likely that the use of wavelength in describing light would not have become so prevalent, frequency would have been used from the beginning in the science of spectroscopy, and there would not be the awkward situation of mixed usage of wavelength and frequency in spectroscopic practice that, alas, exists today.

F. Units used in spectroscopy

Although wavelength units as large as the centimeter and even the meter are convenient in the radio frequency end of the electromagnetic spectrum, the optical region of the spectrum is more conveniently described in smaller units of wavelength. In the infrared region of the spectrum wavelength is usually expressed in microns, abbreviated μ; $1\ \mu = 10^{-3}$ mm. Visible and ultraviolet spectroscopists commonly prefer to express wavelengths in millimicrons, $m\mu$; $1\ m\mu = 10^{-3}\ \mu = 10^{-6}$ mm. In the far ultraviolet region and the x-ray region of the electromagnetic spectrum wavelength is normally expressed in Ångstrom units, $\mathring{A}$; $1\ \mathring{A} = 10^{-1}\ m\mu = 10^{-8}$ cm.

Even in the radio frequency end of the spectrum the frequency unit cycles per second is too small and megacycles per second is commonly used. In the optical region of the spectrum the frequencies are so high that their numbers expressed in megacycles per second tend to become unwieldy. A convenient frequency unit now universally employed in optical spectroscopy is the number of waves per centimeter, or the *wave number*, as it is usually called. Consideration of the sketch on p. 3 and equation 1-2 shows that the number of waves per centimeter, ω, is

$$\omega = \frac{\nu}{c}, \tag{1-4}$$

where ν is frequency in cycles per second and c is the velocity of light, 3×10^{10} cm/sec. The dimensions of ω are centimeters^{-1}; hence ω can be expressed in units of *reciprocal centimeters;* the frequency is spoken of in "so many reciprocal centimeters," and in writing this frequency measure is abbreviated "cm^{-1}."

Equation 1-2 now becomes $\lambda \cdot c\omega = c$, or $\lambda\omega = 1$. If wavelength is expressed in microns in place of centimeters, this equation is

$$\lambda\omega = 10^4. \tag{1-5}$$

As we have already mentioned, frequency is the more useful concept for specifying light radiation, as it is directly proportional to light energy, whereas wavelength is inversely proportional to energy. The infrared literature is rapidly going over to exclusive use of frequency (in units of cm^{-1}); but many infrared spectroscopists still employ wavelength (μ), most infrared spectra are still published on a scale linear in wavelength, and upward of 70% of the infrared spectrometers sold are equipped with charts linear in wavelength. Thus

Fundamental properties of electromagnetic radiation　　5

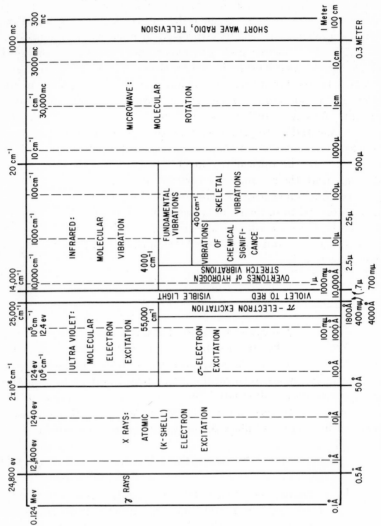

FIGURE 1-1   The "molecular" region of the electromagnetic spectrum.

6

the infrared spectroscopist must be bilingual and be able to "think" in units of both frequency and wavelength.

II. The electromagnetic spectrum

In order to place the infrared region in proper perspective to other regions of the electromagnetic spectrum, a brief review of the spectral regions adjacent to the infrared region is in order. Figure 1-1 is a schematic representation of a portion of the electromagnetic spectrum. Prominent in this diagram are the various molecular processes which are the result of absorption of radiation in the frequency region indicated, for this is what is of interest to spectroscopists.

The chart, logarithmic in form, is plotted with frequency increasing to the left, in the manner in which the great majority of molecular spectra are presented. The units used on the chart are those normally employed in that region of the spectrum; wavelength appears at the bottom. In a similar fashion, frequency designation appears at the top. The exact placement of the heavy lines which separate the various regions of the electromagnetic spectrum is somewhat arbitrary, for there is, of course, no sharp boundary between adjacent spectral regions. The reasons for the separation of the infrared region into subregions and the significance of their labels on the chart will become obvious as our study proceeds.

III. Blackbody radiation

The only source of radiation satisfactory for the infrared region at present is that emitted by a "blackbody" heated to a temperature at which it becomes incandescent. It is necessary to understand the characteristics of this so-called "blackbody radiation," for it is of fundamental importance in spectrometer design and operation.

If a black (i.e., completely nonreflecting in the spectral region concerned) object is at a finite temperature T, it will emit radiation whose intensity distribution is a function of frequency ν and is given by

$$B_\nu \, d\nu = \frac{h\nu^3}{c^2(e^{h\nu/kT} - 1)} \, d\nu, \qquad (1\text{-}6a)$$

where $B_\nu \, d\nu$ is radiant power per cm^2 per solid angle emitted in the frequency interval ν to $\nu + d\nu$ (or *brightness* per frequency interval $d\nu$), k is Boltzmann's constant, and the other symbols have the values already defined. Equation 1-6 is Planck's radiation law. (See, for example, Reference 2 for a complete discussion.)

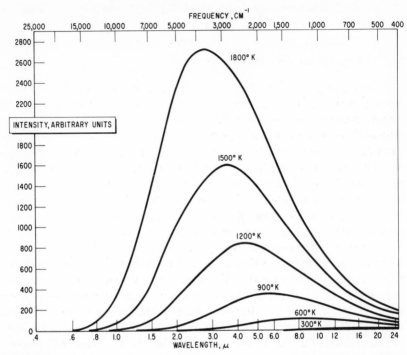

FIGURE 1-2 *Energy distribution of radiation from a blackbody at various temperatures. Curves are for constant frequency intervals (equation 1-6a).*

Planck's law can also be expressed in terms of wavelength. Since

$$\nu = \frac{c}{\lambda},$$

$$|d\nu| = \frac{c}{\lambda^2}\,d\lambda;$$

hence

$$B_\nu\,d\nu = B_\lambda\,d\lambda = \frac{hc^2}{\lambda^5(e^{hc/\lambda kT} - 1)}\,d\lambda. \qquad (1\text{-}6b)$$

This form is somewhat more useful in monochromator design considerations. (See Chapter 3, p. 52 ff.)

A plot of B_ν versus log λ (or log ν) is given in Figure 1-2 for several temperatures. Two important considerations should be noted particularly.

8   *The nature and properties of infrared radiation*

1. As the temperature increases, the total radiation output increases, but far more rapidly at high than at low frequencies. The frequency of the intensity maximum, ν_{max}, increases with rising temperature in accordance with the equation

$$\omega_{max} = 1.96\,T, \qquad (1\text{-}7)$$

where ω is frequency in cm^{-1}, T is absolute temperature (Kelvin). Equation 1-7, known as the Wien displacement law, is readily derived by differentiation of equation 1-6a with respect to ν.*

2. The fall-off of radiation intensity with decreasing frequency is relatively slow when out of the region of the peak intensity. It is this property of blackbody radiation—a reasonably steady *continuum* of energy—that makes it adaptable as a source of infrared energy in spectrometers.

The curve of Figure 1-2 for $T = \sim1500°K$, peaking at $\sim3\frac{1}{2}\,\mu$ is approximately that describing the emission by a body at "bright red" heat; a suitable blackbody at this temperature is generally used as a source in infrared spectrometers. Were a significantly higher temperature employed, the shift of ω_{max} to higher frequency with the resultant rapid increase of the ratio of short-wave radiation output to long-wave radiation would have undesirable consequences, as will be seen later. A source temperature significantly lower than $\sim1200°K$ simply does not give enough energy. A source at about "bright red heat" has been found to be the best compromise for simple prism spectrometers in chemical applications in the region of ~2–$20\,\mu$.

IV. Optical materials in the infrared region

As the properties of infrared radiation are different from those of visible light, optical elements of special materials must be employed in the infrared region. Glass, for example, is essentially opaque throughout most of the region in which we are interested. Hence we devote the remainder of this chapter to consideration of optical materials suitable to the infrared.

---

* This form of the Wien displacement law is derived on the basis of constant intervals of $d\nu$, which seems the natural form when considering absolute emission of a blackbody. When derived on the basis of constant intervals of $d\lambda$ (differentiation of equation 1-6b with respect to λ), the law has the form $\omega_{max} = 3.45\,T$, usually found in texts, which is more useful in monochromator design considerations. (See Chapter 3.)

A. Transmission: windows

In order to make cells, enclose optical equipment, etc., windows transparent to infrared radiation are necessary. Below is a table which gives the "cutoff" wavelengths of some of the materials required in infrared work. Cutoff is here defined as the approximate wavelength higher than which a 2-cm layer of the material transmits less than 50% of incident light.

Table 1-1

Glass	$\sim$2.5 μ	NaCl	$\sim$16 μ
Quartz (fused)	$\sim$3.5 μ	AgCl	$\sim$22 μ
LiF	$\sim$6.0 μ	KBr	$\sim$25 μ
CaF$_2$	$\sim$8.5 μ	CsBr	$\sim$35 μ
BaF$_2$	$\sim$11 μ	CsI	$\sim$52 μ
	ThI$_2$ · ThBr$_2$ eutectic (KRS-5)	$\sim$40 μ	

Glass and quartz find some application as prism materials. (See discussion of prisms, Chapter 3.) They make excellent window materials because of their great resistance to chemical corrosion but can be employed only in the spectral region below 3 μ, of course.

LiF and CaF$_2$ also find extensive use as prism materials. They are seldom used for windows, for they offer little advantage over NaCl in most applications.

BaF$_2$ has special applications because of its ability to transmit infrared radiation to relatively long wavelengths and its essential imperviousness to corrosion by water.

Of all the window materials employed in the infrared region, NaCl is the most common, for it is relatively cheap and easily ground and polished; it transmits radiation over most of the spectral region of chemical interest and is fairly resistant to fogging by water if reasonable care is exercised. It is also the most common prism material.

KBr also enjoys extensive application as a prism and a window material for any work in which the region between 15 and 25 μ is of interest. It fogs more easily than NaCl, hence is rarely substituted when NaCl will do.

ThI$_2$ · ThBr$_2$ eutectic (KRS-5) is worked only with difficulty and has an inconveniently high index of refraction; it is toxic and has for the most part been rendered obsolete by CsBr, which finds application as a prism and window material for any work in the 25–35 μ region. CsBr fogs easily in only slightly humid air and is difficult to work because of softness; hence it is not used as window material when other materials will serve. Fogging rarely impairs its value in the 25–35 μ region, however, for the discontinuities of the fogged surface are small and cause virtually no loss in transmission of long-wave radiation above 25 μ. CsI is a prism and window material applicable to the 35–52 μ region, just as CsBr is in the 25–35 μ region. Its easy corrosion by water vapor, high cost, and difficulty of working because of softness militate against its use anywhere than in the 35–52 μ region.

AgCl is far too soft to be useful as a prism material or for windows of cells requiring any accuracy at all. Further, the material darkens under the influence of visible light, thereby becoming unfit as a window material. However, AgCl does have the advantage of high transmission throughout most of the infrared region together with complete insolubility in water; hence it finds some application in the preparation of certain materials for infrared examination. (See Chapter 5.)

B. Focus: lenses and mirrors

Lenses are rarely employed in infrared spectrometers because of chromatic aberration. A lens made of, say, NaCl presumably would function over the range of 2–16 μ. However, the refractive index of NaCl for 2 μ radiation is quite different from its value for 16 μ radiation, thus causing radiation of different wavelengths to be brought to a focus at different points. This difficulty rules out lenses in infrared monochromator designs.

Front surface mirrors, of course, lack the disadvantage of chromatic aberration, hence are used almost exclusively for focusing infrared radiation in monochromators. A front surface mirror commonly consists of a glass blank of the appropriate figure which is coated with aluminum by evaporation. Aluminum, when exposed to oxygen (or air), readily forms on its surface a few molecular layers of oxide, which is quite corrosion-resistant. Good front surface aluminum mirrors reflect 98+ % of the incident radiation in the infrared region of the spectrum, another of their advantages. Various geometric figures (sphere, paraboloid, ellipsoid, etc.) are employed in making monochromator mirrors, as discussed in Chapter 3.

Selected references

1. Strong, J., *Concepts of Classical Optics*, Freeman, San Francisco, Calif., 1958.
2. *Treatise on Physical Chemistry*, Vol. 1, Taylor and Glasstone, Van Nostrand, Princeton, New Jersey, 1942. (Blackbody radiation theory: pp. 175 ff.)
3. *Synthetic Optical Crystals* (revised edition), The Harshaw Chemical Co., Cleveland, Ohio, 1955.

2

Elementary theory.
The absorption of infrared
radiation by molecules

Before describing some of the experimental techniques of infrared spectroscopy, it would perhaps be advisable to understand why and under what conditions molecules absorb infrared radiation, for measurement of this absorption is the whole purpose of our experimental procedure. We begin by describing the elements of classical and quantum vibration theory, consider vibrations of some simple molecules, and then show how the infrared absorption spectrum of a molecule results from excitation of these vibrations by infrared radiation.

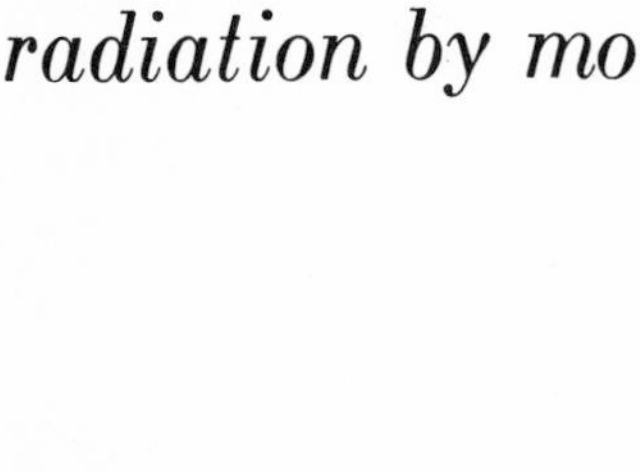

X = 0

FIGURE 2-1 *A particle of mass* m *constrained to vibrate in the* x *direction.*

I. The classical harmonic oscillator

Consider a particle held by springs between two rigid walls, as illustrated in Figure 2-1. Let us say that this particle of mass m is constrained to move only in the x direction, that it is at equilibrium when $x = 0$, and that the springs obey Hooke's law: The force they exert on the particle is proportional to the displacement away from $x = 0$, or

$$F = -kx, \qquad (2\text{-}1)$$

where k = the proportionality constant, or *force constant*.

If the particle is displaced to $x = x_0$ and then released, it will execute harmonic vibrational motion about the point $x = 0$. Solution of the differential equation

$$F = ma = m\frac{d^2x}{dt^2} = -kx \qquad (2\text{-}2)$$

yields the equation of motion

$$x = x_0 \cos\left(\sqrt{\frac{k}{m}}\,t\right), \qquad (2\text{-}3)$$

where x is the instantaneous displacement from equilibrium at any time t, x_0 is the original displacement of the particle, or the *amplitude* of vibration, and k and m are the force constant and mass, respectively. This immediately shows that the frequency of oscillation is

$$\nu = \frac{1}{2\pi}\sqrt{\frac{k}{m}} \qquad (2\text{-}4)$$

or, if we wish to express the frequency in terms of wave numbers,

$$\omega = \frac{1}{2\pi c}\sqrt{\frac{k}{m}}. \qquad (2\text{-}5)$$

We see that the *frequency* of a harmonic oscillator depends only on k and m and is independent of amplitude.

Let us now consider the energy of the mass undergoing harmonic oscillation. If there are no friction losses, the harmonic oscillator, once set in motion, will maintain a constant total energy. At any given instant the energy is partly potential, partly kinetic, depending on the position of the particle. In Figure 2-2 the curve represents the potential energy of the particle at any point x. The curve is a parabola as a result of the Hooke's law force:

$$F = -kx$$

$$PE = \int_0^x \mathbf{F}\,dx = \int_0^x kx\,dx = \tfrac{1}{2}kx^2. \qquad (2\text{-}6)$$

If the initial displacement of the particle is x_0, then at the point x_0 its kinetic energy is zero; and, as total energy $E = PE + KE$, it follows that the total energy of the particle as it moves between x_0 and

The classical harmonic oscillator **13**

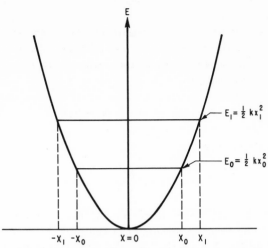

FIGURE 2-2　The potential energy of a harmonic oscillator as a function of displacement from equilibrium.

$-x_0$ is

$$E = \tfrac{1}{2}kx_0{}^2. \tag{2-7}$$

This is illustrated by the horizontal line in Figure 2-2. During this motion at any given point the potential energy is given by equation 2-6; hence the kinetic energy is $\tfrac{1}{2}k(x_0{}^2 - x^2)$.

As the total energy depends only on the force constant k and initial displacement x_0, clearly any energy value is allowed, for the initial displacement might have been x_1, say, whose total energy is also illustrated in Figure 2-2. This fact—that any energy level is allowed—is the distinguishing mark of a *classical* harmonic oscillator.

II. The quantum-mechanical harmonic oscillator

It has been found that the results of classical physics are inadequate to describe the dynamical properties of small masses, such as molecules, atoms, and electrons. Only the methods of quantum mechanics can correctly describe energy relations of small particles. We have space here only for the results of quantum mechanics when applied to the harmonic oscillator.

A. An outline of quantum mechanics

One of the postulates of quantum mechanics is the concept that associated with any observable mechanical property is a mathematical

14　Elementary theory.　Absorption of radiation

operator; of particular interest are the operators associated with energy. The total energy operator, called the Hamiltonian (H), is formulated by a certain combination of mathematical operators in accord with this concept.

A second postulate is that there exist various functions of the Cartesian coordinates of the particle we wish to describe [usually abbreviated $\psi(x, y, z)$] such that when any one of these functions is operated on by H it remains unchanged, except that it is multiplied by the numerical value of the total energy E:

$$H\,\psi(x, y, z) = E\,\psi(x, y, z). \tag{2-8}$$

This is the well-known Schroedinger equation: the functions are called the eigenfunctions, or *wave functions*, of the system, the values of E are known as the eigenvalues, or *energy* levels.

A third postulate is that $\psi^2(x, y, z)$, the *square* of the wave function, expresses the *probability** of finding the particle at point x, y, z.

To determine the wave functions, or ψ's, Schroedinger's equation, which is a differential equation of second order, must be solved. Acceptable solutions will not exist for any arbitrary values of the energy parameter E; usually in the solution of the differential equation it will be found that only for a *very few discrete values* of E will acceptable solutions exist at all. It is this mathematical feature that leads directly to an important characteristic of quantum mechanical systems: the allowed energy levels of a mechanical system do not form a continuous spectrum, as is the case in classical mechanics, but consist of a few discrete levels only.

B. Energy levels of the quantum-mechanical harmonic oscillator

In the case of the quantum mechanical one-dimensional harmonic oscillator the Schroedinger equation has the form

$$\left(-\frac{h}{8\pi^2 m}\frac{d^2}{dx^2} + \frac{1}{2}kx^2\right)\psi(x) = E\,\psi(x). \tag{2-9}$$

This equation, after a simple change of variable, is equivalent to the Hermite differential equation, which possesses solutions for only certain discrete values of its parameter. The solution of Hermite's

---

* To express the probability on an absolute basis, the wave function must be constructed so that it is "normalized" to unity:

$$\int_\infty \psi^2(x, y, z)\,dx\,dy\,dz = 1.$$

equation, when applied specifically to its form in equation 2-9, leads directly to the result that E is allowed to have only the values

$$E = \left(n + \frac{1}{2}\right)\frac{h}{2\pi}\sqrt{\frac{k}{m}} \qquad n = 0, 1, 2, 3, \cdots . \qquad (2\text{-}10)$$

Using the relation of equation 2-4 between the frequency of a harmonic osciallator, force constant, and mass, we now have the important result

$$E = (n + \tfrac{1}{2})h\nu \qquad (2\text{-}11)$$

or (in wave numbers)

$$E = (n + \tfrac{1}{2})hc\omega. \qquad (2\text{-}12)$$

The result is expressed in words: *the energy of a quantum-mechanical harmonic oscillator can have only the values of positive half-integer multiples of hcω*, all other conceivable energy values not being allowed. To be noted in particular is the result that the lowest energy possible for a quantum-mechanical oscillator is $\frac{1}{2}hc\omega$; the oscillator can never lose this so-called "zero-point energy," which implies that even at 0°K all molecules still possess this half quantum of vibrational energy.

Actually, all oscillators, either those of molecular masses or those of masses of the order of grams, obey the laws of quantum theory. Well-separated energy levels are not observed in the latter case because the value of $(h/2\pi)\sqrt{k/m}$ in equation 2-10 is extremely small when m is

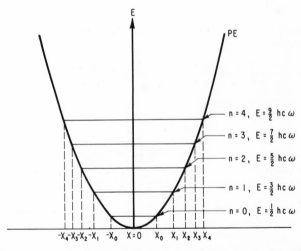

FIGURE 2-3   Energy levels of the quantum-mechanical oscillator.

16   *Elementary theory.   Absorption of radiation*

not of the order of molecular masses, thus making ΔE between any two adjacent states unobservably small. Therefore the energy spectrum for oscillators of large mass (grams) is essentially a continuum, as observed.

Let us now examine the energy-level diagram for the quantum-mechanical oscillator shown in Figure 2-3. The diagram has the same form as Figure 2-2, but here the positions of the horizontal lines illustrating the constant total energy of each state are determined by the quantum condition of equation 2-12. An important point to note is that the energy levels, or states, of the quantum-mechanical harmonic oscillator are equally spaced, the energy interval between any two adjacent states being $hc\omega$.

The amplitude of a given state (say, x_1, for the first excited state) is given by equation 2-7, which is the equation of the parabola in Figure 2-3. Hence for the quantum-mechanical harmonic oscillator not all amplitudes are allowed, but only those corresponding to the discrete energy levels.

The form and implications of this plot should be borne in mind, for we shall return to it when considering transitions between states.

III. The diatomic molecule

The simplest molecule that can have an internal vibration frequency is, of course, a diatomic molecule. We may picture the diatomic molecule as consisting of two masses, m_1 and m_2 connected by a spring.

This system will oscillate with harmonic motion if the spring obeys Hooke's law, and the diatomic molecule is closely approximated by such a mechanical representation. The frequency of oscillation is

$$\omega = \frac{1}{2\pi c} \sqrt{\frac{k}{m_r}}, \qquad (2\text{-}13)$$

where m_r is the *reduced mass*, and is given by

$$m_r = \frac{m_1 m_2}{m_1 + m_2}. \qquad (2\text{-}14)$$

If one of the masses, say m_1, is small with respect to the other mass, the reduced mass is approximated by

$$m_r = \frac{m_1 m_2}{m_1 + m_2} \approx \frac{m_1 m_2}{m_2} = m_1.$$

The frequency is then

$$\omega \approx \frac{1}{2\pi c} \sqrt{\frac{k}{m_1}},$$

essentially that of a point oscillator whose mass is that of the light atom. This approximation is useful in considering hydrogen stretching vibrations. (See Chapter 10, Volume II.)

Provided our assumption of the nature of a diatomic molecule is reasonable, the vibrational levels allowed for a diatomic molecule will be those of any harmonic oscillator,

$$E = (n + \tfrac{1}{2})hc\omega.$$

The energy-level diagram will be like that in Figure 2-3, but the space parameter will be r, the distance between atomic centers, and the equilibrium configuration will be at $r = r_{eq}$ (rather than $x = 0$). These energy levels are a characteristic property of a given diatomic molecule and form the basis for its identification by infrared absorption, as we shall see.

IV. Absorption of radiation by molecular vibration: selection rules

Infrared absorption spectra arise because a molecule absorbs infrared radiation energy in the transition from one vibrational state to another. How this process takes place, and the limitations on it, are now discussed for the case of the diatomic molecule.

A. Dipole-moment change: symmetry selection rule

Consider a vibrating heteropolar diatomic molecule A-B in one of its allowed energy levels. As the interatomic distance changes during the vibration, the dipole moment of the molecule changes. We may thus consider that the vibrating diatomic molecule is producing a stationary alternating electric field whose magnitude changes periodically with time at a frequency equal to the vibration frequency. It is this stationary alternating electric field that interacts with the *moving* electric field of electromagnetic radiation.

If the diatomic molecule is homopolar, there is no dipole-moment change with vibration and no alternating dipolar electric field is produced. In this case no interaction of the type we shall discuss can occur between the molecule and infrared radiation; the molecule will have no infrared absorption, hence no absorption spectrum.

Later we shall see that when polyatomic molecules have elements of symmetry often several of the possible vibrations will not produce infrared absorptions because no change in dipole moment occurs during these vibrations. Such an absence of dipole-moment change is the result of certain symmetry relationships; these relationships constitute the symmetry selection rules, which are discussed in detail in Chapter 8.

B. The absorption process: energy relations

Suppose now that we expose a vibrating heteropolar diatomic molecule (i.e., a stationary alternating electric field) to infrared radiation, which consists of "energy packets" or "wave packets" of *moving* alter-

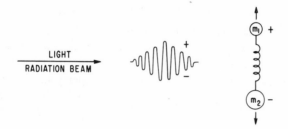

nating electric field. If the molecule is to absorb the energy of the radiation quantum, the energy absorbed must be such that the molecule will just exactly reach a higher allowed energy level; for example,

$$E_{\text{quantum}} = \Delta E_{\text{molecule}} = [(1 + \tfrac{1}{2})hc\omega_{\text{vibration}} - (0 + \tfrac{1}{2})hc\omega_{\text{vibration}}]$$
$$= hc\omega_{\text{vibration}}.$$

But

$$E_{\text{quantum}} = hc\omega_{\text{quantum}}$$

from equation 1-3. Hence

$$\omega_{\text{quantum}} = \omega_{\text{vibration}}, \tag{2-15}$$

or, in order for the quantum of radiation to be absorbed, the *molecular vibration frequency must be identical to the frequency of the radiation.* We can illustrate this transition on the energy-level diagram of the quantum-mechanical oscillator. (See Figure 2-4.) The solid arrows represent the transitions between adjacent levels; the heavy arrow is that between levels 0 and 1.

Absorption of radiation by molecular vibration **19**

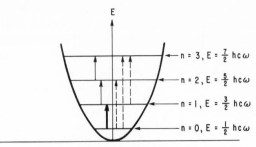

FIGURE 2-4 *Transitions between energy levels of a quantized harmonic oscillator.*

If the frequency of the radiation is not equal to the molecular vibration frequency, no interaction between molecule and radiation occurs that can lead to a change in vibrational state. Not only are the correct energy requirements not fulfilled, but consideration of the instantaneous interaction of changing dipole moment and moving alternating electric field shows that if these frequencies differ such instantaneous interaction eventually will be canceled by one of exactly opposite phase. To use other words, unless the frequency of one harmonic phenomenon is equal to that of the other, they do not interact.

These two situations—that an oscillating dipole will absorb infrared radiation whose frequency is equal to its vibration frequency and will *transmit unchanged* all other frequencies—result in the *absorption spectrum* of the molecule. The frequency range over which absorption occurs is generally referred to as an *absorption band*, for it has a finite width, as we shall discuss in a later chapter.

C. The harmonic oscillator selection rule

We have noted that if the alternating dipole is to absorb the energy of a light quantum the energy of the quantum must be exactly equal to the energy difference between two of the allowed energy levels of the oscillator. In our example we supposed the two levels to have been adjacent, but let us now consider transitions between non-adjacent levels, as indicated by the dashed arrows in Figure 2-4. For example,

$$E_{\text{quantum}} = \Delta E_{\text{molecule}} = [(n + 2 + \tfrac{1}{2})hc\omega - (n + \tfrac{1}{2})hc\omega] = 2hc\omega_{\text{vibration}}$$

and therefore

$$\omega_{\text{quantum}} = 2\omega_{\text{vibration}}.$$

20   *Elementary theory. Absorption of radiation*

Energetically such situations are possible, but a further result of quantum theory imposes a restriction. This quantum theory result arises from the fact that the probability of any transition between levels n and m, $P_{n \to m}$, is given by

$$P_{n \to m} = K \int_{\infty} \psi_n(x) \mathbf{p} \, \psi_m(x) \, dx, \tag{2-16}$$

where K is a proportionality constant, $\psi_n(x)$ is the wave function of the oscillator system for initial state n, $\psi_m(x)$ is the wave function for final state m, and $\mathbf{p}$ is the operator associated with the dipole transition, which in this case is proportional to x, the space variable. If the wave functions are those of the harmonic oscillator, it is found that

$$\int_{\infty} \psi_n(x) x \psi_m(x) \, dx = 0,$$

unless

$$n = m \pm 1. \tag{2-17}$$

This condition, known as the *selection rule* for a harmonic oscillator, states that the *only allowed transitions for a harmonic oscillator are those between adjacent levels.* (The case $n = m + 1$ would be that of transition from the higher to the lower level with *emission* of a quantum of light; we are not interested in this possibility in the practice of absorption spectroscopy.) Hence the transitions in Figure 2-4 indicated by dashed lines do not occur for the case of a strictly harmonic oscillator.

The magnitude of $P_{n \to m}$, the *probability* of the transition $n \to m$, is proportional to the square root of the *intensity* of the absorption band. We discuss intensities and their applications at some length in a later chapter.

D. "Hot" bands

Transitions between adjacent states other than 0 and 1 (1 and 2, 2 and 3, etc.) are theoretically allowed but occur with low probability for another reason. In order for a transition to occur between states 1 and 2, for example, a quantum of radiation of appropriate frequency must meet a molecule in state 1. However, according to the Boltzmann distribution law, the ratio of molecules in state 1 to those in state 0 is given by

$$\frac{N_1}{N_0} = e^{-(E_1 - E_0)/kT} = e^{-hc\omega/kT} = e^{-1.44\omega/T}, \tag{2-18}$$

which indicates that at room temperature this ratio will be less than a few per cent if ω is much over ~ 600 cm^{-1}. Furthermore, even if the fraction were larger, such a transition would be indistinguishable from the transition between levels 0 and 1 and would actually contribute to its observed intensity, for all energy levels of the strictly harmonic oscillator are equally spaced, so that $\Delta E_{0 \rightarrow 1} = \Delta E_{1 \rightarrow 2}$, hence $\omega_{0 \rightarrow 1} = \omega_{1 \rightarrow 2}$.

In high resolution studies in the vapor phase the existence of these transitions must be considered; they are generally referred to as "hot" bands. In most spectroscopic work, however, particularly analytical applications in condensed phases, these transitions can be neglected.

E. Fundamental absorptions

Finally, in the light of the foregoing considerations, we have but one transition to be concerned with in harmonic oscillators: the transition between state 0 (the ground state) and state 1 (the first excited state). This transition is known as the *fundamental absorption* or simply the *fundamental*. It is illustrated schematically in Figure 2-4 by the heavy solid arrow.

As discussed in great detail in later chapters, the infrared fundamentals of interest to chemistry fall between ~4000 cm^{-1} (the highest infrared absorption fundamental, that of HF, is 3958 cm^{-1}) and ~400 cm^{-1} (most fundamentals below this frequency appear to have little useful correlation with chemical structure). This is the reason for our division of the infrared region of the spectrum, as in Figure 1-1. The remainder of this book, then, with the specific exceptions in Chapter 15, Volume II, is concerned with the nature of the molecular spectroscopic phenomena in the region 400–4000 cm^{-1} and the apparatus and techniques for their measurement.

V. Anharmonicity and overtones

The vibrations of real molecules are not strictly harmonic. A harmonic oscillator, it will be recalled, has a parabola as its functional relation between displacement from equilibrium and potential energy. The relation between potential energy and displacement from equilibrium for the case of stretching a chemical bond is *not* strictly parabolic but has a form shown by the solid curve in Figure 2-5. The dashed curve is a parabola, drawn for comparison.

We see that *in the region of low energy* the parabola is a close approximation of the true potential energy curve. In this region real molecules obey the harmonic oscillator energy relation

$$E = (n + \tfrac{1}{2})hc\omega$$

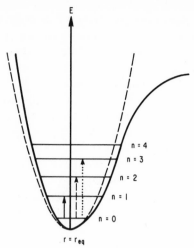

FIGURE 2-5 *Potential energy and energy levels of an anharmonic oscillator.*

to reasonably good approximation. However, if higher states are to be considered, the energy is more closely approximated by

$$E = hc\omega[(n + \tfrac{1}{2}) - (n + \tfrac{1}{2})^2 x], \qquad (2\text{-}19)$$

with the result that the energy difference between states n and $n - 1$ is given by

$$\Delta E = hc\omega(1 - 2nx). \qquad (2\text{-}20)$$

x is generally a small fraction of unity and is known as the anharmonicity constant.

If x is a positive number, the energy spacing between successive levels *decreases* with higher n. This situation is known as *positive anharmonicity* (or usually simply *anharmonicity*). However, if x is a negative number, the energy spacing between successive levels *increases* with higher levels. This situation, known as *negative anharmonicity*, occurs whenever the potential-energy function is steeper than a parabola; positive anharmonicity results if the potential curve is *less steep* than a parabola. (In Figure 2-5 the right-hand branch of the curve is much less steep than a parabola, whereas the left branch is only somewhat steeper. The net result for bond stretching is usually positive anharmonicity.)

Because real molecules are not strictly harmonic oscillators, the harmonic-oscillator-selection rule of equation 2-17 needs correction,

Anharmonicity and overtones **23**

and transitions such as illustrated by the dashed and dotted arrows in Figure 2-5, known as the first and second overtones, respectively, are now allowed. These transitions do take place, but usually with intensity much lower than that of the fundamental; the first overtone is an order of magnitude weaker than the fundamental, the second overtone an order of magnitude weaker still. The smaller the value of x in equation 2-19, the closer the approximation of the strictly harmonic oscillator and the less intense the overtones. Conversely, an unusually intense overtone implies a large degree of anharmonicity.

It should be noted that for cases of positive anharmonicity the first overtone will be observed at slightly *less* than twice the frequency of the fundamental, whereas if the first overtone is observed at slightly *greater* than twice the frequency of the fundamental it is an example of negative anharmonicity. (See equation 2-20.)

VI. Polyatomic molecules

A polyatomic molecule will have several possible vibrational modes. Each mode that leads to change of dipole moment during vibration can cause infrared absorption by the molecule of a frequency equal to that of the particular molecular vibration. In this section we consider briefly some of the simple facts about polyatomic molecular vibrations and how their infrared absorption spectra arise. A more complete discussion of the theory of polyatomic molecular vibrations is given in Chapter 8.

A. The number of fundamentals

Consider a molecule of N atoms. Because each atom has three degrees of space freedom, corresponding to the three Cartesian coordinates, the system of N atoms has $3N$ degrees of freedom. Not all of these degrees of freedom can lead to internal vibrations, however, for among the $3N$ independent linear combinations of these atomic degrees of freedom three will describe translation of the molecule as a whole (along space-fixed Cartesian coordinates) and three will describe rotation of the molecule as a whole about its three mutually perpendicular axes through the center of mass. Therefore the number of fundamental vibrations of a general N-atom molecule is just $3N - 6$.

If all N atoms lie on a single straight line, however, there are only *two* axes about which rotation of the molecule as a whole will concern us. This is so because no combination of the $3N$ atomic Cartesian coordinates can describe rotation about the axis on which the atoms lie; further, such rotation has zero moment of inertia (if we neglect the mass of the electrons). Hence the number of molecular vibrations of a strictly linear N-atom molecule is $3N - 5$.

B. *Energy levels and spectral transitions*

Energy-level diagrams, such as those used to describe the diatomic molecule (Figure 2-5), can illustrate the dipolar radiation transitions in polyatomic molecules, except that there will be one such diagram for each of the $3N - 6$ fundamental vibrations of the molecule, and the abscissa of each diagram is in units of the *normal coordinate* for that vibration (see Chapter 8) rather than in units of a simple Cartesian axis. Some of these potential energy curves will represent vibrations that are essentially stretching motions and will have the form shown in Figure 2-5; others will represent potential energy functions of other types of vibrations and may have different forms. Figure 2-6 illustrates what might be the energy-level diagrams for a few of ·the $3N - 6$ modes of a molecule. In each the symbolism is as before.

The three solid arrows correspond to three different fundamental absorptions. These will usually give rise to three fairly intense infrared absorption bands. Each fundamental absorption has associated with it a first (and higher) overtone, as indicated by the three dashed arrows. The overtones will also give rise to absorption bands, but they are usually of an order of magnitude weaker than the fundamentals.

Suppose a polyatomic molecule were exposed to light quanta of energy exactly equal to the sum of energies of two fundamental transitions, that is, $\omega_{\text{quantum}} = \omega_n + \omega_m$. If all the oscillators were strictly

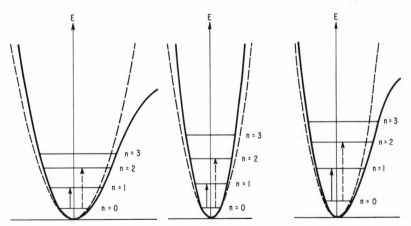

FIGURE 2-6 *Typical energy level diagrams of a few vibration modes of a polyatomic molecule.*

harmonic, there would be no interaction. However, we have seen that real molecules are not strictly harmonic. Such transitions as these are actually observed; absorption bands appear in the spectrum whose frequencies are the sum of two fundamentals. They are called *combination bands* and have intensities comparable to overtones: they are usually much weaker than the fundamentals, and the intensities depend on the degree of anharmonicity of the fundamentals that make up the combinations.

An energy transition $\omega_{quantum} = \omega_n - \omega_m$ might also be possible. Again such transitions, known as *difference bands*, actually do occur. They, too, would be forbidden for strictly harmonic oscillators and are observed only because real oscillators are not strictly harmonic, but have low intensity. These absorptions, however, are temperature-sensitive and are somewhat analogous to "hot" bands; a quantum of frequency $\omega_n - \omega_m$ must interact with a molecule having one quantum of vibrational energy of ω_m, and the process leaves the molecule with one quantum of vibrational energy, ω_n. If ω_m is a low frequency (~ 600 cm^{-1} or below), such a difference band is often observed; if ω_m is a significantly higher frequency, statistics indicate that the number of molecules with a quantum of vibrational energy, ω_m, is low (equation 2-18) and difference bands involving it are not likely to be observed.

C. Degeneracy

It may happen that among the various potential energy curves of a molecule (Figure 2-6) two or more are identical. If this is the case, and if the atoms connected by the identical forces have identical masses, two (or more) of the $3N - 6$ fundamentals will have identical frequency and will be observed as a single absorption frequency in the infrared spectrum of the molecule. This is known as degeneracy: two different vibrations with identical frequency are said to be degenerate.

Degenerate vibrations will occur in any molecule having an axis of threefold or greater symmetry (examples: the symmetrical axis of ammonia, the axis perpendicular to the benzene ring at its center, and the parallel axis of a linear molecule). In certain cases, if a group of atoms having in itself a threefold or higher symmetry axis is a sufficiently isolated portion of a less symmetrical molecule (such as a methyl group in a complex unsymmetrical molecule), that group may have one or more pairs of degenerate vibrations.

The question of degeneracy and symmetry is considered in greater detail in Chapter 8, but we shall describe one simple example here.

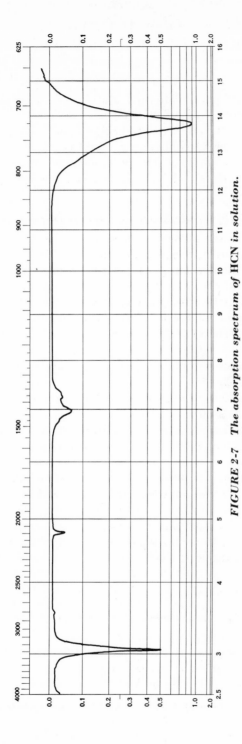

FIGURE 2-7   The absorption spectrum of HCN in solution.

Consider the linear CO_2 molecule, which has $3N - 5 = 4$ fundamental vibrations. One such vibration is obviously a bending motion,

$$0 {=\!\!\!\!=}^{C}{\diagdown}_0 \qquad 0 {=\!\!=} C {=\!\!=} 0 \qquad {}^{0}{\diagdown}_{C} {\diagup}^{0}$$

sketched at its one equilibrium and two extreme positions. This vibrational motion describes a plane. Obviously, if this vibration had occurred in the *other* (perpendicular) plane containing the molecular axis, the energy requirements would be identical. Hence these two bending modes have identical potential energy functions and identical frequencies and are observed as a single *degenerate* infrared absorption.

D. A typical infrared absorption spectrum: assignments

Figure 2-7 is the absorption spectrum of $H—C{\equiv}N$ in solution in suitable transparent, nonabsorbing solvents. HCN is linear and has $3N - 5 = 4$ fundamentals. The strong fundamental absorption at 3270 cm^{-1} results from a vibrational motion that is essentially hydrogen stretching; the absorption at 2085 cm^{-1} is also a fundamental and results from a vibration that is essentially $C{\equiv}N$ stretch. The strong absorption at 727 cm^{-1} is the *doubly degenerate* bending fundamental.

The first overtone of the bending fundamental is observed as a weak band at 1433 cm^{-1}. The overtones of the other fundamentals are not in the frequency range shown in the spectrum. A weak absorption is noted at 2800 cm^{-1}, which is the *combination tone* of the $C{\equiv}N$ stretching (2085 cm^{-1}) and the bending (727 cm^{-1}) fundamentals; a weak absorption at 1370 cm^{-1} is the *difference tone* of these same two fundamentals.

This spectrum was obtained in solution rather than in the vapor state so that only the vibrational spectrum would be observed. When infrared spectra are obtained in the gas phase, they show a superposition of vibrational and rotational transitions, which makes the appearance of the spectrum quite complex. Rotation-vibration spectra of gases are discussed in Chapter 8.

Selected references

1. Strong, J., *Concepts of Classical Optics*, Freeman, San Francisco, Calif., 1958; pp. 61 ff.
2. Pauling, L., and E. B. Wilson, *Introduction to Quantum Mechanics*, McGraw-Hill, New York, 1935.
3. Herzberg, G., *Infrared and Raman Spectra of Polyatomic Molecules*, Van Nostrand, Princeton, New Jersey, 1945.

3

Spectrometer optics:
the basic infrared monochromator

In the next two chapters we describe the construction and performance of the apparatus that obtains the infrared absorption spectrum: the infrared spectrometer.   There are many types of infrared spectrometers, each having its own particular advantages and disadvantages, hence uses.   But certain features are common to all such devices, most important being the design and operation of the basic monochromator, which this chapter discusses.

I. Design and discussion of the basic monochromator

Figure 3-1 is a schematic diagram of a typical infrared monochromator as seen from above, showing the light path through each of the optical components.   Each of these components is described directly below; a more thorough discussion of some of the components and their function is presented in later sections.   The actual optical layout in Figure 3-1 represents a bit of a simplification over most commercial spectrometers, but all the essential principles are illustrated.

A. The source and source optics

Part *a* in Figure 3-1 is the source of infrared radiation.   As we saw in Chapter 1, any physical body at a finite temperature emits radiation.   The source, then, is an object that is heated to a high temperature, commonly by passage of electric current, so that it emits radiation suitable for use in an infrared spectrometer.   As discussed in

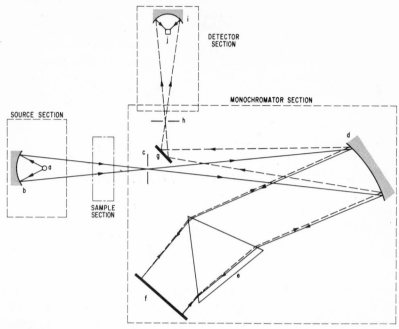

DETECTOR
SECTION

MONOCHROMATOR SECTION

SOURCE SECTION

SAMPLE
SECTION

FIGURE 3-1 *A schematic view of the monochromator parts as seen from above:* (a) *source,* (b) *source mirror,* (c) *monochromator entrance slit,* (d) *collimating mirror,* (e) *prism,* (f) *Littrow mirror,* (g) *plane mirror,* (h) *exit slit,* (i) *detector mirror,* (j) *detector.*

Chapter 1, the radiation intensity emitted is a function of frequency and temperature, as given by equation 1-6 and illustrated by Figure 1-2. The nature of this curve should be borne in mind, for it imposes some design limitations on the spectrometer, as we shall see.

Sources may be constructed in several ways. Three common types in use in spectrometers are the Globar, the Nernst Glower, and a nichrome wire coil.

The Globar consists of a rod of silicon carbide through which a high current is passed. Its dimensions, hence its current requirements, must be commensurate with the size of the rest of the optics. It is usually run at a temperature of $\sim 1300°$K. The Globar, when heated, emits reasonably uniformly over its surface and is a good blackbody radiator. It suffers from the disadvantage that silicon carbide has a negative temperature coefficient of resistance: the resistance is greatest at the ends of the rod at the electrical connections where the temperature is lowest. The resultant high dissipation of energy at the connections tends to cause their eventual arcing and burn out, thereby limiting electrode life.

A simple closely wound spiral of nichrome wire can be used effectively as an infrared source, the wire being heated to ~1200–1500°K by passage of electric current. The advantage of this device is its great stability. Nichrome has a positive temperature coefficient of resistance, hence lacks the problems of a Globar. The nichrome spiral is often employed in applications in which the source must run continually without attention for long periods of time. A disadvantage of the nichrome spiral is that optical images of the source are not uniform, as are those from a Globar; this is an important consideration in the design of double-beam spectrometers. (See Chapter 4.) This disadvantage may be overcome by surrounding the coil with a uniform ceramic tube, which in turn is heated to ~1400°K by the nichrome coil, an arrangement that combines the desirable electrical properties of nichrome with the desirable optical properties of the uniform source. Figure 3-2 is a sketch of this construction.

The Nernst Glower consists of a small rod of mixed rare-earth oxides which is heated by passage of electric current. This material is nonconductive at room temperature, and the rod must be preheated before current will flow. Once at operating temperature, however, the source readily conducts enough current to maintain the temperature. The Nernst Glower is capable of being run at higher temperatures (~1800°K) without warping from excessive heat, hence a large energy output may be obtained. As Figure 1-2 shows, most of

FIGURE 3-2   A small ceramic tube used as an infrared source.

this increase in output will be in the shortwave region, but the increase at long wavelength is enough to be useful. The Nernst Glower, therefore, offers advantages for short wavelength applications over the other sources (except in the region 3–4 μ, where its emissivity is somewhat lower than the blackbody value). It gives only small advantage at long wavelength, plus the disadvantage of the increased problem of elimination of stray radiation resulting from the intense, short wavelength radiation. This problem, however, seems to be less serious when double monochromators and modern filters are employed. (See Section IV-D.)

The basic monochromator   31

The radiation from the source is imaged on the entrance slit c by the source mirror b. (Mirrors used in spectrometers are nearly always made of glass, the reflecting surface being formed by an aluminum coat, as described in Chapter 1.) The source mirror is a concave sphere. It will be recalled from the principles of simple geometrical optics that an object on the mirror axis between the focal point and center of curvature of a spherical mirror will produce an enlarged image at some point between the center of curvature and infinity, in accordance with the familiar law:

$$\frac{1}{d_o} + \frac{1}{d_i} = \frac{1}{f}. \tag{3-1}$$

The amount* of light such a mirror can "transfer" from object to image depends on the light-gathering ability of the mirror. This ability becomes greater as the mirror is made larger and more completely "surrounds" the object, thus gathering more of its emitted light. However, the larger we make the solid angle of the spherical mirror, the further the departure of optical behavior from the "ideal" relation of equation 3-1 becomes. This departure is known as spherical aberration and results in loss of definition of the optical image. Some compromise, therefore, between size, position, and focal length must be made.

Because the sole purpose of the source mirror is to fill the collimating mirror d with light from the source, via an image at the entrance slit c, the placement, size, and figure of the source mirror depend on the geometry of the collimating mirror, the purpose of which we shall now describe.

B. The collimating mirror

As an optical image of the source exists at the entrance slit c, let us consider this slit image as the light source for the collimating mirror d. (We discuss the function of the slits below.) The purpose of the collimating mirror is to focus the diverging light from the entrance slit into a parallel beam for passage through the prism.

The geometrical curve that reflects all rays from a common point outward and parallel is a parabola, not a circle. Hence, in order to render the light from the central point of the entrance slit perfectly

---

* In spectrometer design it is the *brightness* of the image that is important. Brightness is (light) radiant power per unit area per solid angle.

parallel, the collimator must be a paraboloid. The monochromator entrance slit is placed at the focus; hence the focal length of the collimator establishes the position of slit with respect to collimator.

As is apparent from Figure 3-1, the path of the light to and from the collimator cannot be located on the mirror axis but must be several degrees off its axis. Light from a point off the axis cannot be rendered absolutely parallel by use of the central portion of a paraboloid. However, if a section is cut from a paraboloid so that its center is *not* on the paraboloid axis, a mirror so formed can be used to render strictly parallel the light coming from a point off the axis. A mirror cut in this manner is called an off-axis paraboloid; its center must be as many degrees off the paraboloid axis as the angle between the light beams arriving at and leaving the collimator. (See Figure 3-3.)

If the monochromator design is such that a long focal-length collimator is used (see p. 46 ff.), a sphere can be used in place of a paraboloid without much error, provided that the angle between incident and reflected radiation is not large.

After the light is returned from the prism to the collimator, still as parallel light, the collimator performs the function opposite to the former one: it focuses this parallel light onto the monochromator exit slit (via the small plane mirror *g*). Geometrically, the two operations are identical; hence the same mirror figure can be used without introducing any new aberrations.

The degree of perfection required in the figure and surface of the collimating mirror, as with all the optical surfaces in the monochromator, is high. If the collimator is to be an off-axis paraboloid,

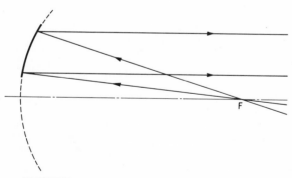

FIGURE 3-3   *A paraboloid mirror used off-axis.*

The basic monochromator   **33**

this is difficult to achieve. For this reason the quality of the collimator often limits the performance that might ideally be obtained from the monochromator.

C. The dispersing element

The purpose of the monochromator is to separate the continuous blackbody radiation into its component wavelengths. To accomplish this, some element that causes change in direction of a light ray as a function of wavelength is necessary. Probably the simplest device is the familiar prism, denoted e in Figure 3-1. When parallel light is passed through a prism, it is refracted to greater degree the shorter its wavelength. We discuss the actual dispersive properties of various materials used to make prisms and their specific applications in Section II of this chapter.

Theory of refraction of light by a prism has shown that aberrations are at a minimum (a) when the prism is traversed by parallel light, moving through the prism parallel to its base; (b) when the slit is parallel to the vertical edges of the prism; and (c) when the light passes through the prism at "minimum deviation."

Minimum deviation, the path of least angular displacement of a ray of given wavelength, results when the angles of refraction at each prism face are equal. We shall accept these statements without proof; infrared prism spectrometers are always constructed so that these conditions are fulfilled as far as possible.

In order to use the prism most efficiently, the light, after having passed through the prism, is sent back through the prism a second time by reflection from a plane mirror, denoted f in Figure 3-1, and called the Littrow mirror. The light is thus dispersed twice as effectively as if only one passage through the prism were used. As we have already mentioned, the collimator focuses the parallel light returning from the prism onto the monochromator exit slit.

Although the prism is the most common dispersing element at present in spectrometers for chemical use, the plane diffraction grating is becoming ever more important. A plane grating suitable for use in an infrared spectrometer is made from a glass block onto which a thin layer of aluminum is applied by vacuum evaporation; a series of fine parallel lines is ruled on this surface. Briefly, a grating disperses light radiation because the angle of diffraction is a function of the wavelength of incident radiation. For application in monochromators a plane reflection grating replaces the prism and Littrow mirror combination.

A good grating properly employed is capable of somewhat greater angular dispersion than is a prism. A more detailed discussion of the use of gratings in infrared spectrometers is given in Section III.

D. The entrance and exit slits

The monochromator entrance and exit slits, c and h in Figure 3-1, each consist of two pieces of metal having sharply machined edges facing each other to form a long narrow aperture. (See Figure 3-4.) The purpose of the slits is to define sharply the light image which is to be refracted or diffracted and to limit the width of the image, thereby increasing the ability of the prism or grating to resolve the incoming light into its component wavelengths. This can perhaps best be visualized by imagining the source to be replaced by a bright-line atomic discharge, such as a sodium vapor lamp. The rays of the two yellow D lines, say (whose wavelengths are 5890 and 5896 Å), will be bent at slightly different angles by the prism and will be refocused at two different points on the exit slit jaws. If the slit width were large, for a certain position of the optical parts both lines would pass through the slit; hence the lines would not be resolved. However, if

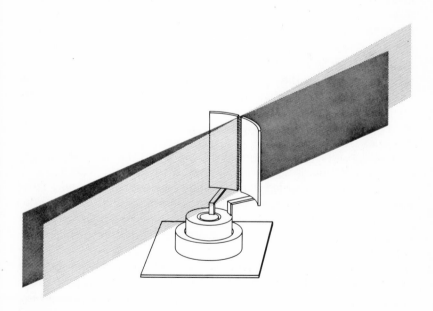

FIGURE 3-4 Schematic representation of a bilateral slit at the focus of the radiation beam.

The basic monochromator 35

the slit aperture were narrow, the D lines could be focused so that one would emerge from the exit slit, the other would not; in this case these lines would be resolved.

As was implied, the monochromator is constructed symmetrically about the dispersing element so that the slits have identical arrangements with respect to collimator and prism (or grating); that is, in principle the source optics and detector optics could be interchanged with no change in monochromator operation. Because this is so, change in either slit width effects the resolving power equally. Hence the slits are usually set so that they are the same width, and, if their width is to be changed for any reason (see Section IV), the mechanism performing this function is made so that both slits are varied equally together.

To preserve the symmetry of the monochromator, the slits are made so that both jaws move equally in such a way that the center of the slit aperture remains stationary. Such slits are called *bilateral*.

If the slits were points instead of narrow lines, all light would travel through the prism parallel to its base. However, the finite length of the slits means that some light radiation will be off the collimator axis in a direction for which no correction can be made, hence will pass through the prism in a ray not parallel to the prism base. The result is that a bright line image falling on the exit slit is not straight, but curved. To compensate, the exit slit could be curved. Usually, however, the entrance slit is curved so that the exit slit image is straight, which is advantageous for refocusing the exit slit image on the detector. The image of the source on the entrance slit is so wide that no light is lost by making this slit curved.

E. The detector and detector mirror

In order to detect the presence and determine the intensity of infrared radiation, a device is required to convert the light signal to some more easily recorded signal, usually an electrical voltage. There are several sorts of devices that perform this function. A discussion of their nature, theory, and performance is given in Chapter 4. We state here only that all types have a very small sensitive area on which the light must be focused.

The ellipsoid has the property that all light originating at one focus and reflected from the ellipsoid surface will pass through the other focus. Hence an ellipsoidal mirror will change this image size *without spherical aberration*, the image ratio depending on the eccentricity*

* The eccentricity of an ellipse is the ratio of its minor to major axis: $e \leqslant 1$.

of the ellipse:

$$\text{image ratio} = \frac{1 + e}{1 - e}. \tag{3-2}$$

Therefore an ellipsoidal mirror of an image ratio of ~7:1 is used to focus the radiation from the exit slit onto the very small surface of the detector. The exit slit is at one focus of the ellipse, the detector at the other.

F. Operation of the monochromator as a whole

Imagine for a moment that the monochromator exit slit is replaced by a photographic plate bent along a suitable curve. For given positions of all the optics, the radiation from the source will be presented along the photographic plate; the exact spot on which any given quantum of radiation falls is dependent on its wavelength. If the source were replaced by a bright-line atomic emission source (which consists of several discrete wavelengths or emission lines), the photographic plate, when developed, would yield the characteristic bright-line emission spectrum of the element in the emission source. (Such an arrangement is essentially that used in emission spectrographs.)

Replacing the photographic plate by a fixed slit, we see that for a given position of the other optical parts only a specific narrow wavelength region can pass through the exit slit. If it is desired that a large region of the spectrum be examined minutely, interval by interval, or *scanned,* we could do so by moving the slit and detector optics along a horizontal curve tangent to the slit jaws. This, of course, is mechanically inconvenient. The spectrum is usually scanned by varying the position of the Littrow mirror about a vertical axis through its front surface. This is mechanically convenient and tends to keep the ray that does pass through the exit slit near minimum deviation on its passages through the prism. As the angle of the Littrow mirror is varied, the various wavelengths emitted by the source are successively presented to the exit slit so that they will pass through and be focused on the detector. If the monochromator employs a grating, the spectrum is scanned by rotation of the grating about a vertical axis through its front surface.

If the motion of the Littrow mirror (or diffraction grating) can be coupled to motion of chart paper, and if the detector signal can be suitably amplified and used to drive a recording pen, a continuous plot of radiation intensity transmitted by the sample at each frequency, known as a scanned spectrum (Figure 2-7), can be pro-

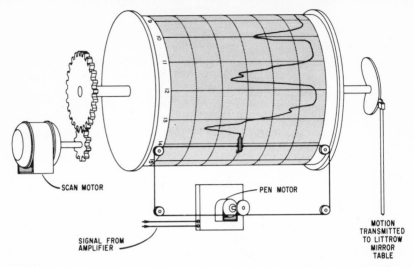

FIGURE 3-5 *Schematic illustration of the recording spectrometer principle.*

duced. To do this the Littrow mirror (or grating) position is controlled by a lever arm riding on a cam of suitable shape, which in turn is mounted on the shaft that drives the chart paper. A constant angular velocity of the Littrow mirror does not produce equal wavelength intervals on a chart driven at constant velocity; hence the need for a cam, which must be shaped to give the type of presentation desired on the chart paper (linear wavelength intervals, linear frequency intervals, or some other convenient scale). This is illustrated schematically in Figure 3-5.

The chemical substance that is to absorb certain wavelengths of radiation, thereby producing the infrared absorption spectrum, is usually placed in the infrared beam between the source mirror and the monochromator entrance slit. (See Figure 3-1.) The manner in which the sample is prepared is discussed in Chapter 5. It is important to realize that the intensity of light transmitted by the sample is what is measured by the spectrometer and presented as the ordinate on the recorder chart.

The foregoing discussion is intended as a brief over-all view of the operation of an infrared spectrometer. In the remainder of this chapter and in Chapter 4 certain features of the monochromator are discussed in greater detail. Other details of operation can perhaps best be found by consulting the manufacturer's operation manual supplied with the spectrometer.

38 *Spectrometer optics: the basic infrared monochromator*

II. Prism properties and materials

The most common dispersing agents used in the chemical region of the infrared spectrum are prisms of various materials. In this section we describe the general properties of prisms and discuss the specific uses of prisms made from the various materials having utility in the infrared region.

A. The prism as a disperser of radiation frequencies

The angular dispersion of light frequencies by a prism results because the index of refraction of the prism is a function of wavelength. In Figure 3-6 it is shown that successively shorter wavelengths suffer greater refraction; to use other words, the shorter the wavelength of light, the higher the refractive index of a prism material. This statement is generally true for all prism materials throughout their range of transmission in the optical region of the electromagnetic spectrum.

Figure 3-7 is a plot of refractive index as a function of wavelength for NaCl. (The shape of this curve is typical; other prism materials have similar curves.) The significant feature of such a curve is that the slope becomes increasingly large as cutoff (i.e., wavelength beyond which a useful amount of light is no longer transmitted) is reached. The ability of a prism to disperse, or the angular dispersion $d\theta/d\lambda$, in terms of the change in refractive index per wavelength change $dn/d\lambda$, the first derivative of the curve, is given by the expression

$$\frac{d\theta}{d\lambda} = \frac{2 \sin (\alpha/2)(dn/d\lambda)}{[1 - n^2 \sin^2 (\alpha/2)]^{1/2}}, \tag{3-3}$$

where n is refractive index and α is the apex angle of the prism.

This expression is generally true for any prism and prism material at minimum deviation. Thus we have the general result that *a prism has its highest dispersive power in the infrared wavelength region just below its cutoff*.

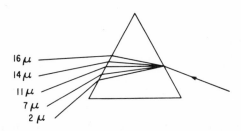

FIGURE 3-6 *Dispersion of infrared radiation by a prism.*

It is this fact that explains why an infrared spectrometer does not lose resolution as the wavelength is increased, even though the slits are being opened ever wider to compensate for the blackbody emission profile of the source. (See Sec. IV-C.) The rate of refractive index change with wavelength, hence angular dispersion, increases at a rate rapid enough to far more than compensate for resolution loss because of slit width increase. The net result is that in prism spectrometers the resolving power is always best when working at wavelengths just below that of a given prism cutoff.

B. Comparison of prism materials

For work in different regions of the spectrum prisms of different materials must be used because of long-wave cutoff (discussed in Chapter 1) and varying dispersive power (illustrated in Figure 3-7). Figure 3-8 is a series of curves showing the first derivative of refractive index n as a function of wavelength for various common prism mate-

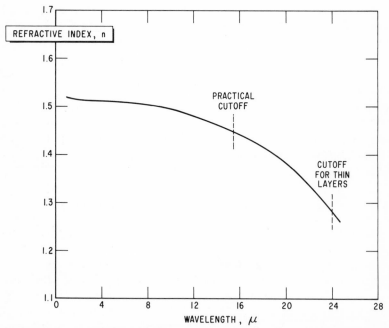

FIGURE 3-7 *Refractive index of* **NaCl** *(rocksalt) as a function of wavelength.*

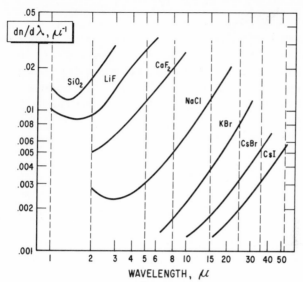

FIGURE 3-8 **Dispersion of optical materials used in various ranges of the infrared region.**

rials. The dashed vertical lines show the region in which each prism should be used for the best general results.

As is apparent from the figure, in order to do the best possible work throughout the chemical infrared region, all prisms from LiF through KBr should be available. However, in practical chemical infrared work it is often more desirable to get reasonable data rapidly and on one piece of paper. Hence NaCl (rocksalt) is usually chosen as a best "compromise" prism material, and most chemical applications of infrared spectroscopy today are done with spectrometers having NaCl optics.

III. The use of plane gratings in infrared spectrometers

The great advantage of properly made gratings is their high resolving power. In fact, the resolving power of which a grating spectrometer is capable is often so high that in analytical applications this "extra" power can be traded for energy through-put (hence signal-measurement accuracy) by operating the spectrometer with slits "extra" wide. (See later.) The recent availability at reasonable prices of a variety of grating types suitable for chemical infrared spectrometers has made consideration of their use in this application important.

The use of plane gratings in infrared spectrometers **41**

A. The properties of plane gratings

Figure 3-9 shows a much enlarged view of a plane reflection grating surface as seen in a section through the grating, perpendicular to the grooves. If FF_i is the wavefront of the incident ray, the condition for formation of the diffracted ray wavefront FF_d is that points F and F_d must be at the same phase. This will be true only if the distance F_i-O-F_d is equal to an integral number of wavelengths. This condition leads to the relation between α and β, the angles of incident and diffracted rays with the grating normal (FN):

$$(\sin \alpha + \sin \beta) = \frac{n\lambda}{d}, \qquad (3\text{-}4)$$

where λ is the wavelength, d is the distance between two adjacent grooves (called the grating constant), and n is the integral number of wavelengths in distance F_i-O-F_d, usually called the *order*. (Figure 3-9 illustrates the first-order diffracted ray.) It will be noted from equation 3-4 that the short wavelengths have *less* angular deviation from the incident ray than long wavelengths—just the opposite situation from prism refraction.

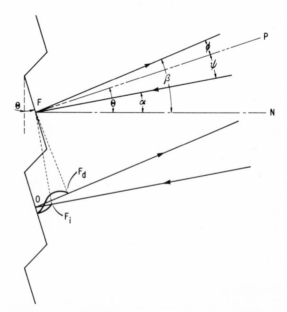

FIGURE 3-9   *Diffraction by a reflection grating.*

Spectrometer optics: the basic infrared monochromator

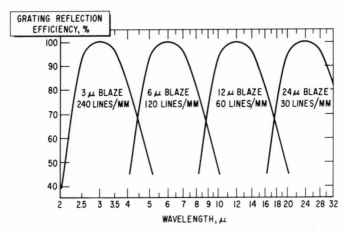

FIGURE 3-10   Grating efficiency as a function of wavelength near the
blaze angle.

The light diffracted from a grating will be at maximum intensity
when the angle between incident and diffracted light is the same as
for specular reflection; that is, when ψ, the angle between incident
ray and normal to groove surface (FP), equals ϕ, the angle between
diffracted ray and normal to groove surface.   (See Figure 3-9.)   For
a given angle of groove face, or "blaze" angle (θ in Figure 3-9), the
intensity of the diffracted ray will be a maximum for a unique wavelength, and the grating is said to be *blazed* at this wavelength.   The
diffracted rays of longer or shorter wavelength than this value will
have lower intensity; the greater the departure from the wavelength
for which the grating is blazed, the lower the intensity.   For this
reason a diffraction grating will give most efficient operation over a
relatively narrow wavelength range, a situation much analogous to the
necessity for use of various prism materials.   Figure 3-10 shows a set
of curves for diffracted light intensity versus wavelength for an arbi-
trarily selected series of gratings which might be used throughout the
"chemical" region of the infrared spectrum.   Each curve peaks at the
wavelength for which the grating was blazed.   The grating spacings,
usually expressed as lines per millimeter, are typical values for their
respective regions of the spectrum.

B. The problem of order separation

As can be seen by consideration of equation 3-4 one unique wavelength does not emerge at angle β, but instead any wavelengths will

The use of plane gratings in infrared spectrometers   43 emerge that can be expressed as the first-order wavelength divided by an integer. For example, suppose the diffracted ray at angle β in Figure 3-9 were 12 μ light; superimposed on it will be 6, 4, 3 μ, etc., light corresponding to λ, $\lambda/2$, $\lambda/3$, $\lambda/4$, etc. These wavelengths are spoken of as the first-order, second-order, third-order, fourth-order, etc., diffracted rays. Although the grating has high ability to resolve 12 μ light from 12.005 μ light, say, it does have the disadvantage that the orders must be separated by some auxiliary means if the grating is to be used in spectrometer applications.

Because the problem in order separation is to separate wavelengths relatively far apart, only a relatively crude device is necessary. One such method is the use of filters. Suppose it is necessary to work in the region $8\frac{1}{2}$–15 μ, for which a 12 μ blazed grating is being employed; a filter is required which transmits light in the region $8\frac{1}{2}$–15 μ but transmits no light at $7\frac{1}{2}$ μ (the second order of 15 μ) or below. To cover the entire infrared region of chemical interest obviously requires the use of a series of filters. Filters such as this have only recently become available. They are made by deposition of successive layers of materials of various refractive index on a substrate (such as germanium); the optical interferences arising between transmitted and reflected rays at each phase boundary allow transmission of some wavelengths, reflection of others. Variation of the thickness and refractive index of the materials constituting the successive layers allows selection of the radiation to be transmitted. The transmission characteristics of a typical filter of this type is shown in Figure 3-11.

A second method for order separation is to arrange an auxiliary prism monochromator in tandem with the grating monochromator. If the gratings have been well chosen, the requirements of this prism monochromator are not stringent. It is necessary that the prism monochromator be arranged at all times to pass the same wavelength for which the grating monochromator is set; two cams—one to program the grating position, the other to program the Littrow mirror of the grating monochromator—must thus be driven together. It is usually advantageous to place the prism monochromator ahead of the grating monochromator; such an arrangement is known as a fore-prism grating monochromator. Grating spectrometers for the chemical infrared region, employing either a fore prism or a series of filters, have now become commercially available.

Unlike a prism, one grating used in but one order will *not* suffice for use over any reasonable portion of the infrared region of chemical interest. (See Figure 3-10.) One single grating can be used in *different orders*, however. For example, a grating with 30 lines/mm

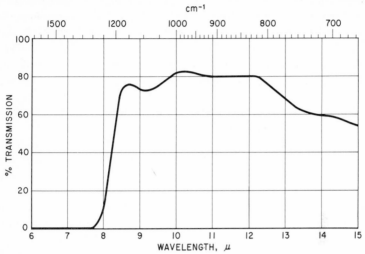

FIGURE 3-11 *Transmission of a long wave pass interference filter (#237-1012, Perkin-Elmer Corp.).*

and blazed at 24 μ could be used in the second order (where $\sin \alpha + \sin \beta = 2\lambda/d$) in somewhat the same manner as a grating with 60 lines/mm and blazed at 12 μ or could be used in the fourth order in somewhat the same manner as a 120-line/mm grating blazed at 6 μ. This application cannot be carried on indefinitely, however, for two reasons. The first is that more stringent requirements are imposed on the fore prism at higher orders. When operating in the second order, for example, the fore prism is merely required to separate 12 μ light from 24 and 8 μ light (first and third orders, respectively), a relatively simple matter. But when operating in the eighth order, say, the fore prism is required to separate 3.00 μ light from 3.43 and 2.78 μ light (seventh and ninth orders, respectively), a nearly impossible task for a fore prism which is also supposed to transmit light beyond 24 μ! (See discussion of prisms in Section II.) The second reason is that when the grating is used in a high order, such as, say, the eighth, the grating efficiency will fall to a low level between the seventh and eighth orders and also between the eighth and ninth orders. Hence the 24-μ blaze 30-line/mm grating of our preceding example could be used in the eighth order over only a *very* narrow wavelength range near 3 μ.

It is possible, however, to use one grating in a few orders with a single fore prism if the study of only a somewhat narrower range

The use of plane gratings in infrared spectrometers   **45**

of the spectrum is required; this situation is similar to the selection of NaCl as a simple compromise prism in prism spectrometer application. But, in order to obtain the best results from optics of given size, a series of different gratings must be employed.   (See Figure 3-10.)

IV. Monochromator quality and performance

The design factors which influence spectrometer optical performance have only been implied by our brief, over-all survey of the monochromator.   In this section we consider in more detail some of the factors that lead to improved resolving power and energy transmission.

A. Factors affecting resolution

If it is assumed that all the optical surfaces are as perfect as can be made, the resolving power, or ability to distinguish between two closely adjacent frequencies, depends directly on only three factors:

1. The *angular dispersion* of the prism (or grating), usually expressed as $d\theta/d\lambda$.   This number, a measure of the ability of the dispersing optic to bend successively further each successively shorter wavelength, depends on the wavelength region being measured and the prism material and geometry, or the number of lines per millimeter on a grating surface, as discussed in the preceding sections.

2. The focal length of the collimator.   In order to separate two closely adjacent wavelengths as well as possible at the exit slit, $\Delta\theta$ is translated there into a linear distance as long as possible by making its radius, the focal length of the collimator, as large as possible.

3. The slit width.   The narrower this aperture, the greater its ability, obviously, to discriminate between closely adjacent wavelengths.   As we have already noted, the entrance and exit slits have equal effect on the monochromator, are generally kept at equal width, and are varied together.

The effect of these factors is quantitatively summarized by an expression which we shall now consider.   The incremental angle of resolution formed by the exit slit $\Delta\theta$ is the slit width s, divided by the focal length f, hence

$$\Delta\theta = \frac{s}{f} = \frac{d\theta}{d\lambda}\Delta\lambda. \tag{3-5}$$

Now, as

$$\lambda = \frac{c}{\nu} \qquad |\Delta\lambda| = \frac{c\,\Delta\nu}{\nu^2},$$

and therefore

$$\Delta \nu = \frac{\nu^2}{c} \frac{s}{f} \frac{1}{d\theta/d\lambda}.$$ (3-6)

But this is not the only factor limiting spectrometer operation. Another term, the so-called diffraction limiting term, must be made a part of the complete expression for $\Delta \nu$. For Littrow prism spectrometers, in which light passes through the prism twice,

$$\frac{d\theta}{d\lambda} = \frac{4 \sin (\alpha/2) (dn/d\lambda)}{[1 - n^2 \sin^2 (\alpha/2)]^{1/2}},$$ (compare with equation 3-3)

and the limiting resolution is often approximated by the expression

$$\Delta \omega = \omega^2 \frac{[1 - n^2 \sin^2 (\alpha/2)]^{1/2}}{4 \sin (\alpha/2)(dn/d\lambda)} \frac{s}{f} + F(s) \frac{\omega}{2b(dn/d\lambda)},$$ (3-7)

where ω is the frequency in cm^{-1}. The second term of the expression arises from the diffraction limit of a prism of finite size. Here b is the height of the prism base in centimeters, and $F(s)$ is a function of the slit width, the exact nature of which is still in doubt, but it is sometimes assumed to be ~ 0.9 for narrow slits and ~ 0.5 for the widest slits.

The first term in the expression is the slit-limiting term, the most important in energy-limited spectrometers because the slit must be made quite wide in order to obtain sufficient detector response. (See Chapter 4.) In other branches of optical spectroscopy, in which spectrometers are usually not energy-limited, the slit may be made much narrower, and the second term in equation 3-7 is usually the limiting term. For infrared prism monochromators of good quality the first term is about three times as large as the second.

An analogous expression for grating monochromators is

$$\Delta \omega = \omega^2 \frac{d \cos \theta}{2n} \frac{s}{f} + F(s) \frac{\omega}{Mn},$$ (3-8)

where n is the grating order, d is the grating constant (distance between successive lines), θ is the angle of incidence or diffraction (essentially equal), M is the total number of lines on the grating, and $F(s)$ has the same significance as in equation 3-7. For a reasonably good grating monochromator the second term (the diffraction-limiting term) is quite small compared to the first term (the slit term).

$\Delta \nu$ (in cycles per second, $\Delta \omega$ in cm^{-1}) is properly called the *spectral slit width* and is defined as one half the width of the frequency range passed at the exit slit. This number is an effective statement of the minimum frequency interval that can be resolved by the spectrometer Because, in infrared spectrometers, the first term in its expression is the most important, spectral slit width is essentially proportional to the physical spectrometer slit aperture. Spectral slit width is most conveniently expressed in $\Delta\nu$ frequency interval (usually expressed, however, in terms of cm^{-1}, hence properly denoted $\Delta\omega$), because many absorption bands of chemical substances have half bandwidths of roughly the same magnitude when expressed in frequency interval; this would not be true if they were expressed in terms of wavelength interval.

It is desirable to have the spectral slit width as small as practically possible, for this enables us to determine accurately the frequencies of adjacent bands, which is important in chemical applications. For example, in Figure 3-12 (a) might be a typical portion of a spectrum obtained with low resolution (or high spectral slit width), whereas (b) would be a spectrum of the same material obtained at higher resolution. If any spectral studies concerned with accurate frequency determination are to be made of molecules in the vapor phase, where individual rotation lines are extremely sharp, high resolution is imperative.

A second reason for desiring high resolution is the matter of accurate absorption-intensity determination. Unless the spectral slit width of the monochromator is essentially narrower than the width of the absorption band whose intensity we wish to measure, the intensity so determined will not be a precisely calculable function of molecular concentration and the usual intensity relations used in quantitative analysis will not be valid. The second point is discussed in more detail in Chapter 6.

For a given prism material or a given grating, then, we can increase resolution by increasing collimator focal length and decreasing slit

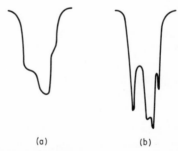

(a)   (b)

FIGURE 3-12   Effect of resolution on a spectrum.

48   *Spectrometer optics: the basic infrared monochromator*

width. However, both operations (other things being equal) decrease the energy transmitted by the spectrometer. Before a spectrometer can resolve two closely adjacent bands it must at least be able to detect the signal, and lowering the transmitted energy makes this a real problem in the infrared region. Therefore before we can leave the subject of monochromator quality we must consider the factors that affect signal strength at the detector.

B. Factors affecting transmitted energy

If it is again assumed that all the optical surfaces are as perfect as can be made, for a given spectral slit width the amount of energy received by the detector of an infrared spectrometer depends only on the amount of light passing through the entrance slit in the solid angle subtended by the collimator. In the monochromator portion of the spectrometer this depends on three factors.

1. The size of the solid angle. Consideration of Figure 3-1 shows that the greater this is, the more light that can pass through a slit aperture of given size. The solid angle is defined as

$$\Omega = \frac{A}{4\pi r^2} = \frac{A}{4\pi(2f)^2} = \frac{A}{16\pi f^2}, \tag{3-9}$$

where A is the area of the optical surface of the collimator and f is its focal length.* However, as we have remarked, the focal length must be made as great as possible in order to obtain high resolution. Thus, to keep the solid angle high, the area of the collimator must be as large as possible.

As the collimator passes parallel light to the prism (or grating), the size of the prism must be such that all light from the collimator can be utilized. A useful increase of the magnitude of the solid angle at the entrance slit, therefore, dictates that the size of the prism (or grating) be increased.

2. The length of the slit. The longer the slit (if it is properly illuminated), the more light it will pass. However, as the slit is made longer, the light passed by the slit further from the slit center will travel through the prism in a path less parallel to the prism base, with resulant increase of aberration in the exit-slit image. (See p. 36.)

---

* The solid angle is also equal to $\frac{1}{64}$ of the square of the ratio of collimator diameter to focal length, the latter ratio being known as the "f number" of a mirror. The f number, usually expressed in the form $f/8$, say, means that the ratio of focal length to diameter of optical surface is $8:1$. The lower the f number, the "faster" the mirror is said to be, for the solid angle is greater.

The longer the focal length of the collimating mirror, the smaller the errors, hence the greater the slit length that may be used.

In view of these considerations, the source and source mirror must be placed so that the solid angle at the slit is equal to the solid angle which correctly fills the collimator. The source must be long enough to illuminate uniformly the full length of the slit being used. The source can be made to emit more energy by increasing its temperature, but most of this increase is in the short wavelength region. (See Figure 1-2.)

3. The slit width. As the slit aperture is quite narrow, increasing it will not introduce any important aberrations but will clearly pass more light in proportion to its width. A distinction must be made here, however: energy *per spectral slit width* and spectral slit width itself are proportional to the actual spectrometer slit aperture (see equations 3-6, 3-7, 3-8, and 3-10); but *absolute energy* passed by the monochromator, important in signal versus noise considerations (see Chapter 4), is proportional to the *square* of the spectrometer slit aperture. (See equation 3-11.)

The interrelation between the factors of resolution and energy can be given a quantitative expression which we shall now derive. The absolute radiant power in the spectral range $\Delta\nu$, which leaves the exit slit and falls on the detector and which we shall designate P_ν, depends on (a) the brightness B_ν (see equation 1-6) per spectral slit width of the radiation focused from the source onto the entrance slit; (b) the solid angle $\Omega = A/16\pi f^2$ subtended by the effective prism aperture; (c) the area of the entrance slit s (width) times h (slit height); and (d) the spectral slit width $\Delta\nu$. Thus

$$P_\nu = (B_\nu \, \Delta\nu) \, \frac{sh\,A}{16\pi f^2} \, T_\nu, \qquad (3\text{-}10)$$

where T_ν is a factor which rates the optical efficiency of the various monochromator optical parts; its subscript ν indicates that it is a function of frequency.

Now, if we are dealing with an *energy limited spectrometer*, that is, if the second term in equation 3-7 or 3-8 is small with respect to the first, we may use equation 3-6,

$$\Delta\nu = \frac{\nu^2}{c} \frac{s}{f} \frac{1}{d\theta/d\lambda}$$

as an expression of the spectral slit width and combine it with equation

3-10 to obtain

$$P_\nu = B_\nu \frac{hs^2 A T_\nu}{16\pi f^3} \frac{\nu^2}{c} \frac{1}{d\theta/d\lambda} \tag{3-11}$$

This equation demonstrates our earlier statement that absolute energy transmitted by a monochromator depends on the square of the slit aperture. Also, it is useful because it shows how the spectrometer slit width can be varied to produce a constant value of $P\nu$ over the frequency range being scanned.

We may use this same substitution in another way to eliminate the slit aperture entirely:

$$P_\nu = \left[B_\nu (\Delta \nu)^2 \frac{c}{\nu^2} \right] \left[\frac{hA(d\theta/d\lambda)T_\nu}{16\pi f} \right]. \tag{3-12a}$$

This equation is often seen in the form

$$E_\nu = I_\nu \frac{hADT}{f}, \tag{3-12b}$$

where E_ν is called radiant power per spectral slit width $(P_\nu/\Delta\nu)$, I_ν is the source brightness $(B_\nu \Delta\nu)$, and $d\theta/d\nu = (d\theta/d\lambda)(c/\nu^2)$ is abbreviated D. In this form the equation specifies the radiant power per spectral slit width as a function of the spectrometer parameters.

Another useful form of the equation is obtained by solving equation 3-12a specifically for $\Delta\nu$:

$$\Delta \nu = \left[\left(\frac{\nu^2}{B_\nu c} \right) \frac{16\pi P_{\nu \min}}{LA(d\theta/d\lambda)T_\nu} \right]^{\frac{1}{2}}, \tag{3-13}$$

where L is the ratio of slit height to focal length h/f. This equation gives the ultimate resolving power of a spectrometer in terms of the minimum power $P_{\nu \min}$ that can be detected as a signal by the detector employed. This situation is known as energy-limited resolution and occurs in infrared spectroscopy because of the low efficiency of thermal detectors. (See Chapter 4.)

If the number $L = h/f$ is increased significantly, serious aberrations will result (as previously discussed). Hence an attempt to increase either energy through-put or energy-limited resolution of a monochromator, either by decreasing focal length or by increasing slit height, does not lead to a useful result after a level of L has been reached above which aberrations rapidly becomes serious.

In Part A of this section we noted that widening the slit decreases the resolving power of the spectrometer. Also, as shown by equation

3-12a, slit width is the parameter by which we may control spectrometer performance but which does not effect monochromator quality. Therefore

wide slits allow a higher energy (proportional to the square of the slit width) through the monochromator, hence a larger signal with which to work, but give lower resolution;

narrow slits give higher resolution but allow less energy through the monochromator, hence result in a smaller signal.

To summarize these points and those in Part A, we see that in order to improve monochromator performance it is desirable to have the following:

1. The size of the collimator and prism (or grating) as large as possible.

2. The ratio of slit height to focal length as large as possible but not large enough to produce serious aberrations.

These parameters, then, are an index of the quality of results to be expected from a monochromator employing a given prism or grating type and having optical surfaces completely free of any imperfections. This condition of optical perfection is, of course, never wholly attainable.

C. The blackbody curve and the necessity for programmed slits

Reference to Figure 1-2 shows that $B_\nu \Delta\nu$—the brightness of a blackbody source in frequency interval $\Delta\nu$—varies considerably throughout the region in which infrared spectrometers are generally employed for chemical applications. Furthermore, B_ν is only one factor that varies rapidly with frequency; equation 3-11 shows that radiant power also depends on ν^2. Comparison of equations 1-6a and 1-6b shows that $B_\nu \cdot \nu^2/c = B_\lambda$. Hence a plot of B_λ is somewhat more revealing of the problem here than the plot of B_ν in Figure 1-2. Such a plot is shown in Figure 3-13.* This is the usual form of illustration of Planck's law.

From the figure it is easily seen that when a spectrum is scanned (usually from short to long wavelength) the radiant power falls drastically with increasing wavelength and the detector will be given ever less energy. Now, in order to scan a spectrum in a useful manner (see Chapter 4) over a reasonably wide frequency range, it is necessary

* The Wien displacement law derived by differentiation of B_λ is $\omega_{max} = 3.45T$; this form predicts the maxima of the curves in Figure 3-13.

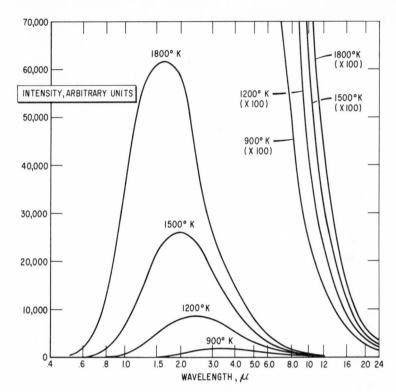

FIGURE 3-13 *Energy distribution of radiation from a blackbody at various temperatures. Curves result from constant wavelength intervals (equation 1-6b).*

to hold the power input to the detector essentially constant. This can be done by programming the slits in such a way that the factor $B_\nu s^2 \nu^2 T_\nu / (d\theta/d\lambda)$ of equation 3-11 remains constant throughout the spectral region of interest. (Since $d\theta/d\lambda$, and presumably T_ν, do not vary rapidly with frequency, Figure 3-13 graphically illustrates the problem.) The net result of these considerations is that as the spectrometer scan procedes from short to long wavelength the slits must be continually widened. This is usually accomplished by a shaped cam on which rides a lever arm controlling the slits. The "slit cam" may be mounted on the same shaft as, and adjacent to, the cam used to move the Littrow mirror.

It would seem from the foregoing that resolving power would become poorer as wavelength increased in a scanned spectrum. Fortunately, other factors more than compensate for this situation.

Monochromator quality and performance   **53**

Equation 3-6 shows that although the spectral slit width does indeed increase with increasing slit aperture it also increases as the inverse *square* of wavelength and the inverse of angular dispersion, $d\theta/d\lambda$, of prisms and gratings. The latter increases with increasing wavelength, as discussed in Sections II and III. Therefore, as we pointed out in the discussions of prisms and gratings, better resolution is always available at the *long wave end* of any region in which a prism or grating is used, despite the increase of slit aperture.

D. Scattered light

No matter how carefully a monochromator is constructed, it will always have some imperfections. Most common of these are imperfections in the optical surfaces, which can cause small amounts of light of wavelength different from that for which the monochromator is set to pass to reach the detector surface, hence to become part of the amplified signal. Such radiation, variously known as "scattered light," "stray radiation," or "false energy," presents a problem in quantitative infrared applications. When scattered light is present, the transmission value of an absorption band will always appear too high. At high levels of transmission this error is not so serious, but for absorption bands of low transmission completely misleading results can be obtained from a spectrometer having appreciable scattered light in that region. This is illustrated in Figure 3-14.

The scattered light problem is usually most serious at the longest wavelengths employed, for in regions in which a prism transmits

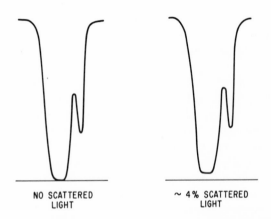

NO SCATTERED
LIGHT
~ 4% SCATTERED
LIGHT

FIGURE 3-14   The effect of scattered light on absorption bands of low transmission.

only a small amount of light a small fraction of some scattered light from the short wavelength region, where source emission is higher (see Figure 3-13), can be a substantial part of the detector signal.

The fundamental cure for scattered light is, of course, extreme care in monochromator design and construction. However, since absolute perfection is never possible *filters* are often employed to reduce scattered radiation. A filter for this purpose is made from some material that is transparent to long wavelength radiation but opaque to short wavelength radiation. Often this filter consists of a thin layer of Ag_2S on an AgCl plate, which passes essentially all radiation above ~ 7 μ but whose transmission gradually falls to zero in the region 7 to 3 μ and transmits no light of wavelength shorter than 3 μ. This filter may be switched into the optical beam at some convenient time during the infrared scan, say at $7\frac{1}{2}$ μ.

A second and very effective method of reduction of scattered radiation is the use of a double monochromator. Double monochromator types are described in Chapter 4, Section II.

For work at wavelengths longer than ~ 25 μ the scattered light problem becomes much more serious, and various combinations of special filtering techniques are employed. These are described more fully in Chapter 15, Volume II, in which far infrared spectroscopy is discussed.

Selected references

1. Sawyer, R., *Experimental Spectroscopy*, Prentice-Hall, New York, 1944.
2. *Synthetic Optical Crystals* (revised edition), The Harshaw Chemical Co., Cleveland, Ohio, 1955.
3. Strong, J., "Resolving Power Limitations of Grating and Prism Spectrometers," *J. Opt. Soc. Am.* **39**, 320 (1949).
4. Williams, V., "Infrared Instrumentation and Techniques," *Rev. Sci. Instr.* **19**, 135 (1948).
5. Strong, J., *Concepts of Classical Optics*, Freeman, San Francisco, Calif., 1958.
6. Lecomte, J., "Spectroscopie dans l'infrarouge," *Handbuch der Physik*, Band XXVI (pp. 262 ff), Springer-Verlag, Berlin, 1958.
7. Brügel, W., *An Introduction to Infrared Spectroscopy*, Wiley, New York, 1962.
8. Bauman, R. P., *Absorption Spectroscopy*, Wiley, New York, 1962.

4

The performance and operation of infrared spectrometers

In Chapter 3 we described the optical parts of a basic monochromator and their functions. In this chapter we discuss the photometry systems, construction of various practical spectrometer types, and practical points of spectrometer operation. It is well to understand at the outset that the limitations in spectrometer performance at present result from the low signal level supplied to the amplifier by the detector. If a highly efficient photoconductive detector or some equivalent device should ever be made to perform in the long wavelength infrared region of interest to the chemical spectroscopist, much of this chapter would become either unnecessary or obsolete.

I. Infrared radiation detection and signal amplification

Because a quantum of infrared radiation is only a small amount of energy, its detection (i.e., its transformation into an electrical signal) is not easy. In this section the various types of detectors in use, the theory of their operation, and how their output signal is amplified for recording purposes are described.

A. Detector types

Infrared detectors can be classified into two groups: thermal and photoconductive. At present only the thermal types can be applied throughout the infrared region of chemical interest, namely, 2–25 μ.

The thermal types in common use are the following:

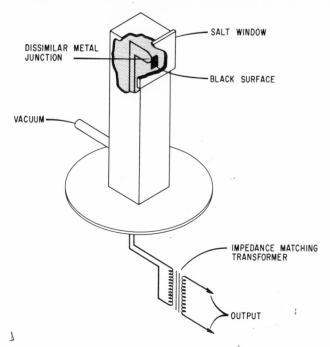

FIGURE 4-1 *Schematic illustration of a thermocouple detector.*

The thermocouple. A thermocouple detector is essentially a junction of two unlike metals, the junction being coated with evaporated gold to make it as nearly "black" as possible in the range in which it is to be employed. A potential difference exists at the junction of the two metals, this potential increasing with rising temperature. In order to form a complete circuit, the two dissimilar metals must meet at some other point, at which a potential difference in opposition to that at the blackened junction will exist. However, the difference at the second junction, if kept at room temperature, will be smaller than that of the junction at higher temperature. When the blackened junction receives infrared radiation, which is absorbed and thereby brings this junction to higher than room temperature, a measurable potential difference will exist in the circuit and will be directly proportional to the number of infrared photons falling on the blackened surface. Figure 4-1 schematically illustrates a thermocouple.

The bolometer. A bolometer is essentially a small piece of conductor suitably blackened to absorb infrared radiation and whose resistance is a linear function of temperature. If a small, constant direct current

Infrared radiation detection and signal amplification   **57**

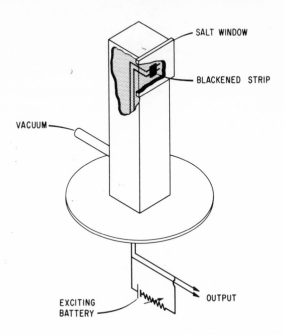

SALT WINDOW

BLACKENED STRIP

VACUUM

EXCITING BATTERY

OUTPUT

FIGURE 4-2   Schematic illustration of a bolometer detector.

is passed through the bolometer, the voltage drop across it will vary with its temperature, which, in turn, depends on the number of photons falling on its surface.   The advantage of the bolometer over the thermocouple is that the light-receiving surface can be made larger for the same voltage sensitivity as produced by a thermocouple, thereby placing less stringent requirements on the detector ellipse which condenses the light from large optics to a small surface.   As a result of the larger size, however, the heat capacity of the bolometer is larger, which leads to certain disadvantages.   Figure 4-2 schematically illustrates a bolometer.

The pneumatic detector (Golay cell). This device consists of a small gas chamber, one wall of which is an infrared absorbing film and serves as the detector surface, the opposite wall being a flexible mirror. Absorption of radiation by the film heats the gas in the chamber, causing the flexible mirror to be deformed.   This deformation is measured by an auxiliary optical system employing visible light and a photocell whose output signal is an electrical voltage. Figure 4-3 schematically illustrates a Golay cell.   The advantage of this system is that the infrared absorbing film can be made optimum for just this purpose; it does not need to have the additional requirement that it conduct electricity, as in a bolometer or thermocouple. In practice, it appears that in most of the infrared region of chemical interest the Golay cell offers only slight advantage, but at successively longer wavelengths it becomes increasingly efficient, compared to a thermocouple or a bolometer, for the evaporated gold coating on these devices becomes a less perfect absorber at longer wavelengths.

At the present writing the photoconductive types of detectors are not yet well enough developed to serve in the longer wavelength regions of interest to the chemist. They do, however, find important use in the near infrared region (0.7 to 3 μ) and therefore are discussed more fully in Chapter 15, Volume II.

Should the range of infrared photoconductive detectors ever be extended as far as 25 or even 15 μ, infrared instrumentation will probably be revolutionized. It is probably safe to say that the limiting factor in infrared spectrometer operation today is the insensitivity of thermal-type detectors, whose performance characteristics are discussed later in this section. There is some indication that advances have been made in this direction, but no practical photoconductive detectors suitable for infrared spectrometers are commercially available at present.

B. Amplification of the detector signal for recording

As discussed subsequently, it is advantageous to work with an ac signal. Toward this end, the detector signal is made alternating by chopping the radiation beam. The chopper usually consists of a semicircular plate which is continuously rotated in and out of the infrared beam, commonly at some point between source and monochromator entrance slit. As a result, the radiation reaching the detector is

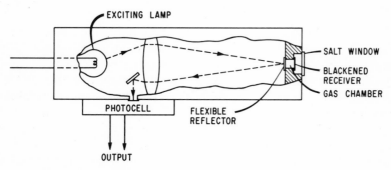

FIGURE 4-3   Schematic illustration of a Golay detector.

Infrared radiation detection and signal amplification   **59**

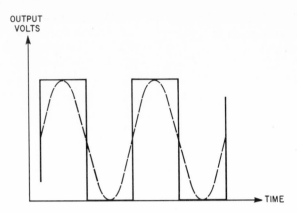

OUTPUT
VOLTS

TIME

FIGURE 4-4   *A square wave signal and its largest sine wave component.*

regularly interrupted and consists of alternate dark and light cycles of equal length.   The signal output from the detector will be a square wave.   (See Figure 4-4.)

An ac amplifier can now be used to amplify the square-wave signal. It will be recalled that the biggest component in the Fourier development of a square wave is the sine wave of the same frequency.   The amplifier is therefore designed to pass this sine-wave frequency and amplify it to sufficient strength for recording purposes.

There are three significant advantages in the use of a sharply tuned ac amplifier:

1. An ac amplifier is essentially drift-free; that is, small changes that may gradually occur in its circuit components do not produce significant changes in output signal level.

2. An ac amplifier sharply tuned to the desired signal frequency will pass it while tending to reject all other frequencies, such as random noise originating in the detector.

3. Only the chopped signal is amplified, an important consideration, since every part in the spectrometer, being at finite temperature, emits infrared radiation according to Planck's law.   Should any of this radiation reach the detector, no signal resulting from it would be amplified because, not being chopped, it would be seen by the amplifier as a pure dc signal.   Without use of chopped radiation and an ac amplifier, any variation in ambient temperature of spectrometer parts would become a signal.   At long wavelength, where the emission from the high temperature source is only slightly greater than that of objects at room temperature, such a signal could conceivably be an

inconveniently large fraction of the desired radiation signal, clearly an undesirable situation.

After suitable amplification the signal is rectified to a dc voltage. This is accomplished by a switching circuit which operates at the same frequency as the chopper and is actuated by the same shaft that drives the chopper. The dc signal is now passed through a capacitance-resistance network which changes the pulsating dc signal to a smooth dc voltage. The values of capacitors and resistors in this filter are quite important, for they determine in large measure the *time constant* of the recording system (i.e., the time delay between change in light intensity at the detector and recognition of this by the recording system). Although a long time constant will have certain disadvantages (see Section III), it has the advantage that possible sudden "noise crashes" will not be passed by the filter system. A quantity indicative of noise passage is called the "band pass" of the system and is proportional to the reciprocal of time constant. We shall refer to the effect of band pass in consideration of detector performance factors.

Finally, the filtered dc voltage, usually of the order of ~0.01 volt, drives the actual recorder through a power amplifier.

C. Detector theory and performance

The intimate details of thermal-detector theory require a complex exposition, which is not our purpose here. To simplify the picture (perhaps to oversimplify), we may regard a thermal detector as a form of heat engine operating between temperatures T_2 and T_1. The detector element is brought to the higher temperature T_2 by absorption of radiation and cools to the lower temperature T_1 on the "black" portion of the chopping cycle. The maximum thermodynamic efficiency of the process is then

$$\frac{E_{\text{out}}}{E_{\text{in}}} = \frac{T_2 - T_1}{T_2} = \frac{\Delta T}{T}. \qquad (4\text{-}1)$$

In order to have some grasp of the detector problem, we must consider the order of magnitude of certain energy, temperature, and voltage values. The radiation power falling on a detector from a reasonably high resolution monochromator is $\sim 10^{-7}$ watt. The fraction that can be detected reliably is, of course, the amount of power that will produce a signal voltage E_s, something larger than the average noise-level voltage E_j, which at room temperature is $\sim 10^{-9}$ volt. Thermal detectors have a voltage sensitivity per power input of approximately 5–10 μ-volts/μ-watt. Therefore the minimum power detectable as a useful signal, P_{min}, is $\sim 10^{-10}$ watt. Now, the resistance of the detector circuit is ~ 10 ohms. Therefore, when operating at *minimum detectable signal*, the electrical power delivered by the detector is $E_s^2/R = \sim(10^{-9})^2/10$, or $\sim 10^{-19}$ watt. Hence the efficiency of a thermal detector at P_{min} is $\sim 10^{-19}/10^{-10}$, or $\sim 10^{-9}$, a truly appalling figure. To use other words, when a thermal detector is being used in its threshold range, it operates with an efficiency of $\sim 10^{-9}$; when detecting stronger signals, it will be somewhat more efficient.

Returning to our concept of a thermal detector as a heat engine, we see that equation 4-1 indicates that at P_{min} the minimum detectable ΔT is $\sim 10^{-6}$°K when operating at room temperature. Another interesting point is shown by equation 4-1: if the ambient temperature T were reduced to ~ 4°K (the boiling point of He, for example), a hundredfold increase in detector sensitivity should be obtained. At the present writing progress is being made in this direction, but no commercially available apparatus yet exists for cooling infrared detectors in chemical spectrometers to this temperature.

Mentioned above was the fact that noise-level voltage of the detector is a most important concept and the fundamental origin of ultimate limitation in spectrometer operation. No matter how great the voltage gain of the amplifier, it cannot lift an inherently weak signal out of the noise level. It is generally agreed that in present infrared thermal detectors the so-called "Johnson noise"—the average value of electrical potential arising from random thermal drift of electrons in a conductor—forms the limiting noise level in infrared spectrometers, although other types of noise are known to be present. The Johnson noise voltage is given by

$$E_j^2 = 4kTR(\Delta f) \times 10^{-7}, \tag{4-2}$$

where k is Boltzman's constant (1.38×10^{-16} erg/°K), T is the absolute ambient temperature, R is the resistance of the detector, and Δf is the so-called "band pass" of the amplifier employed in recording or a number inversely proportional to amplifier time constant. (See p. 78.) The factor 10^{-7} converts the units of ergs to joules, to be commensurate with E_j in practical volts.

An important consequence should be noted: Johnson-noise voltage is proportional to the square root of amplifier band pass or the square root of the reciprocal of amplifier time constant. This is equivalent to saying that the longer the time spent making a measurement with

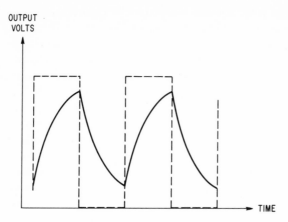

FIGURE 4-5 *Detector output as a result of finite detector heat capacity.*

a thermal detector, hence the longer the time constant the recording circuit can use, the lower the *square* of limiting noise voltage. This fact is important in the discussion in Section III on recording time.

Finally, the heat capacity of the thermal detector must be considered. The higher this heat capacity, the longer it will take the signal voltage to reach the steady-state value both at T_2 and T_1. The result of finite heat capacity is that, rather than a square wave signal, the output of the detector is similar to the form shown in Figure 4-5, where the dotted lines represent the square wave that would be produced for zero detector heat capacity. For this reason it is desirable to make the chopping speed as low as possible in order that temperatures T_2 and T_1 may come as near their steady-state values as possible.

On the other hand, as each chop is an "information bit," it is desirable to have the chopping speed as *high* as possible from the point of view of having more "information bits" per second. A compromise is therefore necessary, the chopping speed usually being in the range of 5–15 cps.

II. Photometry: single- and double-beam spectrometers

The per cent of infrared light radiation transmitted by a chemical substance can be measured in different ways. The principal methods used in spectrometers for chemical applications are the single-beam spectrometer, the double-beam optical-null spectrometer, and the double-beam ratio-recording spectrometer. These instruments differ only in electronic and mechanical components and in certain minor optical details; all employ the basic monochromator discussed in Chapter 3.

A. The single-beam spectrometer

The basic monochromator, with suitable amplifier and recording mechanism, constitutes the so-called single-beam spectrometer. Figure 4-6 is a block diagram of the arrangement. The square-wave detector signal is fed through a tuned ac amplifier, rectifier and filter, and power amplifier and recorder, as described in Section I-B. The position of the pen on the chart, then, depends on the magnitude of the signal arriving at the detector (which is a function of sample transmission and slit width) and the setting of the amplifier gain control. For condition of no absorption by the sample, spoken of as "100% transmission," or "I_0" (see Chapter 6), the pen position on the chart is set at a convenient point either by varying the slit setting, thereby varying the detector signal, or by varying amplifier gain.

We recall from Chapter 3 that if a scan is to be made it will be convenient to program the slit width in such a way that a signal of constant level is developed at the detector. The gain control, therefore, is not varied during the scan. If greater resolution is required, the entire slit program must be changed so that a narrower slit width will be obtained at all points in the scan program but still with constant signal maintained at the detector throughout the scan. If narrower slits are used, less energy will be received at the detector, hence the amplifier gain must be increased to obtain full-scale deflection on the recording chart. In addition to increasing the signal

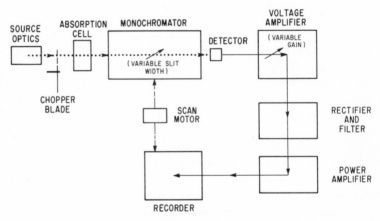

FIGURE 4-6 Block diagram of a single-beam spectrometer.

voltage, increasing amplifier gain also magnifies the random noise voltage from the detector, thereby giving a "noisy" record. (The relations between signal, noise, and recording time and the practical operating conditions dictated by these relations are discussed in much greater detail in Section III.)

The single-beam-spectrometer arrangement has certain advantages and disadvantages which determine in what situations it is best employed. Its advantages are the following:

1. Simplicity and reliability. This arrangement is usually the most accurate method by which measurements of transmission can be made. The simplicity of the system implies that fewer things can "go wrong" in the operation, and maintenance of the spectrometer is much simpler than with double-beam types.

2. Greater versatility in certain cases. The single-beam spectrometer can be used for scanning operations conveniently if the slits are programmed to produce constant energy. It can also be used in a convenient manner for measurements made at a single fixed wavelength. The simplicity of photometry and of the geometry of the sampling area allow it to be used in special applications in which double-beam types might not be convenient.

3. Amenability to determination of improper performance. Should some malfunction arise, such as a change in source condition, or a variation in amplifier output as a result of misbehavior of an electronic component, it is usually immediately obvious in the operation of a single-beam spectrometer. This is not always so in double-beam-spectrometer operation, as we shall see.

The disadvantages of single-beam operation are these:

1. When a scan is made, even with slits programmed for constant energy, the "I_0" line, or 100 % transmission line, is not smooth. With no sample in the spectrometer, a desirable situation would be the production of a perfectly straight line near the top of the recorder chart representing 100% transmission at all wavelengths scanned. A slight variation of any component in the spectrometer, however, either optical or electronic, will change the position of this line on the recorder chart. Such disturbances as source fluctuations, absence of perfect amplifier stability, small imperfections in the slit programming cam, etc., all lead to a nonsmooth I_0 line. Most of these irregularities can be canceled out in double-beam systems.

2. Presence of atmospheric absorptions. It is difficult to remove the last traces of H_2O and CO_2 vapors from the air in a spectrometer.

Both gases have strong absorption bands; hence any spectrum obtained on a single-beam spectrometer will always have their spectra superimposed on it unless rather elaborate flushing and drying procedures are employed. This difficulty can be eliminated to some extent by a double-beam system.

3. The signal recorded by a single-beam spectrometer is the absolute energy transmitted by the absorption cell, solvent, solute, and optics of the monochromator. In order to obtain the per cent transmission of the solute alone, or I/I_0, the ratio of transmitted to incident radiation, a "blank" spectrum must often be obtained. Also, direct differential comparison of two materials is not possible, as it is with double-beam instruments.

The foregoing limitations and advantages of a single-beam spectrometer thus indicate that (a) in most cases it is not used to best advantage in any application in which a scanned spectrum is desired (as in studies of band frequencies and qualitative analysis); (b) the single-beam spectrometer is normally more accurate and reliable in applications in which transmission is to be measured at a fixed wavelength or over a short scanned region (as with intensity measurements and quantitative analysis); (c) in special applications the versatility of the single-beam spectrometer may make its use preferable, whereas in certain other special applications in which a double-beam spectrometer is necessary it will not serve at all.

B. The double-beam optical-null spectrometer

The spectrometer enjoying the widest use today in chemical applications is the *double-beam optical-null* type. From the entrance slit through the tuned ac amplifier it is identical to the single-beam spectrometer. However, the source optics and chopper are different, as is the method of recording the signal.

The arrangement of the optical parts between source and monochromator-entrance slit is illustrated in Figure 4-7 for an optical-null spectrometer. Again this figure represents a simplification over systems actually used in commercial spectrometers, but all the essential points are illustrated.

The source is represented by a; b and b' are two separate source mirrors, each by itself employed in exactly the same manner as in the single-beam spectrometer; here, however, the two mirrors now produce two equivalent beams, called the *sample beam* and the *reference beam*. The exit windows of the source housing are c, c'; the entrance windows to the photometer section are c'' and c'''. The area between sets of windows is where absorption cells, containing samples whose

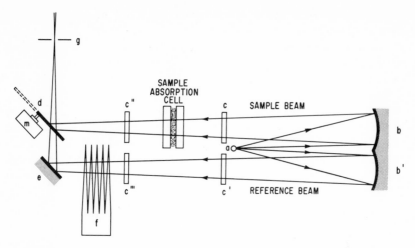

FIGURE 4-7 *Optical parts unique to a double-beam spectrometer.*

spectra are to be determined, are placed.   The chopping mirror *d* is a semicircular front-surface plane mirror, rotated in and out of the beam by a motor, *m*, so that the sample beam and reference beam (with the aid of plane mirror *e*) are alternately focused onto the monochromator entrance slit *g*.   The light attenuator *f* consists of a comblike device, the position of which in the reference beam determines the amount of light transmitted by the reference beam.   Its function is described below.

If the radiation intensity in the two beams is not equal, a squarewave signal is developed at the detector.   This signal is proportional to the energy *difference* between the two beams; it bears no relation to the energy content of either one.   Let us imagine that in the process of scanning a spectrum a situation exists in which the substance in the sample beam is transmitting slightly less radiation than the reference-beam attenuator in the reference beam.   The essentially square wave signal developed at the detector will then have the appearance of Figure 4-8.   This signal, suitably amplified and rectified (see preceding section), is used to drive the referencebeam attenuator into the reference beam so that less light is transmitted by the reference beam, and the square-wave-detector signal tends to become zero, or *null*.   If the square-wave signal at the detector results from *more* light energy in the sample than in the reference beam, it will be amplified in such a way that the referencebeam attenuator will be driven *out from* the reference beam.   A

Photometry: single- and double-beam spectrometers **67**

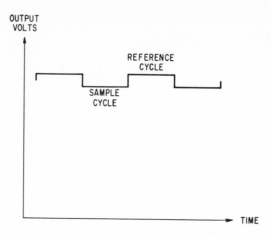

FIGURE 4-8 Signal developed at the detector of a double-beam spectrometer.

servomotor drives the reference-beam attenuator by a series of wires and pulleys; to this same wire is attached the recorder pen, so that its position on the recording chart is a direct linear measure of the position of the reference-beam attenuator. The position of the light attenuator in the reference beam gives the fraction of incident light the sample in the sample beam transmits, and this is recorded as per cent transmission, or I/I_0. Thus, as the spectrometer scans through an absorption band, the light attenuator is driven by the amplified detector signal in an attempt to make the reference-beam light intensity equal to the sample-beam light intensity at all times, and the band shape produced on the spectrometer chart is a record of this presumably successful attempt.

The reference-beam attenuator usually consists of a comblike structure whose linear advancement into the reference beam causes a linear reduction of light intensity. An attenuator of the comb type must be placed at the monochromator entrance slit or an image of the entrance slit. (This detail is not illustrated by Figure 4-7, which has been somewhat oversimplified for purposes of illustration.) This is necessary because each point on the slit image illuminates the entire collimator surface equally, and an attenuator placed at the slit image will therefore uniformly reduce the light over the entire collimator surface as it is driven into the beam (i.e., no shadows of comb teeth are formed on the collimator). Furthermore, at the slit image the light beam is narrow, and a linear comb will attenuate the beam uniformly across its width; at some point which is not a slit image the light beam will be wider, and one side of the beam will be attenuated to a different degree than the other side as a result of the slope of the comb teeth.

Other types of attenuators that need not be placed at the slit or a slit image permit some simplification and flexibility in spectrometer design. But as the majority of commercial spectrometers in common use employ a comb-type attenuator, we shall not take space here to describe other types.

The double-beam spectrometer has several advantages:

1. Linearity of ordinate ($\% T$) measurement depends only on the linearity of the attenuator comb. This takes a good deal of the design exactness load off the amplifier and electric circuits, for their only requirement is to determine the beam that is most intense and to move the reference-beam attenuator accordingly. It is a relatively simple matter to make the taper on comb teeth quite linear.

2. Double-beam spectrometers give a much flatter I_0 line (i.e., the locus of points representing 100% transmission at all wavelengths). This is useful and desirable in scanned spectra and results from the fact that minor fluctuations in source temperature, amplifier behavior, or slight imperfections in the slit-width-control cam are canceled out, for they affect both beams in an identical manner.

3. The strong absorptions of CO_2 and H_2O, always present in the atmosphere, are nearly completely canceled out.

4. The spectrometer records directly the ratio of I, the light intensity emerging from the material in the sample beam, to I_0, the light intensity in the reference beam, which is the same as the light intensity incident on the sample ($\% T = I/I_0$). Difference spectra between two samples, including such techniques as compensation of solvent bands or simplification of spectra of mixtures by compensating out some of the components, can therefore be obtained. (This technique is discussed at length in Chapter 7.)

The double-beam spectrometer also has certain disadvantages when compared to a single-beam spectrometer:

1. Only the *difference* between sample- and reference-beam energy is available as a signal; a signal proportional to the light energy in either beam of the spectrometer is not available. This is unfortunate, for it is the latter signal that is an index of the spectrometer's performance or its ability to perform. Should some difficulty arise while a spectrum is being obtained, as a decrease in source output or amplifier gain, it is not readily apparent, and thus a spectrum with poor ordinate

accuracy may be produced without the operator's knowledge of its shortcomings. Such a situation, should it occur when quantitative analyses are being made, can be most troublesome.

2. The double-beam spectrometer, being more complex than the single-beam, is more likely to get out of order and usually does. The large "servo loop," which includes nearly every component in the spectrometer, is difficult to maintain and has several problems associated with it (discussed in the next section).

3. Because there are two beams in proximity in the sampling area, certain bulky sampling systems, such as multireflection gas cells and microscope devices, cannot be accommodated in the sample beam without disturbing the reference beam unless special design precautions are taken. Therefore in this sense the double-beam spectrometer is somewhat less versatile than the single-beam spectrometer.

The foregoing considerations indicate that double-beam spectrometers generally find their greatest use in production of scanned spectra for qualitative analysis, survey spectra, frequency studies, and similar applications. The double-beam optical-null spectrometers have become the "work horses" of laboratories that are primarily concerned with study and analysis of organic compounds.

C. The double-beam ratio-recording spectrometer

The biggest single disadvantage of the optical-null double-beam spectrometer—the absence of a signal describing the light energy with which the spectrometer operates—is overcome by the ratio-recording double-beam type. This system of photometry does not employ a light attenuator in the reference beam but measures the light intensity in both beams more or less independently and records the electrical *ratio* of their amplified signals.

In order to do this, it is necessary that the amplifier system be able to distinguish between the signals of the two beams. This may be accomplished in various ways by a judicious choice of multiple chopping so that two different frequencies are produced at the detector. These frequencies are chosen so that each of the two signals produced is some simple function of the light intensities in both beams. One possible method is illustrated by Figure 4-9: (*a*) is the form of chopper used, and (*b*) is the square waveform generated by the detector. If the chopper rotates at frequency f, the electric signal is a superposition of a signal of f cps, proportional to $I_0 - I$, and a signal of $2f$ cps, proportional to $\frac{1}{2}(I_0 + I)$. This waveform (*b*) is amplified by a broadband amplifier; the signals are then "demodulated" by a suitable

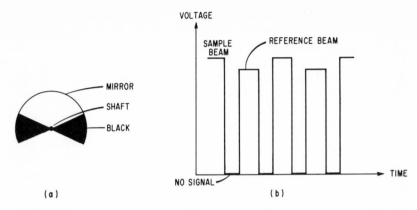

VOLTAGE

SAMPLE
BEAM

REFERENCE BEAM

MIRROR

SHAFT

BLACK

NO SIGNAL

TIME

(a)

(b)

FIGURE 4-9   One method of chopping in a ratio-recording spectrometer.

switching circuit (synchronized with the chopper) and filtered. The result of the switching and filtering operation is two dc voltages, one proportional to the light intensity of the sample beam, the other to the light intensity of the reference beam. The *ratio* of these voltages, obtained with a resistance network, is equal to $I/I_0 = \% T$ and is further amplified and recorded. (This and several other possible systems of ratio recording are described in Reference 6.)

An electric null system is used in the actual recording process. A part of the resistance network that obtains the voltage ratio is a slidewire; this slidewire and the recorder pen are actuated together by a servomotor. If the intensity of the sample beam should change in relation to the reference beam, a voltage is produced in the resistance network which drives the servomotor and moves the slidewire until this driving voltage is balanced out, or nulled. As a result, the only components in the recording servo loop are slidewire, power amplifier, and servomotor, compared to the optical-null system whose servo loop includes nearly every optical, electronic, and mechanical component in the spectrometer.

The ratio-recording type of double-beam spectrometer has certain advantages over the optical-null type:

1. A signal proportional to the reference-beam energy is available as a check on the ability of the spectrometer to perform and is useful in programming the amplifier response for certain special purposes. (See Chapter 7.)

2. The size of the servo loop is reduced, including now only the final stages of electronics and the servomotor. Also, the filter section,

Photometry: single- and double-beam spectrometers   **71**

the biggest factor in determining the time constant, is now outside the servo loop, which decreases in great measure certain servo-loop problems encountered in optical-null spectrometers. (See Section III-E.)

3. Some of the difficulties of using a light attenuator are avoided. (Some of these difficulties have already been noted, others are discussed in detail; see especially Section III-E.)

4. In an electric ratioing system it is a simple matter to expand a weak signal over a larger portion of the chart by making a few changes in the resistance network; ordinate expansion in an optical-null spectrometer requires several additional mechanical or electric parts.

However, the ratio-recording system has certain disadvantages when compared to the optical-null system:

1. The linearity of response of the optical-null spectrometer depends only on the linearity of the light-attenuating device (usually easily made linear over most of its range, except the very low end), whereas in a ratio-recording system the linearity of response depends on a large number of electronic components whose aggregate response is made linear only with some difficulty.

2. The simultaneous chopping of both beams at different frequencies in the ratio-recording system leads to periods in the chopping schedule when both beams are dark at the same time. Obviously, this situation results in lower inherent electric signal strength for given light intensity, and the effective signal-to-noise ratio (see next section) will therefore be lower by a factor as large as 2 (depending on the chopping and demodulating system) compared to an optical-null system.

Ratio-recording infrared spectrometers are not in common use in most chemical applications at the present time. Whether this situation will change is hard to predict.

D. Double monochromators

In Chapter 3 it was pointed out that the only way in which a single-prism monochromator can be improved in design is by the use of larger optics. Beyond a certain point this rapidly becomes expensive and impractical. If greater resolution is a necessity, it can be achieved in another way—with a double monochromator.

A second great advantage of the double monochromator is the virtually complete elimination of stray radiation. As a practical matter, *only* a double monochromator will ever be completely free from stray radiation when used in the region just above the practical cutoff of its prism (e.g., $7\frac{1}{2}$–8 μ with CaF_2 prisms, 14–15 μ with NaCl prisms, 22–24 μ with KBr prisms).

A double monochromator may be made in two ways. The first consists of two monochromators (see Chapter 3) arranged in series so that the exit slit of the first monochromator also serves as the entrance slit of the second. This arrangement gives better resolution at equivalent energy through-put than a single monochromator. If both monochromators are to be of high quality, the arrangement will be expensive but probably less so than a single monochromator of comparable performance made with large optics. This sort of double monochromator may be used in either a single-beam or double-beam spectrometer type.

The second method is the so-called "double-pass" system, in which the light normally arriving at the monochromator exit slit from the collimator is reflected back to the collimator for a second trip through the collimator-prism-Littrow-mirror combination. This system also gives improved performance but at only small extra cost. There is, however, a difficulty in the double-pass system: Since the geometry of the system (see Figure 4-10) demands some crowding of optical parts, certain light frequencies from the first pass will reach the exit slit directly and will be of different frequency than light reaching the exit slit from the second pass (the desired signal). These signals can be separated, however, by placing a light chopper at the small mirrors used to reflect the light from the first pass back for the second pass. The light emerging from the exit slit after only one pass is therefore not chopped, hence its signal is not amplified by the ac amplifier, whereas light from the second pass is chopped and amplified as a signal.* This arrangement is quite satisfactory in single-beam spectrometer application, but no one has yet devised a way to make a spectrometer both double-beam and double-pass without the use of multiple choppers and chopping frequencies.

The double monochromator in which both monochromators are the prism type will probably soon become obsolete because of the advent of gratings. In practical application a grating monochromator *must* be preceded by a prism monochromator (see Chapter 3); hence, if a double monochromator is to be constructed, the second portion of it should be the grating type, for this combination is capable of considerably higher resolving power than a double-prism monochromator.

---

* Placing the chopper at this point has the disadvantage that any radiation originating between the source and the chopper will become a signal. Most important is the heating or cooling of the entrance slit jaws, which will cause the spectrometer to drift.

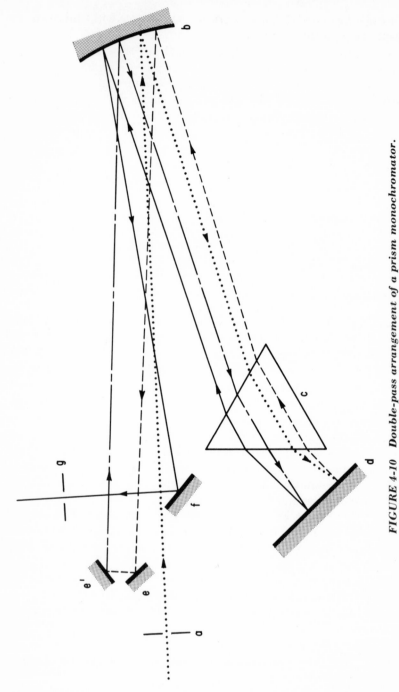

FIGURE 4-10 Double-pass arrangement of a prism monochromator.

74

We have included this discussion of double-prism monochromators simply because they are still in wide use today.

III. The limitations in practical operation of a double-beam optical-null spectrometer

The limiting optical factors of spectrometers were discussed in Chapter 3, and the limitations of infrared detectors were noted in Section I of this chapter. We now discuss the relation of these and certain other limiting factors to practical spectrometer operation. Because, as we have noted, the optical-null double-beam spectrometer is the one enjoying widest use today in chemical applications, the following discussion of limitations in spectrometer operation is based on this spectrometer type. The discussion in this section can be applied to other spectrometer types with only slight and usually obvious modifications.

A. Spectrometer Block Diagram

It will be helpful in the following discussion to visualize the spectrometer as consisting of several large "blocks." (The details of the construction of each block have been outlined in this and in the preceding chapter.) The diagram is given in Figure 4-11.

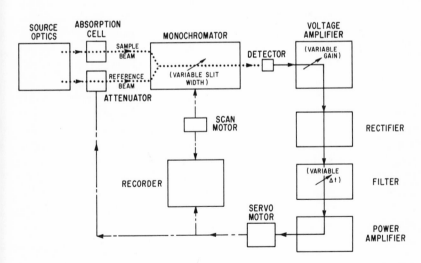

FIGURE 4-11 Block diagram of the optical-null double-beam spectrometer.

The dotted lines represent light signal, the solid lines, electric signal, and the dot-dashed lines, the mechanical signal which drives the recorder and reference beam attenuator, thereby closing the servo loop. The slanted arrows in the monochromator, amplifier, and filter sections illustrate that detector output, amplification value, and servo time constant can be varied by changing the setting of slit width, amplifier-gain control, and resistor-capacitor values, respectively. The effect of each of these controls on spectrometer performance, and their interrelation with each other, is now considered.

B. Noise

As discussed above, probably the largest contribution to the noise level in the spectrometer is the *Johnson noise* in the detector, which was given by equation 4-2:

$$E_j{}^2 = 4kTR(\Delta f) \times 10^{-7}.$$

For average practical values of the parameters in this equation the noise level is of the order of 10^{-9} volt at the detector.

As we have seen, an electronic amplifier is necessary to increase the detector output signal to a voltage suitable for driving a recorder. But while this is being done the noise signal is also amplified and will appear on the recorded spectrum. The noise level on the recorded spectrum, then, depends on the parameters in equation 4-2, which are largely fixed (except for Δf—see later), and amplifier gain; for the purpose of this discussion we shall say that the noise level depends only on the setting of the amplifier-gain control.

Now, the recording servo demands a certain level of energy input to make it operate accurately. This level can best be described in terms of signal volts produced per unit displacement of the light attenuator. If this value is too low, the recording servo is sluggish and does not follow the changes in signal level rapidly enough to produce a faithful recording of the detected signal. On the other hand, if this value is too high, the servo system will break into oscillation, or "hunt." (See later.) Depending on the magnitude of the signal at the detector, then, the *gain control* must be set to deliver the correct value of volts-per-unit-attenuator-displacement to the recording servomotor, and *the noise level on the recorded spectrum depends on this setting.*

A desirable condition of noise level exists when the average peak-to-peak distance (the usual method of expressing recorder noise level) is not significantly greater than the thickness of the line drawn by the recorder pen. The noise becomes the limiting factor in spectrometer operation when the average peak-to-peak level is so high that a small absorption band cannot be determined in it. (See the sketches of these situations.)

"Good" noise level
(low gain)

"Poor" noise level
(high gain)

C. Signal and signal-to-noise ratio

The signal voltage produced at the detector in the optical-null spectrometer depends on the difference of absolute light intensity in the two beams (sample and reference cycles). Hence the greater the light intensity in the two beams, the greater the difference signal that can be developed between them. For a given optical arrangement the detector signal can therefore be increased only by widening the monochromator slits. As discussed in Chapter 3, the signal strength at the detector depends on the *square* of the slit setting. (In this case we are interested in *absolute* energy, not in energy per spectral slit width.)

If the monochromator slits are widened and detector output signal thus increased, the amplifier gain must be decreased in order that the servomotor receive the correct value of volts-per-unit-attenuator-displacement. When the amplifier gain is reduced, the recorded noise level is decreased and the situation is described as a good or high signal-to-noise ratio. On the other hand, should the slits be made narrower, the signal strength at the detector will be reduced, and the gain must be increased to provide the correct level of volts-per-unit-attenuator-displacement for the servomotor. This results in increased noise level, and the situation is described as poor, or low, signal-to-noise ratio.

It will be recalled that narrower slits lead to better resolution, whereas use of wide slits leads to poorer resolution. What is gained in resolution by narrowing the slits is lost in increased recorded noise level, and, conversely, what can be gained in lower recorded noise level by widening the slits is lost in resolution. Note the sketches

Narrow slits, high gain:
high resolution,
high noise.

Wide slits, low gain:
low resolution,
low noise.

which illustrate these conditions. It should be borne in mind, however, that resolution (spectral slit width) is proportional to the *first* power of slit width, whereas signal-to-noise ratio is proportional to the *square* of the slit width.

D. Recording time

When the spectrometer is scanning an absorption band, the recorder pen (and light attenuator) is always a bit behind the actual transmission of the chemical sample being measured because it takes a finite amount of time for the difference signal at the detector to be amplified, rectified, filtered, and recorded. The over-all time delay results principally from three factors: (*a*) the band pass of the amplifier, (*b*) the time constant of the R-C network of the filter section, and (*c*) the mechanical inertia of the moving parts in the recorder and attenuator. These factors are effectively equivalent: all have the effect of increasing the time necessary for the recorder to recognize a change in the detector signal and respond to it. These factors therefore determine Δf, the so-called servo-loop band pass, to which the time constant is inversely proportional. In view of equation 4-2,

$$E_j{}^2 = 4kTR(\Delta f) \times 10^{-7},$$

it is apparent that Johnson noise, presumably the largest contribution to limiting noise level, can be *decreased* by decreasing the amplifier band pass, increasing the inertia in the pen servomotor-light attenuator mechanical system, or by increasing the capacitance or resistance in the filter section of the electronics; the last is the most convenient to adjust in practice. However, in order to take advantage of these effects, the speed of scan must be reduced, ˉfor although noise level has been limited so also has the speed with which the amplifier can respond correctly to a detector signal. Thus, if a lower noise level is required, it can be attained by increasing the time of scan and adjusting Δf accordingly. Because E_j is proportional to $\sqrt{\Delta f}$, it follows that *signal-to-noise ratio is proportional to the square root of scan time.*

If better resolution is required, scan time could be increased but with slits narrowed so that increased signal-to-noise ratio is traded for increased resolution. Since signal-to-noise ratio is proportional to the *square* of slit setting, whereas spectral slit width is proportional to the *first power* of slit setting, it follows that resolution is proportional to the *fourth root* of scan time. Thus, in order to obtain a twofold increase in resolution at equivalent signal-to-noise ratio, the scan time must be increased by the obviously impractical factor of 16.

E. *Some additional considerations of servo response*

When the servo system is at or near balance, the ratio of the value of volts-per-unit-attenuator-displacement to that of amplified detector-noise voltage is what determines the ultimate accuracy with which the system can record a signal. For a given slit setting and time constant, this ratio is independent of gain control setting, for both its factors vary linearly with amplifier gain. But if the servo system is even to begin to record at all accurately, the value of volts-per-unit-attenuator-displacement must be held within close limits, as we have already mentioned and the reasons for which we shall now amplify.

If the amplifier-gain control is set too low, and the value of volts-per-unit-attenuator-displacement is thus too low, the pen servo system simply lacks the power to respond to small correction signals or to reach the correct balance point in a time consistent with servo time constant and scanning rate. Under these conditions the spectrometer is said to be "dead." A "dead" spectrum is characterized by square corners (or "stairsteps") in place of a smooth curve representing rise or fall in transmission.

"Dead" spectra can result from causes other than insufficient amplifier gain. Malfunction of the detector or excess friction in the recording pen and light attenuator mechanical system are occasionally responsible. More insidious, however, because it is less easily noted, is the deadness that is produced by simultaneous absorption of light intensity by both sample and reference beams over a short region of the spectrum. We have noted that one of the advantages of double-beam spectrometer operation is the ability to cancel atmospheric (or other) absorptions so that they are not observed in the spectrum. But the atmosphere is still in the spectrometer and is absorbing radiation at its characteristic frequencies. As the spectrometer scan enters such a frequency region, the light intensity in both beams is rather suddenly reduced, so that any difference signal between the two beams will also be reduced and will result in a drop in the value of volts-per-unit-attenuator-displacement. The spectrometer will therefore be "dead" over this frequency region; because such a region is often narrow, the effect on the spectrum is likely to be overlooked or ignored. Transmission measurements made in these regions will be less reliable as the amount of light removed from both beams is greater, unless the value of volts-per-unit-attenuator-displacement is maintained at its usual level throughout the scan (see discussion of servo-energy programming in Chapter 7). Situations of absorption in both beams of the spectrometer usually develop from atmospheric absorptions or absorption bands of solvents commonly used in infrared work. The frequencies of many of these absorptions are given in Chapter 5.

On the other hand, if the gain control is increased to a level that is too high and the value of volts-per-unit-attenuator-displacement becomes too high, then when the servo system is slightly out of balance a correction signal exists which is too large. As a result, the pen and attenuator are driven too rapidly and, because of the finite time delay between detector signal and servo response, go right through the balance point and far enough in the opposite direction so that the new correction signal is larger than the original. The attenuator now moves back through the balance point more rapidly than before; the process is continually repeated, with more and more violent pen motion, until, in extreme cases, the pen is waving wildly across the entire recording chart. The servo system is said to be in oscillation, or "hunting," when this occurs; the frequency of this oscillation depends on the magnitude of the servo time constant.

Even with the gain control set at reasonable level, a somewhat similar problem develops when the servo system is momentarily far out of balance. This occurs when the spectrometer is in the process of scanning over a deep, sharp band; the servo time delay causes it to be far out of balance when on the side of a sharp band, hence the servomotor is momentarily given a large surge of power, causing the pen to move rapidly. As the servomotor, pen, and attenuator have inertia, they will tend to stay in motion and may easily coast past the point where balance would occur. This difficulty is known as *overshoot*.

In order to avoid overshoot (and, in extreme cases, oscillation) on one hand and a sluggish servo system with resultant "dead" spectra on the other, yet not place a nearly impossible accuracy requirement on gain-control setting, the servo system must be *damped*. The damping device must have the property that it will exert a force counter to the driving force when the system is in motion but must exert no force at all when the system is stationary or moving only slowly. Any device that has this property will serve; since damping can be accomplished in a variety of ways, one finds different methods in use in different makes and models of spectrometers.

As with gain-control setting, the level of damping is important. If the servo system is underdamped, overshoot will be observed. The presence of overshoot gives the recorded spectrum a false look of high resolution: the sharp bands become sharper yet, and "valleys" between adjacent sharp bands become deeper. However, band intensities so recorded will tend to be incorrect and unreproducible; overshoot should therefore be avoided. If the servo system is overdamped, it will come to equilibrium too slowly and thus will not have enough "time" to find correctly the maxima of sharp bands (although broader bands will not be affected). A useful compromise is to arrange the damping system and gain control so that about 5% overshoot of the balance point results if a partially opaque object (such as a screen) is suddenly thrust into the sample beam.

Ideally, the servo system should be stationary when an absolute zero signal is being received (i.e., when both sample and reference beam are completely blocked). In practice, however, the servo system will usually drift slowly in one direction or the other, because any slight dc voltage in the filter system will cause the servomotor to turn and no correction signal will be made as the result of attenuator motion. A small amount of drift is tolerable, but a rapid drift at zero signal can be overcome by a desired signal only with difficulty, hence must be eliminated. A potentiometer circuit is therefore incorporated at some point in the power amplifier which will provide adjustment of drift.

Another problem of the optical-null servo system exists in regions of very low sample beam light transmission. As the pen travels to zero transmission on the recorder chart when scanning through a band having total absorption, the reference-beam attenuator closes completely, with the result that no light reaches the detector from either beam of the spectrometer. At this point, the spectrometer is "dead," for the servo system is being given no signal to adjust attenuator position. If the servo-system drift causes the pen to creep to lower transmission, the zero "bottom" of the absorption band will be misshapen and peculiar in appearance.

Furthermore, it is difficult to make a light attenuator strictly linear in the last 2 or 3% transmission above complete cutoff. Bits of dust or dirt or small errors in the comb easily render the attenuator nonlinear in this region. Hence the region of $\sim$3% and lower transmission is not accurate.

The first difficulty can be circumvented to some extent by arranging the servo system so that it always has a small amount of upward drift. Now, when the light attenuator closes completely in the midst of a completely absorbing band, the servo drift will move the attenuator open until the signal generated returns the pen position and light attenuator to zero. This process will repeat continuously until the region of total absorption by the sample beam is passed.

A much better solution to both problems of the attenuator in the region of low transmission is the so-called "light bypass" system. (See Reference 4.) This device is arranged so that about 4% of the reference-beam energy (which normally is being discarded during the sample-beam half of the chopping cycle) is bypassed around the sample and recombined with the sample beam on the sample-beam half of the chopping cycle. This always keeps a constant 4% of the total energy in the sample beam, even at complete absorption by the sample, so that the attenuator is never driven further closed than 4% of transmission. Hence the lower nonlinear portion of the attenuator is never used; also, the servo system always has energy, even at complete sample absorption, and the problem of a "dead" zero is avoided.

Because of these difficulties with the light attenuator at low transmission, it is probably best to avoid intensity measurements for quantitative analytical applications on any absorption bands having transmission minima below about 5%. It should be remarked that ratio-recording systems of double-beam photometry do not have these problems of the light attenuator.

F. Practical spectrometer operation and testing

Experience has shown that in the comparative study of infrared spectra, as a method of elucidation of organic structure, greater skill and better understanding of the process result when all spectra are obtained under the same conditions (this point is discussed further in Chapter 5). As we have already seen, no fixed set of conditions for spectrometer operation is ideal for every case, and if we insist that all spectra be obtained under such fixed conditions certain compromises must be made.

For purely practical reasons an elapsed time of about 15 minutes is a good compromise for obtaining a spectrum in the region 2–15 μ with a double-beam prism spectrometer with rock-salt optics. (This kind of spectrometer will probably continue to be the most common in chemical applications until grating spectrometers come into wider use.) This is about the minimum time in which a chemical material can be weighed, diluted with proper solvents to make quantitative solutions, and placed in an absorption cell, or about the time required to prepare a satisfactory oil mull or pressed halide disk. (See Chapter 5.) For this reason there is little advantage in running the spectrometer more rapidly; samples could not be prepared fast enough to take advantage of this possible time economy.

On the other hand, we have seen that improvement in signal-to-noise ratio is proportional to the *square root* of scan time, whereas improvement in resolution is proportional to the *fourth root* of scan time. The large factor of scan-time increase necessary to improve the spectrum materially is simply not warranted for the production of spectra in condensed phases which are to be used in characterization of organic structures or for simple quantitative analysis. The few exceptions to this rule are usually in the realm of special quantitative analytical applications and are discussed in Chapters 6 and 7. If better resolution than is obtainable with the optimum prism in a particular spectral region is mandatory, it is best done with a grating spectrometer; an attempt to produce it with a prism spectrometer by increase of scan time is impractical.

The magnitude of the time constant of the servo loop must be consistent with the established recording time. If it is determined that this standard time shall be, say, 15 minutes, the time constant must be set at such a value that reasonable compromise will be struck between noise level and ability of the recording system to reproduce faithfully small, sharp absorption bands.

Slit setting is to some extent a matter of preference. The collective years of experience of many people have shown that operation at noise levels greater than 1 % of full scale, even for qualitative applications, does not inspire confidence in the spectrum. It seems preferable to keep the noise level at or below this low value, and thus have a reasonably high "confidence level" in the spectra produced, and to accept the resolution produced. If resolution obtained under these circumstances is not felt to be sufficient, improvement or replacement of the spectrometer would appear in order.

The slit-width program *should not be altered* from the value that will produce the desired resolution and noise compromise, as just described, except for special applications. Some of these applications are described in the following chapters; usually they require *increase* of the slit-aperture program.

The higher the amplifier-gain control, the better the spectrometer can record faithfully a complex spectrum with sharp absorptions up to the point at which the capacity of the damping device is exceeded and the servo system shows excessive overshoot. It is the author's opinion that for given slit setting the gain control should be set at such a value that overshoot will be about 5% when a partially opaque object (such as a piece of wire screen) is suddenly thrust into the sample beam.

All three of the parameters just discussed—speed and time constant, slit width, and gain—influence the spectrometer noise level. Therefore all must be adjusted together to optimum standard values, as described above. Once these values have been established, the parameters *should not be "tinkered with."* It is a great temptation to organic chemists to "twiddle the knobs" when many such knobs present themselves for twiddling. The parameters we have discussed should be varied *only when a specific, previously considered purpose is served* by doing so (usually an increase in signal-to-noise ratio for a special quantitative analysis—see Chapters 6 and 7). It cannot be emphasized too strongly that skill in interpretation of spectra will best be attained if the spectra studied have always been obtained under similar conditions.

An I_0 trim adjustment is found on all double-beam spectrometers. This device consists of a sort of partial "light attenuator" in the sample beam which will take up to $\sim 30\%$ of the radiation out of this beam. This adjustment is provided so that different chemical samples, with different inherent transparencies in regions of no spectral absorption, may all produce spectra of comparable I_0. The sample-beam light intensity is reduced with this adjustment for highly transparent samples (as solutions in well-polished cells) or is increased for less highly transparent samples (such as mulls, pressed disks, or old foggy cells).

The spectrometer should be tested regularly; if it is in constant use, it should be tested at least once a day. A comprehensive test program, which can be completed in reasonable time and which checks most of the critical performance points of spectrometer operation, is now described. (These tests or their equivalent, and sometimes additional ones as well, are described in the operation manual of most commercial spectrometers.)

Drift. As we have noted, at condition of zero signal in both beams the recording servo may tend to drift in one direction or the other. A small amount of drift is tolerable, but tests should be made to see that it is not large. It is checked by placing opaque objects in both beams of the spectrometer and noting the speed of pen motion, which should be small. An adjustment is provided somewhere in the spectrometer electronics to correct it. On certain commercial spectrometer models the drift must be set so that it has a slight upward value. (See previous discussion.)

Servo-loop energy (volts-per-unit-attenuator-displacement). The method by which this energy can be measured varies with spectrometer makes and models. If measurement of this value is provided for in the spectrometer, the gain control is set so that the recommended value is obtained. If no such method for measurement is provided, the gain should be set just comfortably short of servo oscillation, as previously discussed.

Overshoot and dead spot. With a screen or some other partially opaque object in the sample beam such that $\sim 50\%$ of its light is transmitted, a completely opaque object is inserted in the sample beam and suddenly withdrawn. In returning to the 50% transmission level, the recorder pen should overshoot about 5% before coming to balance. An opaque object is then placed in the reference beam and suddenly withdrawn. After overshooting about 5% in the other direction, the pen should come to the same balance point as before, within a value of the noise level at which the spectrometer is to operate ($\frac{1}{2}\%$ of full scale or less).

I_0 *check.* The spectrometer is scanned over its full range with nothing in either beam. Noise level should be less than $\sim \frac{1}{2}\%$, and the line produced on the recording chart should be essentially flat. Appearance of positive or negative "absorption bands" indicates dirt on optical parts peculiar to sample or reference beam, respectively.* (This particular test probably need not be done each day.)

* When the scan goes through regions of atmospheric absorption (especially CO_2 at ~ 2350 cm^{-1}) the spectrometer momentarily becomes dead, and often a small, peculiar-appearing discontinuity will be produced in the recorded spectrum. This is unavoidable unless the spectrometer is evacuated or well purged with dry CO_2-free air.

Zero and scattered light check. The spectrometer is scanned over its full range with a thin piece of glass in the sample beam. From the point at which glass ceases to transmit infrared radiation ($\sim 5\mu$) to the long wave limit of the spectrometer the recorder pen should be reasonably colinear with the zero per cent transmission line of the chart. Also, a 0.1-mm absorption cell containing CS_2 and another containing CCl_4 (see Chapter 5) should be scanned in the regions 6–7 and 12–14 μ, respectively. These solvents are totally absorbing in the regions indicated, and the recorded spectrum in these regions should be very nearly colinear with the glass zero just obtained. (This is a far more useful *and revealing* test for scattered light than those usually described.)

Standard spectrum. Most important is a comprehensive check of over-all spectrometer performance, both with respect to ordinate and abscissa accuracy. This can probably best be accomplished by obtaining a spectrum of some standard material and checking frequencies and absorption intensities of several of its absorption bands. The choice of a standard material to produce this spectrum deserves some consideration, for its state and concentration must be absolutely reproducible with no question or effort. A thin film of polystyrene plastic gives a spectrum reasonably satisfactory for this purpose, but the spectrum lacks the moderately strong, sharp bands in the longer wavelength region that are most useful for making these tests. Any crystalline solid sample for this purpose is difficult to keep uniform; solutions or gases require strict attention to concentration or pressure; most liquids, when scanned undiluted in absorption cells of reasonable length, produce a spectrum that is too intense to be useful. A standard material that has proven useful is liquid propylene dibromide, CH_3—$CHBr$—CH_2Br, scanned undiluted in a 0.03-mm cell. This particular material produces a spectrum which has a wide distribution of absorptions of convenient frequencies and intensities and no unusual chemical activity; it is conveniently handled and easily purified by distillation. (No doubt other liquids could be found that would perform the function equally well.) The spectrum of propylene dibromide is shown in Figure 4-12, together with I_0 check; glass, CS_2, and CCl_4 zero checks.

In laboratories in which a good deal of analytical infrared work is done and in which more than one double-beam spectrometer is employed it is worthwhile to keep continuous plots of the various band intensities measured from the standard spectra used as instrument checks. Such records provide a good basis for estimation of long-term spectrometer accuracy.

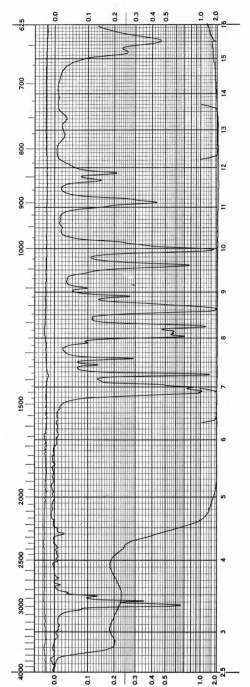

FIGURE 4-12   A recommended daily spectrometer check.

87

IV. Special devices for improving spectrometer performance

The features that have been discussed at some length in these last two chapters are common to all commercial spectrometers. Although they will not better the ultimate performance of the spectrometer (only possible by improvement of optics and detector), certain other devices will nevertheless improve the practical results that may be obtained or increase the convenience with which they can be obtained.

A. Scale expansion

It is possible, by various electrical or mechanical means, to expand either the abscissa (wavelength) or ordinate (transmission) scales. This expansion does not, of course, improve resolution or increase the ultimate accuracy with which transmission measurements may be made, but it may be convenient in a variety of special applications.

Abscissa expansion is especially useful when (a) integrating absorption band areas (see Chapter 6), (b) comparing absorptions of similar frequencies in a series of related compounds, and (c) studying vibration-rotation bands obtained with the high resolution of a grating spectrometer.

Ordinate expansion is effective when very small pen deflections are to be measured. Expansion of the ordinate scale does not alter signal-to-noise ratio, of course, and therefore recorded noise level is raised along with recorded signal level when this expansion is employed. But when noise level has been reduced by widening spectrometer slits ordinate expansion is a method of realizing the full advantage of a high signal-to-noise ratio; this is particularly useful in certain special quantitative analytical applications. (See Chapter 7.)

B. Single-, double-beam interchange

Because the monochromator parts are identical, whether the spectrometer is single- or double-beam, and because the single-beam spectrometer contains no parts not contained in a double-beam system, it is possible to make a double-beam spectrometer also serve as a single-beam instrument with a few simple changes in the electrical circuitry of the servo system and by blocking out the reference beam. On certain commercial spectrometers this change-over can be effected by one simple control to give the user the advantages of both single- and double-beam operation in one instrument. (See Section II.)

C. Automatic speed suppression

Because of the requirement that the recording servo be damped, it takes a not insignificant amount of time for the recording pen to reach the bottom of an absorption band. If the band is sharp, not only must this be done quickly, but the pen must immediately reverse itself and return to a position of high transmission as the spectrometer scan leaves the absorption band. Consequently, it is difficult for the servo system to record the exact absorption maximum accurately. This difficulty could be overcome if the spectrometer scan rate were brought to a small value as each strong, sharp absorption band were entered. It can be done manually, but a much better method has been devised. The amplified ac detector signal is a measure of the imbalance between sample- and reference-beam transmission at any time; hence it is an index of the sharpness of transmission change. Therefore this signal can be used to actuate a suitable electrical device which will cause attenuation of the scan motor speed in such a manner that scan rate is decreased to a low value when the servo system is more than, say, 1% out of balance but at its standard value when the servo system is in balance. The result is a relatively rapid rate of scan through regions of little or no absorption but a slow rate when the spectrometer is scanning a sharp absorption band. Since a spectrum obtained in solution does not usually contain a large number of strong, sharp absorptions, the increase in over-all scan time caused by this device is not significant, but the increase in accuracy of the measured values of sharp absorption maxima is materially increased. This device is known as "automatic speed suppression," and the sketch in Figure 4-13 describes its operation.

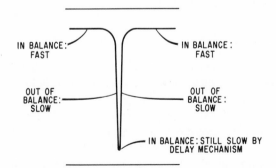

FIGURE 4-13 Illustration of the operation of automatic speed suppression.

Devices for improving spectrometer performance **89**

D. Automatic servo-energy control

One of the disadvantages of the optical-null double-beam spectrometer is that no signal proportional to the energy in the reference beam is available. Such a signal is useful when difference spectra are produced (see Chapter 7) and can be obtained from an optical-null spectrometer by a slight modification. Two small black segments are added to the chopper half-round mirror at its edges, so that as the chopper changes the monochromator view from one beam to the other a small region intervenes in which no energy at all enters the monochromator. This chopper is similar to that shown in Figure 4-9a, but the "black" regions need not be nearly so wide.

The voltage-versus-time curve at the detector (neglecting finite detector heat capacity) now has an appearance similar to that of Figure 4-9b, but again the "black" regions of no signal are narrower. Two signals are present at the detector: an n cps signal, proportional to the intensity difference between beams, and a $2n$ cps signal, proportional to the reference-beam energy *and* the reference-beam attenuator position. The n cps signal is amplified in the usual manner by a sharply tuned n cps amplifier and records the spectrum. The other signal can be separately amplified by a $2n$ cps amplifier, and, when suitably corrected for attenuator position, gives the desired signal proportional to the absolute energy in the spectrometer.

As has been discussed, to make the recording servo perform correctly, the value of servo-loop energy (or volts-per-unit-attenuator-displacement) must be held reasonably constant. In a normal scan, when no material is in the reference beam, this condition is easily achieved, as we have seen. But if a chemical material is placed in the reference beam, as, for example, when difference spectra are being obtained, the reference-beam energy will vary as the scan proceeds; hence the servo-loop energy will vary. However, this value could be kept constant by varying the amplifier gain control or by varying the slit width in an appropriate manner as the energy in the reference-beam changes.

Now, the $2n$ cps signal (after suitable correction for reference-beam attenuator position), being proportional to reference-beam energy, is just the sort of signal necessary to program the gain control or slit width to accomplish this. This signal can therefore be used to drive a second servo system which will vary the amplifier gain in such a manner that, even with fluctuations in reference-beam energy, servo-loop energy will remain constant. This device is known as *automatic gain control* or *automatic slit control* (depending on the method used); its application is discussed fully in Chapter 7.

90   Spectrometer performance and operation

Selected references

1. Strong, J., *Concepts of Classical Optics*, Freeman, San Francisco, Calif., 1958.
2. Williams, V., "Infrared Instrumentation and Techniques," *Rev. Sci. Instr.* **19**, 135 (1948).
3. "Instruction Manual: Perkin-Elmer Infrared Equipment," Vol. 1: *Introduction to Infrared Spectrometry*, The Perkin Elmer Corp., Norwalk, Conn., 1952.
4. Herscher, L., H. Ruhl, and N. Wright, "An Improved Optical Null Spectrometer," *J. Opt. Soc. Am.* **48**, 36 (1958).
5. Lecomte, J., "Spectroscopie dans l'infrarouge," *Handbuch der Physik*, Band XXVI (pp. 248 ff; pp. 275 ff), Springer-Verlag, Berlin, 1958.
6. Golay, M., "Comparison of Various Infrared Spectrometric Systems," *J. Opt. Soc. Am.* **46**, 422 (1956).
7. Brügel, W., *An Introduction to Infrared Spectroscopy*, Wiley, New York, 1962.
8. Bauman, R. P., *Absorption Spectroscopy*, Wiley, New York, 1962.

5

Sample preparation techniques

One of the truly great advantages of the infrared method of chemical analysis is that it can be applied to virtually all materials, almost regardless of phase or phase mixtures, colloidal state, turbidity, molecular weight, solubility, "blackness," and nearly every other gross chemical or physical property. With proper (and usually simple) techniques, nearly any material can be prepared so that its infrared spectrum can be obtained.

Although these techniques are, for the most part, simple and straightforward, it is in this area that lack of careful work is made so painfully evident in the quality of the infrared spectra produced. Most users of infrared methods in chemical applications depend on others for the design, production, and maintenance of spectrometers; but the problem of sample preparation cannot be avoided.

This is an area in which differences of opinion do exist. It will be obvious from the presentation that follows which methods the author prefers, and the reasons cited in their favor are believed to be sound. Nonetheless, the reader should be made aware that one laboratory's *modus operandi*, which will best solve the problems peculiar to it, will not necessarily be the best for another laboratory whose problems may be quite different. Experience appears to be the best guide in making decisions here.

I. Solution techniques

A useful method of obtaining an infrared absorption spectrum of a material is to dissolve it in a suitable solvent which is then placed in an appropriate absorption cell. For this purpose, of course, the solvent must be reasonably transparent to infrared radiation in the region of interest. This is by far the most common method used in quantitative analysis; it also finds extensive use in qualitative analysis.

A. The case for solution spectroscopy

The preparation of accurate solutions requires time and care; the preparation and maintenance of infrared absorption cells, with the inherent problems associated with salt windows, require special techniques. Some of the techniques by which materials can be prepared for infrared examination are simpler and less time consuming than the use of solutions, hence have found wide application. Nevertheless, when spectra are obtained in solution, some definite advantages result.

As we pointed out in the discussion of instrumentation, it is desirable to have all spectra obtained under similar conditions, unless there is a specific reason for the contrary. One of the most important of these conditions is the molecular environment of the chemical substance whose spectrum is being obtained. A molecule's infrared absorption spectrum arises basically from its internal vibrations, and we can best interpret it when the molecule is in the simplest, least complicated, and most reproducible surroundings. When this is done, the correlations between vibrational frequencies and molecular structure will be most useful and facility in their interpretation most easily gained. The gas phase would be ideal from this viewpoint; unfortunately, it is not nearly so widely applicable and has certain other drawbacks for analytical chemical spectroscopy, as discussed in Section III. *Therefore, the best manner in which to keep the molecular environment of all materials similar and simple is to place the materials in dilute solution in an inert, nonpolar solvent.*

It is sometimes argued that when the spectra of pure materials are obtained by methods not employing solutions the complications of solvent-solute interactions are avoided. However, it seems preferable to tolerate the relatively mild interactions between solute and nonpolar solvent than to attempt to interpret the much stronger interactions between neighboring polar molecules in a pure liquid or the still stronger interactions between neighboring molecules in a crystal lattice. Even in a pure nonpolar liquid the interactions of neighboring molecules will certainly be no less serious than interactions between these molecules and nonpolar solvent molecules when in dilute solution.

Furthermore, if all substances studied are examined at a standard concentration and absorption-path length, so that those of similar structure will have their analogous absorptions of roughly similar intensity, it is possible to develop some feeling for the relation of absorption-band intensity to molecular structure and to use this information to aid in identification of molecular structure. This is difficult to do with pure materials, for without dilution many of the absorption bands are inherently so intense that spectra must be obtained from very thin layers in order to have bands of useful intensity; absorption-path lengths of thin layers of sample are difficult to reproduce from sample to sample.

Finally, if the spectrum of the material being analyzed has been obtained in solution and is a mixture of two or more substances, both qualitative *and quantitative* analyses may be made from the same spectrum. If solution techniques are not used, quantitative analysis is a more difficult task and generally yields less accurate results. (See later discussion; see also Chapter 6.)

The difficulty with the solution technique is, of course, that a nonpolar liquid which will be essentially transparent throughout the chemical infrared region and which will dissolve all organic materials simply does not exist. But several liquids are reasonably good solvents and are transparent over reasonably useful ranges of the infrared region. Often a judicious combination—using one solvent in some regions, another solvent in other regions—will provide a most satisfactory method of obtaining spectra in solution. Two of the best solvents in this respect are carbon tetrachloride and carbon disulfide. They are so useful, in fact, that the proper application of the two together makes a nearly ideal situation for infrared solution spectroscopy and forms the basis for a "standard" technique which we shall now describe.

B. *The* CCl_4–CS_2 *solution technique*

The first consideration for a solvent to be used in infrared spectroscopy is its transparency to infrared radiation. Small symmetrical molecules containing little or no hydrogen generally will be more transparent in the 400–4000 cm^{-1} region than molecules containing several hydrogen atoms, for reasons that will become clear in discussion in later chapters. Two such liquids are carbon tetrachloride and carbon disulfide. Figure 5-1 shows the infrared absorption spectrum of each of these materials in a 0.1-mm absorption cell with KBr windows.

Clearly, carbon tetrachloride will serve nicely in the region of 4000–~1330 cm^{-1}; carbon disulfide is satisfactory in the region ~1330–450 cm^{-1}. Also, both materials are fairly good solvents for many organic materials.

Experience has shown that when a concentration of ~10% and a

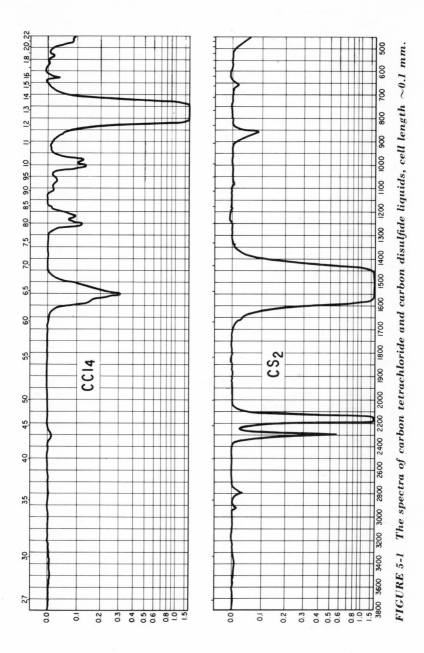

FIGURE 5-1   *The spectra of carbon tetrachloride and carbon disulfide liquids, cell length ∼0.1 mm.*

cell length of ~0.1 mm is used, most organic materials produce spectra in which a good many of their absorption bands are of reasonably convenient intensity. Solutions are probably most conveniently made up on a weight per volume basis: "10%," as used here, means 1000 mg of chemical sample in a volume of 10.0 ml of solution (or 200 mg of sample in 2.00 ml, etc.). It would be desirable to be able to obtain spectra on a constant *mole per volume* basis, but in practice this obviously is impossible when dealing with unknown materials or mixtures. At any rate, a constant weight per volume condition is the best basis on which to obtain spectra of mixtures for quantitative analysis.

Of course there are other concentrations and cell lengths that will yield the same results: 2% solutions in 0.5-mm cells or 20% solutions in 0.05-mm cells, for example. But as the cell length is increased, the few absorption bands of the CCl_4–CS_2 solvents become more intense and transmit less infrared radiation, obviously not desirable. On the other hand, cells thinner than ~0.1 mm are sometimes awkward to fill, rinse, and clean, especially when the more viscous 20% solutions are being used; furthermore, many materials soluble to the extent of 10% in CCl_4–CS_2 are not soluble to the extent of 20%; 10% solutions in cells 0.1-mm long seem to be a good compromise.

However, the so-called "CCl_4–CS_2 technique" has some disadvantages. First, for each spectrum *two* quantitative solutions—one in CCl_4, the other in CS_2—must be prepared. The spectrum must be interrupted at just the right point, namely in the range 1325–1350 cm^{-1}, to change solutions. Absorption cells used for CCl_4 solutions occasionally become contaminated with traces of CS_2, which has a highly intense absorption band maximum at 1522 cm^{-1}, noticeable even at concentrations of 0.1% or less; also, cells used for CS_2 solutions occasionally become contaminated with CCl_4, which has a similarly intense absorption band maximum at 785 cm^{-1}. These objections are only slightly more than trivial.

A somewhat more serious, but fortunately limited, disadvantage of the CCl_4–CS_2 technique is the fact that CS_2 reacts rapidly and often violently with most primary or secondary aliphatic amines.

$$CS_2 + H_2N{-}R \rightarrow R{-}\overset{\overset{\displaystyle H}{|}}{N}{-}\overset{\overset{\displaystyle S}{\|}}{C}{-}S^- \ \overset{+}{H_3N}{-}R$$

$$CS_2 + H{-}N{-}R_2 \rightarrow R_2N{-}\overset{\overset{\displaystyle S}{\|}}{C}{-}S^- \ \overset{+}{H_2N}{-}R$$

$$CS_2 + NR_3 \rightarrow \text{no reaction}$$

96   *Sample preparation techniques*

(Aromatic amines, for the most part, do not react in this way, or at least react much more slowly.) Carbon tetrachloride alone must be used to obtain the spectra of aliphatic primary and secondary amines. Reference to Figure 5-1 shows that this is not unsatisfactory except in the region $\sim$740–820 cm^{-1}, where some other technique must be employed (see later).

A still more serious disadvantage is the upkeep of 0.1-mm cells with NaCl or KBr windows, which are easily ruined if any wet samples are inadvertently introduced and even with the best care eventually become fogged and unusable. The construction, repair, care, and measurement of these cells is considered in some detail in Section II of this chapter.

In spite of these objections, the CCl_4–CS_2 solution technique appears to have such outstanding advantages over other techniques that the only and obvious reasons that it is not used for *every* application are (*a*) possible economy of time in certain applications; (*b*) certain special instances in which studies are made specifically on gas or crystalline phases; and (*c*) materials that are not soluble in CCl_4–CS_2. Reasons (*a*) and (*b*) are expanded elsewhere in this chapter; we shall now elaborate a bit on solubility limitations.

Quite conveniently, CCl_4 and CS_2 have similar solvent characteristics for most organic materials. Substances soluble in one to the extent of 10% are usually soluble in the other to roughly the same extent; substances insoluble in one solvent are almost certain to be insoluble in the other. Few exceptions to this useful rule appear to exist.

There is a reasonably large number of materials which are not soluble in CCl_4–CS_2 to the extent of 10% but which are soluble in CCl_4–CS_2 to the extent of $\sim$1%. At the concentration level of 1% the CCl_4–CS_2 technique is still valuable, but now cell lengths of $\sim$1.0 mm must be employed and some loss in solvent transmission will result. This loss of transmission is not disastrous, however, as illustrated by Figure 5-2, which gives data analogous to Figure 5-1 for CCl_4–CS_2 in a 1.0-mm cell.

Of course, a great number of chemical compounds are simply not soluble in CCl_4–CS_2 to any useful extent. These include ionic materials, both organic and inorganic, highly polar molecules, and most polymeric materials. There are other solvents which readily dissolve such materials, but almost by definition they must be molecules containing polar groups; therefore they are molecules with strong infrared absorption or low transmission. Spectra obtained in solution under these conditions are usually not satisfactory for the identification or

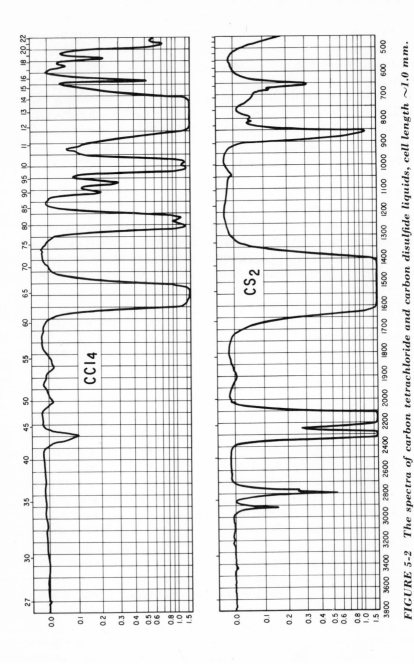

FIGURE 5-2 The spectra of carbon tetrachloride and carbon disulfide liquids, cell length ~1.0 mm.

structure-determination aspects of qualitative infrared analysis; therefore spectra of polar materials for such uses must be obtained by other techniques (see later). However, in a great number of cases solvents can be found which will dissolve polar materials yet will have at least *some* regions of high infrared transmission, so that quantitative analyses may be done by the much preferrred solution techniques. We now list some of these other solvents and discuss their uses and limitations.

C. Use of solvents other than CCl_4–CS_2

In Figure 5-3 are the spectra of several liquids obtained undiluted in a 0.1-mm cell: *n*-hexane, chloroform, methylene chloride, acetone, acetonitrile, dioxane, nitromethane, and dimethyl formamide. These liquids have some value as solvents in which infrared spectra may be obtained.

Simple saturated aliphatic hydrocarbons, such as *n*-hexane, have limited application. Hexane is usually a poorer solvent for organic materials than CCl_4–CS_2 and its transmission is not nearly so useful. In the lower frequency region where it is quite transparent hexane does have some utility, particularly with solutes that react with CS_2 (as aliphatic amines).

The transmission of chloroform is a bit less useful than CCl_4 or CS_2, but is a better solvent than either of them for polar materials. Methylene chloride is a considerably better solvent for polar materials than CCl_4–CS_2 and is only slightly less desirable in infrared transmission properties than chloroform.

Acetone, acetonitrile, dioxane, nitromethane, and dimethyl formamide are excellent solvents for a large variety of polar materials. All, of course, have only limited infrared transmission, but all have some frequency regions free of absorption in which infrared measurements can be made. A judicious choice among these solvents will allow the spectra of a great variety of polar organic materials to be obtained in at least a good share of the region 4000–400 cm^{-1}, particularly if solvent compensation techniques are employed. (See Chapter 7.)

A technique often overlooked is the possibility of mixing one of these polar solvents with CCl_4 or CS_2 in such proportion that the mixture will be a satisfactory solvent for the particular material to be analyzed but will still have enough transmission in some frequency region so that a quantitative analysis can be performed. For example, a mixture of about 10% acetone and 90% CS_2 is an effective solvent for p,p'-bisphenols, which are normally insoluble in CS_2 alone. Figure 5-4 shows a spectrum of 1000 mg of isopropylidene 4,4'-bisphenol in a solvent mixture of 1 ml of acetone and 9 ml of CS_2. Other insoluble

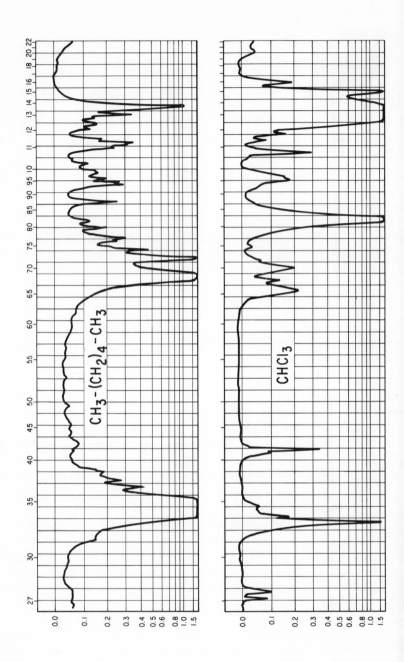

100

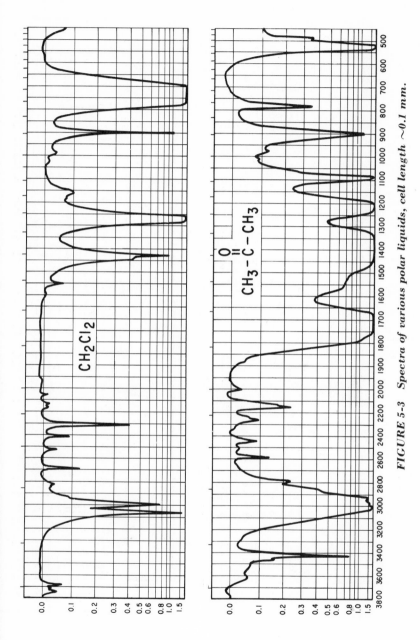

FIGURE 5-3 Spectra of various polar liquids, cell length ~0.1 mm.

101

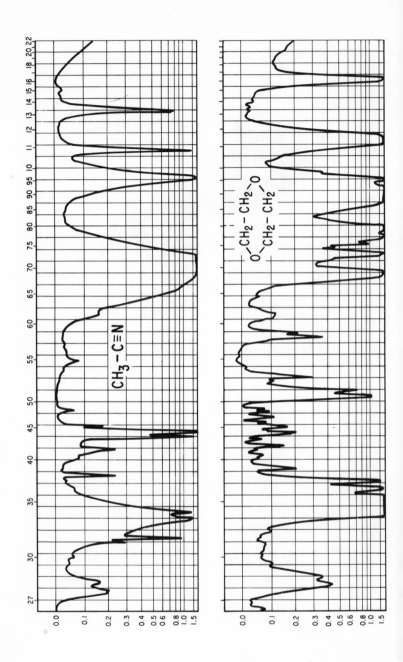

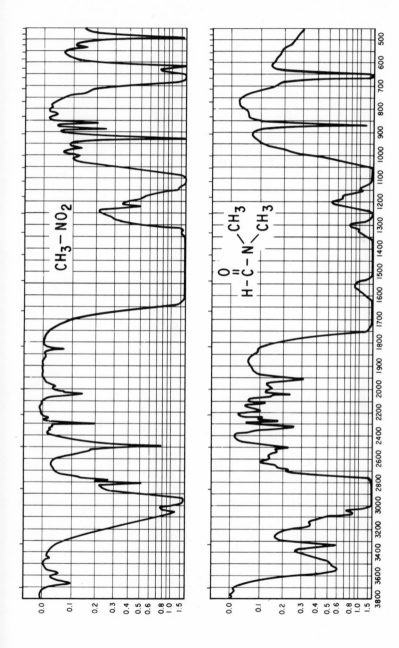

FIGURE 5-3 (Continued)

103

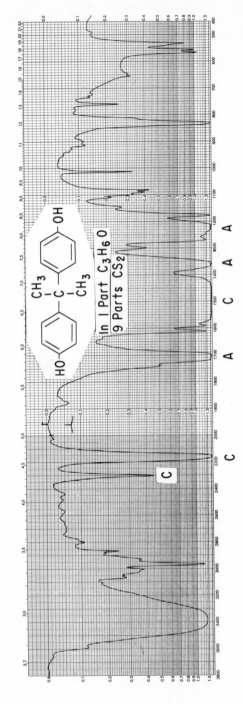

FIGURE 5-4 Spectrum of 1000 mg of isopropylidene-4,4′-bisphenol in solution in 1 part acetone and 9 parts carbon disulfide. Bands labeled C result from carbon disulfide; those labeled A result from acetone.

104

polar materials can often be placed in solution by similar techniques to give regions of reasonably high transmission in which analyses can be made conveniently.

The solvent techniques just described are too tedious for any purpose other than quantitative analysis of materials, the identities of whose components are already known; that is, these techniques are nicely suited to routine assay or impurity-level determination of polar organic materials. For identification of polar materials, or rough quantitative estimates of their composition over wide ranges, however, other techniques subsequently described are better suited. Nevertheless, it should be strongly emphasized that *quantitative analysis by infrared methods is best done in solution.*

D. Compensation of solvent absorptions

One of the greatest advantages of double-beam infrared spectrometers is the ability to "cancel out" atmospheric absorption bands. They can also be used to some extent to cancel out the absorption bands of solvents, thereby giving an I_0 line free of fluctuations. For example, the medium and small absorptions of carbon tetrachloride in a 0.1-mm cell occurring at $\sim$1550, 1250, 1220, 1110, 1070, 1005, 980, 630, 570, 535, 475, and 450 cm^{-1} are easily canceled by placing another matched 0.1-mm cell containing pure CCl_4 in the reference beam of the spectrometer. Also, the smaller absorptions resulting from acetone and CS_2 in the acetone-CS_2 mixture of Figure 5-4 (those at 1090, 900, 855, 785, and 650 cm^{-1}) could have been eliminated from the spectrum by placing an equivalent acetone-CS_2 mixture in the reference beam.

However, cancellation of *total* absorption, such as that in the region 1400–1600 cm^{-1} in CS_2, is not possible. If this were to be attempted by placing a cell filled with CS_2 in the reference beam of a double-beam spectrometer so that a solute absorption in the 1400–1600 cm^{-1} region might be observed and measured, the results would be most misleading, for no absorption band would be observed! The reason is obvious: in this region of the spectrum no radiation whatsoever would fall on the detector under these conditions (except possible scattered light), and the servo system would be completely dead. Therefore, in the region 1400–1600 cm^{-1} a straight but meaningless line will be observed on the recorder chart. (Drift of the servo system might cause the recorder pen to move upward or downward, but the result would still be meaningless.) At the end of this dead region the servo system, as it suddenly becomes alive, will abruptly correct itself if drift has occurred; the recorded result is peculiar looking and can sometimes show in what region a servo system has "gone dead." This is illustrated by Figure 5-5.

If compensation of a strong yet not totally absorbing band (such as 3060, 2990, 1424, or 900 cm^{-1} in CH_2Cl_2) is attempted, difficulties will still be present. When the scan proceeds though such a frequency region, the value of servo-loop energy (volts-per-unit-attenuator-displacement) is changing rapidly, with the result that energy with which to drive the recorder is variable. (See discussion in Section III-E of Chapter 4.) To attempt to perform a quantitative measurement, or even to obtain a reasonable interpretation, of an absorption band will lead to misleading or highly inaccurate results. Methods for correcting this difficulty are discussed fully in Chapter 7.

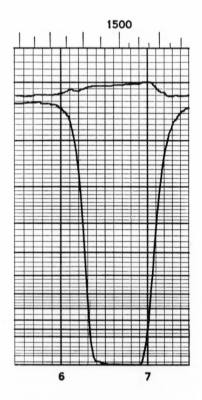

FIGURE 5-5 Lower curve: *A portion of the spectrum of carbon disulfide in a 0.1-mm cell.* Upper curve: *Result of placing 0.1-mm cells filled with carbon disulfide in both beams of a double-beam spectrometer. This result is meaningless (see text).*

106   *Sample preparation techniques*

Reasonably accurate results will probably be obtained if compensation of absorptions whose uncompensated transmission is ~50% or greater is attempted. But without the special methods described in Chapter 7 *under no circumstances* should any reliance be placed on any region of a spectrum in which an attempt has been made to compensate for transmission of ~10% or below.

II. Preparation and use of infrared absorption cells

The care and handling of cells whose windows are soluble in water presents special problems. If any large amount of infrared solution spectroscopy is done, it is inevitable that the cells used will eventually become fogged in the process. It is the author's opinion that infrared absorption cells should be regarded as expendable; if not, important work that should be pursued is neglected because of fear of ruining a cell. However, such cultivated callousness toward the well-being of cells, although productive of results, will become expensive unless the spectroscopist learns to make and repair cells for himself. If he learns these techniques, not only will he save a great deal of time and money in the long run, but he will be able to design and prepare special-purpose cells which might otherwise be unobtainable. This section describes techniques for grinding and polishing windows used in the infrared region, cell assembly and repair, and care and measurement of cells.

A. Techniques for polishing alkali halide plates

Because NaCl windows are by far the most common in use in chemical infrared spectroscopy, we shall first discuss their preparation in detail, then show how the techniques can be modified to work other materials. Rocksalt and other cubic crystal plates are cut to size by cleaving the plate along one of its natural cleavage planes. This technique is rapidly becoming less important because of the availability from commercial suppliers of cleaved and rough-ground salt plates in a variety of standard shapes and sizes. But should there be need for special plates, especially thin plates, it is well to know this technique.

The cleavage must take place along a cleavage plane. Inspection of a freshly chipped corner of a plate will reveal where these planes lie. A firm straight edge is laid along the desired line of cut, and a sharp razor blade is drawn firmly along the edge a few times. The razor blade is then placed in the crack thus formed and tapped with a small hammer until cleavage occurs. Plates can usually be cleaved in this manner without great difficulty; naturally, people less skilled are almost certain to break more plates in the process than those who have used the operation often enough to become more proficient. The surface produced by cleavage will not be perfect, and for most applications must be flattened by grinding.

NaCl plates can be ground flat without difficulty. The grinding process can be done in one operation with one grit size because rock-salt is soft and grinds easily, the plates are usually nearly flat to begin with, and even a rough-ground salt plate can be polished directly; when working glass or other hard materials, a series of successively finer grits must be used. A slurry of #500 Carborundum in water is prepared on a heavy flat glass plate; the NaCl plate is easily ground flat with several circular or figure-8 strokes. The water in which the Carborundum is suspended dissolves the NaCl on the surface being worked, thereby making the cutting action very fast and the task of grinding a plate flat a simple one. At the end of the grinding operation the slurry is washed off the plates with acetone.

Polishing a ground plate to a smooth, flat finish is not so easy, but it can be mastered by most people with sufficient practice. Although it is the most difficult operation in cell making, once it is learned cells can be constructed reasonably quickly and confidently. There are two widely used methods for polishing salt plates: the cloth-lap method and pitch-lap method.

The cloth-lap method. The lap is constructed by stretching a soft, lint-free cloth (a few layers of diaper serve well) tightly over a flat, round, heavy glass plate ($\sim$8 in. in diameter, $\frac{1}{2}$–$\frac{3}{4}$ in. thick). The cloth is held in place by one or more heavy rubber bands stretched around the circular edge of the plate. The polishing agent can be any material of very fine particle size ($\sim$5 μ average diameter) with good hardness: rouge (Fe_2O_3), alumina (Al_2O_3), magnesia (MgO), titania (TiO_2), or several of the various rare-earth oxides. A small amount of one of these agents is sprinkled over the lap and wetted with a few drops of 95% ethanol. The plate to be flattened is polished on this lap with any convenient motion that covers the whole area of plate and pad. During this operation the plate will usually fog in areas adjacent to the fingers holding the plate unless the operator wears surgeon's thin rubber gloves or rubber finger cots. After being polished for a short while in this manner, the plate is slid off the pad and immediately wiped dry by rubbing it on a similar cloth lap (to which no ethanol or polishing agent has been added), or simply on a few layers of cloth laid flat on the bench. If a flat polished surface is not produced, the operation is repeated until this result is obtained. Flatness is checked by interference fringes as later described.

The apparatus required for the cloth-lap technique is simple and easily constructed, and the technique itself is easily learned. The results produced are good, but not so good as those obtainable with the pitch-lap technique.

The pitch-lap method. The preparation and care of the pitch lap itself are somewhat involved, and the polishing technique is a bit more difficult to master; but the result is superior and can be attained in less time than with a cloth lap.

In order to form the grid of the pitch lap, a series of interlocking metal bars must be made. The individual bars are $\frac{1}{8}$ in. thick, $\frac{1}{4}$ in. wide, and long enough to form a circular array of 1-in. squares as illustrated in Figure 5-6a. The assembled bars are placed on a circular metal block 6 in. in diameter. The bars are made just long enough to come to the edge of the block all around. A strip of heavy gummed kraft paper is wrapped about the block, gummed side in, so that a mold ∼1 in. deep is formed. Before filling the mold with optical pitch, the bars and metal block are moistened with a glycerine-water mixture so that they will not stick to the pitch and can be removed when the pitch has cooled.

After the pitch lap has cooled to room temperature, and the paper, bars, and metal block have been carefully removed, the lap is warmed on the bottom, just enough to melt the bottom surface, and firmly pressed onto a heavy steel plate about 8 in. square and $\frac{1}{2}$ in. thick. This plate will hold the pitch lap steady during the polishing operation. A finished lap is shown in Figure 5-6b.

The pitch lap must now be flattened. This is done by flooding the

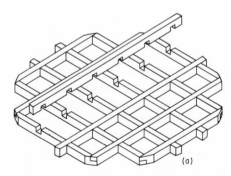

(a)

FIGURE 5-6a   Grid used to mold a pitch lap.

Preparation and use of infrared absorption cells   **109**

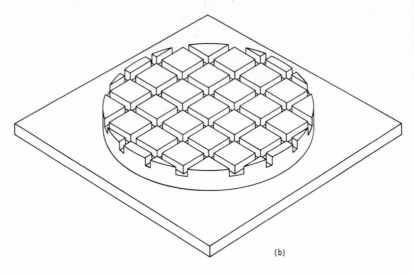

FIGURE 5-6b   The finished pitch lap.

working surface with a very dilute suspension of polishing agent (any used with the cloth lap) in water and placing on the pad a heavy slab of flat glass (a piece about 8 in. in diameter, $\frac{1}{2}$ to 1 in. thick is convenient) which has been warmed slightly.   Additional weight may be placed on the glass, so that the total weight on the pitch lap is 8–10 lb.   The pitch flows slowly under steady pressure, and the pad will begin to flatten.   When flat, the raised squares of the pitch lap will show a uniform bright black through the glass slab; the grooves will be white (if white polishing agent is used).   The glass slab is removed, the slurry washed off, and the pad is ready for immediate use.

A small amount of dilute slurry of polishing agent is placed on the pitch lap.   This slurry is conveniently made by dipping the fingers in water, then lightly in polishing powder, and spreading them over the pitch lap surface.   The slurry so formed should be watery and not in the least pasty.   The salt plate to be polished is now held lightly in the fingers (covered with rubber finger cots) and moved over the lap in some systematic circular manner that will cover plate and lap entirely and uniformly.   When the salt plate is first put on the lap, the water begins to dissolve the plate surface and levels it rapidly (for this reason fine grinding of the plate was unnecessary).   As this operation proceeds, the polishing slurry becomes saturated with salt, and the cutting action stops.   Now the plate is quickly slipped off the lap and dried by rubbing it briskly on a few layers of soft cloth

110   *Sample preparation techniques*

laid flat on the bench. When a wet plate is dried in this manner, a very high luster is developed on its surface. If plate and pitch lap are allowed to become dry during the polishing operation, the plate surface is usually not nearly so bright. A little practice is necessary to master this technique.

As the pitch lap is used it will tend to become either concave or convex and should be treated regularly by the same method used to flatten it originally. The pitch lap should be stored in an icebox near 0°C when not in use, for over a long period of time the lap will flow and lose its shape at room temperature. After each use the pitch lap should be well rinsed under cold tap water before being stored in the icebox. The polishing agent should not be allowed to dry on the pad, for when thoroughly dry it can be removed from the grooves only with difficulty.

Either the cloth-lap or pitch-lap method of polishing can produce plates flat and smooth enough for cell assembly and for other purposes described later in this chapter. Flatness is conveniently checked by placing the salt plate on a glass optical flat and observing the interference fringes. These fringes are easily seen when the work is illuminated with essentially monochromatic light, such as that from a sodium vapor lamp. The plates should be flat to within a few fringes or repolished until this flatness is obtained. A typical fringe pattern for a "good" plate is sketched in Figure 5-7.

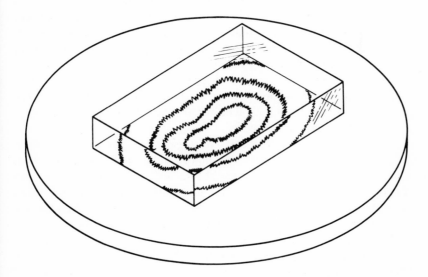

FIGURE 5-7   A typical fringe pattern for a polished salt plate.

Preparation and use of infrared absorption cells   **111**

Polished salt plates are conveniently stored in a desiccator until required.

KBr plates can be cleaved, ground, and polished in the same manner used with NaCl plates. Because KBr is softer and more soluble in water than NaCl, it cuts faster in all operations, and care must be exercised in working it.

CsBr and CsI are too soft to cleave. They are so soft and water soluble that they must be ground carefully, but the operation is simple. Because of their high water solubility they a're probably most easily polished with the cloth-lap technique. These materials fog most readily, and a high-luster surface is produced on them only with difficulty. Fortunately, a high luster is not necessary on CsBr or CsI plates, for presumably they would be used only at long wavelength (20–50 μ) where the slight surface irregularities resulting from fogginess are much smaller than 20 μ in size and are not even "seen" by light of this wavelength.

The fluoride plates—LiF, CaF_2, and BaF_2—are much harder, and range from only slightly soluble to nearly insoluble in water. Because of their hardness they actually cleave more easily than NaCl and KBr, but firm strokes along a straight edge with a sharp razor blade are far more effective than striking in the cleaving operation. Also, as a result of their hardness, they cannot be rendered flat with one simple operation but must be ground with successively finer abrasive grits: #500 Carborundum is used for rough grinding and #600 Aloxite for fine grinding. These materials can be polished by the pitch-lap technique if a solvent can be found: CaF_2, BaF_2, and, to a lesser extent, LiF are effectively insoluble in water. It has been found that concentrated HCl solution ($12N$) attacks these fluoride materials slowly, yet with sufficient speed so that if it is used as the suspending fluid for the polishing agent the pitch-lap method of polishing is satisfactory and produces good results. The usual precautions in handling concentrated HCl must be observed.

Silver chloride is far too soft to be cleaved, ground, or polished. As usually supplied, it has a reasonably high luster and polishing is not necessary. Thin ($\sim$1 mm) sheets are easily cut to size with sharp scissors. Silver chloride, when in contact with any metal higher than silver on the electromotive table, reacts chemically to form free silver metal, the chloride of the metal with which it was in contact, and, since the metal chlorides so formed are often extremely hygroscopic, a mess. Therefore, silver chloride should not be kept in contact with metals for any extended period of time. Also, when exposed to strong visible or ultraviolet light, silver chloride becomes surface-blackened as a result of reduction of silver chloride to free silver. When not in use, silver chloride plates should be kept in a light-tight box. Because of its extreme softness, silver chloride is rarely used for cell windows but does find application to certain other techniques. (See Section IV.)

B. Cell construction and repair

Several different designs for sealed liquid cells have appeared in the literature from time to time. Probably all have merit, and the differences among them are not significant. The cell design described here is one that has evolved through many years of use in the spectroscopy laboratory of The Dow Chemical Company; probably its biggest advantage is its simplicity of construction and repair.

Figure 5-8 shows a "take-apart" view of the cell. Holes are drilled in the back brass plate a to conduct the liquid from the filling arms to the gasket b. One of the windows, c, has two holes drilled in it to allow liquid to flow into the cell space formed by the cell spacer d.

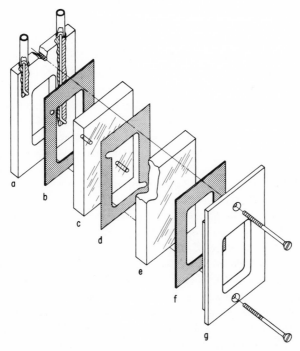

FIGURE 5-8 "Take-apart" view of an absorption cell.

Preparation and use of infrared absorption cells **113**

The other window, e, encloses the cell space. The polyethylene pad f is placed between window e and the mounting plate, g, so that the cell assembly may be tightened without cracking the windows. The mounting plate slides into a suitable track on the spectrometer so that it is properly positioned in the beam.

The holes are drilled in salt plates on a drill press, using the slowest speed, a sharp drill bit, and lubrication with water or oil. (If water is used, the plate surface must be protected in some fashion.) The drill bit is continually disengaged and re-engaged with the work every second or so in order to keep it well cooled and to clean chips from the hole. Halfway through the operation the plate is turned over, and the hole is completed from the other direction; this prevents shattering of the plate surface near the hole upon breakthrough. The slurry of oil and powdered salt is easily washed off the plate with CCl_4 or acetone. The holes are made before the polishing operation.

The cell spacer can be made from almost any thin sheet metal. Usually lead is selected because of its resistance to corrosion. However, for the thinnest cells (0.03 mm or thinner) shim brass is more convenient, for lead of this thickness is hard to handle. The lead (or brass) shim can be cut to shape (see Figure 5-8) with a sharp knife by tracing around an appropriate form. If many cells are to be made, a punch can be constructed to cut the shims rapidly and accurately. After being cut out, the shim is amalgamated with mercury on its surface; the amalgam wets the salt plates and after a few hours "sets up" hard, thereby forming a sealed cell. Lead is easily amalgamated by placing the lead shim in a flat shallow dish with a small amount of mercury and rubbing the mercury over the shim surface with a cotton swab or a loop of pipe cleaner. When brass shims are employed it is usually necessary to wet the swab with dilute nitric acid to provide a freshly cleaned brass surface that mercury will easily wet. The mercury used for amalgamating thin lead shims must be nearly saturated with lead or the shim will dissolve.

To assemble the cell, the block a is placed on a smooth white surface (such as a sheet of paper on the bench top); then the polyethylene gasket b, drilled window c, freshly amalgamated shim d, undrilled window e, polyethylene pad f, and face plate g are successively and carefully placed. The screws holding the assembly together are inserted loosely, and a sodium vapor lamp is positioned so that interference fringes between the cell windows can be observed as they are formed. As the screws are gradually tightened, close watch is kept on the interference fringes; by this method a fairly large degree of control of parallelness of the plates, as well as control of deformation

114 *Sample preparation techniques*

of the plates that may result from making the screws too tight, is achieved. If the cell is assembled while fringes are being observed, and good flat salt plates are used, generally superior cells result. When the screws are snugged into place, there should be three or fewer fringes observed over the area through which the spectrometer light beam will pass. If there are only a few more than three fringes, the screws can be loosened and retightened in an attempt to reduce the number of fringes, which often is successful. However, if there are many fringes (say, 10 or more) it often means that there is a metal burr or dirt particle on the shim, and the cell can never be made parallel. If this is the case, a new shim should be made and the cell assembly process repeated.

In a few hours, after the amalgam has "set up," the cell should be checked for leaks. Probably the simplest way in which this can be done is to place a dilute solution of some highly colored material (such as malachite green dissolved in acetone) in the cell, allow it to stand for a few minutes, and then examine it carefully. Small dried deposits of dye show where the cell has leaked. A leaky cell should be remade, for its use can lead to nothing but trouble.

In order to disassemble an old cell for rebuilding, it will usually be necessary to split the plates from the shim with a sharp razor blade, in an operation similar to cleaving a plate. After the plates are apart and have been ground (if necessary) and repolished, the cell is assembled as in new cell construction. When these techniques have been mastered, an old cell can be rebuilt completely in about two hours.

Occasionally a cell becomes fogged on the outside surfaces of the windows while the inside window surfaces are still in satisfactory condition. The outside faces of the salt plates can be polished without cell disassembly by moistening their surfaces with the breath and rubbing with a facial tissue dipped in a small amount of dry polishing powder. The polishing powder is then wiped off with a clean facial tissue. This operation does not restore flatness to the outside of the cell windows and probably even leads to a departure from flatness, although that is not important for the outside surfaces; luster is restored, which *is* important at short wavelengths.

Although the simplicity of construction, repair, and use make the cell design discussed here a convenient one, this cell has one disadvantage: it requires a fairly large volume of liquid or solution to fill it. Cells of this design of 0.1-mm length require $\sim\frac{1}{2}$ ml of liquid to fill them; the longer cells of 1.0-mm length take somewhat more than 1 ml of liquid. In the vast majority of analytical applications this is not serious, but for microtechniques $\frac{1}{2}$ ml of solution is far too much.

Special designs for much smaller volume cells are discussed in Chapter 7.

C. Use and care of absorption cells

Liquid cells are filled by introducing liquid into the filling arm on the side in which the drilled hole goes to the bottom of the cell; then air is displaced uniformly through the upper hole in the window and bubble formation is minimized. Probably the most convenient way to stopper cells of this design is to place one end of a short length of rubber tube on one arm, the other end on the other arm. The rubber tube provides a convenient "stopper" for the cell and also has the advantage that judicious maneuvering of the rubber tube will force small bubbles which may have formed during the filling operation out between the cell windows and into the upper filling arm. The liquid in the cell space must be absolutely bubble-free if accurate quantitative analysis is to be performed; bubbles in the cell have the same effect on a spectrum as the presence of scattered light. (See Figure 3-14.)

Immediately after use cells should be thoroughly rinsed, using the same solvent with which the solution was prepared (*never* any other solvent, or a precipitate may form in the cell). The cell is then dried with dry compressed air. This air must be *very* dry, for, as the first air is blown through the cell, evaporation of a volatile solvent quickly cools the inner cell surface to a temperature well below 0°C, hence use of even slightly moist air may cause small traces of water to condense and fog the cell.

If solution is spilled over the cell during filling, the cell can be rinsed with solvent and dried with a dry air stream. Solvent should not be indiscriminantly sloshed over the cell, however, for small traces that work up between the brass block and polyethylene pad are not easily evaporated with compressed air, and solvent vapors can easily be transferred to rubber gaskets holding spectrometer windows in place. If this happens, absorption bands of the solvent vapor will be superimposed on the next several spectra.

Often organic materials will contain small amounts of water or other solids or liquids insoluble in CCl_4–CS_2, whereas the bulk of the sample will be soluble in CCl_4–CS_2. When a solution of such a sample is prepared, it will be found to be more or less cloudy or turbid. Introduction of a solution of this type into a salt cell is almost certain to ruin it: traces of water can attack the inside window faces, or small amounts of insoluble solids or liquids can become lodged in the cell which can never be washed out. To prevent this from happening, probably the best procedure to follow is to add granulated NaCl to the solution in the flask in which it was prepared; this will immediately pull all water droplets or droplets of highly polar liquids to the bottom of the flask along with the salt crystals, and the solution can be decanted into the cell if clear, or, if still turbid from suspended solids, can be filtered into the cell through filter paper. In this filtering operation it is advisable to put the tip of the folded filter paper directly into one of the cell filling arms to minimize evaporation of volatile solvent and resulting concentration change. An alternative technique is to filter by drawing the liquid from the flask into a medicine dropper through a small wad of cotton, then deliver liquid from the medicine dropper directly to the cell.

If a sample largely soluble in CCl_4 or CS_2 should contain more than trace amounts of an insoluble solid, the solid may be collected off the filter paper, washed with excess CCl_4 or CS_2, dried, and its spectrum obtained by methods described in Section V. If the sample contains sufficient liquid insoluble in CCl_4 or CS_2 to form a separate layer (generally on top of the CCl_4 or CS_2, since these solvents have high density), the two-phase system may be transferred to a separatory funnel: the CCl_4 or CS_2 layer is drawn off the bottom, powdered NaCl is added to it, the solution is decanted into a cell, and its spectrum is obtained; a spectrum of the upper CCl_4 or CS_2 insoluble layer in the separatory funnel may be obtained by techniques described in Section IV. Both techniques are useful in identification of organic mixtures, for by them the sample becomes separated into highly polar and less polar substances and the spectrum of each type is easily obtained separately, thereby facilitating identification. In fact, these techniques should be regarded as "standard procedure" whenever samples only partially soluble in CCl_4–CS_2 are encountered.

In order that cells be kept in good condition as long as possible, they should be stored in an atmosphere well above the dew point, of course. Although a desiccator will serve nicely, a somewhat more convenient storage place can be made from a small glass-windowed cabinet in which a $\sim$5-watt light bulb has been mounted. This small heat input is just sufficient to keep the cabinet temperature $\sim$2–3 degrees above ambient room temperature; under these conditions no water vapor from the room can condense on a cell window in the cabinet.

D. Measurement of cell length

In order that quantitative comparisons can be made between materials whose spectra are not obtained in the identical absorption cell, the length of each cell must be known accurately. This distance, usually of the order of 0.1 mm, cannot be measured directly to the precision required but can be measured optically to a value whose error is certainly no larger than the variation of cell length itself over the beam area. This method is based on the interference of light transmitted directly through the cell with light that has been twice internally reflected in the cell and is usually called the "interference pattern" method.

Figure 5-9 is a much enlarged view of the inside of a cell. When the cell is empty, the refractive index change at the salt-air interface is high (refractive index of NaCl, for example, is 1.54; refractive index of air is 1.00); hence the fraction of light reflected rather than transmitted is relatively high. (When solution fills the cell, the refractive index change at salt-solution interface is not nearly so severe, and reflection losses can usually be ignored.) Interference in an empty cell arises in the following way: with reference to Figure 5-9, a given beam of monochromatic radiation, ray x, shown as a wave motion to illustrate phase relations, travels through the cell-entrance window, through the cell space, and strikes the other window at point O. At O an abrupt change of refractive index is encountered and a small fraction of the light is reflected (ray y, dashed line), whereas the remainder is transmitted through the cell window. Ray y travels back through the cell space, strikes the cell window at point P, where a small fraction of it is re-reflected back through the cell, shown as ray z (dotted line). (The portion of ray y transmitted through the window at point P does not concern us.) Ray z arrives at point Q where most of it is transmitted by the right-hand cell window (the fraction re-reflected back into the cell space at point Q is small enough

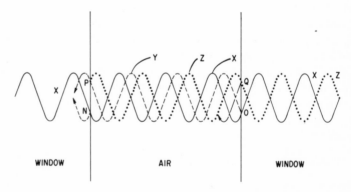

FIGURE 5-9 *Interference resulting from internal reflections in an empty absorption cell.*

118 *Sample preparation techniques*

to ignore). Now, ray x, the completely transmitted ray, and ray z, the twice-reflected ray, will not necessarily be the same phase, which will indeed occur only if twice the cell length is an integral multiple of the wavelength. If the phases are not the same, part of the intensity of ray x will be canceled by ray z, depending on the relative intensities and the phase relation. Only if the phase of both rays is identical is there no diminuation of intensity.

The phase relation between ray x and ray z, hence the intensity of the net resultant ray emerging from the cell, depends on the wavelength of light. If the wavelength is continuously varied, the intensity of radiation emerging from the cell will be a maximum when twice the cell length is an integral multiple of the wavelength and will be a minimum when twice the cell length is a half-integer multiple of the wavelength; wavelengths intermediate between each of these several limits will result in intermediate transmission intensity. If a transmission spectrum of an empty cell is obtained, the result will be as shown in Figure 5-10, the so-called "interference pattern" of the cell.

From this pattern the cell length can be calculated accurately. Remembering that $2b = n\lambda$ at each transmission maximum (b = cell length in microns, λ is wavelength in microns), we can apply it to a transmission maximum at some convenient long wavelength, λ_L, and obtain the relation

$$2b = n_L\lambda_L,$$

and again at some convenient short wavelength and obtain

$$2b = n_S\lambda_S,$$

where n_L and n_S are the appropriate integral number of wavelengths in the twice-reflected ray as it traverses the cell space twice. Now an individual n, say n_L or n_S, cannot be determined, but the *difference* between any two n's is simply the number of complete cycles of transmission maximum and minimum in the spectrum between these wavelengths. Let us call this n; in Figure 5-10 it can be seen to be 51. Hence

$$n_S - n_L = n = \frac{2b}{\lambda_S} - \frac{2b}{\lambda_L} = 2b\frac{\lambda_L - \lambda_S}{\lambda_L\lambda_S}$$

or

$$b = \frac{n}{2}\frac{\lambda_L\lambda_S}{\lambda_L - \lambda_S}. \tag{5-1}$$

If we wish to determine the length in millimeters, the equation is

Preparation and use of infrared absorption cells   **119**

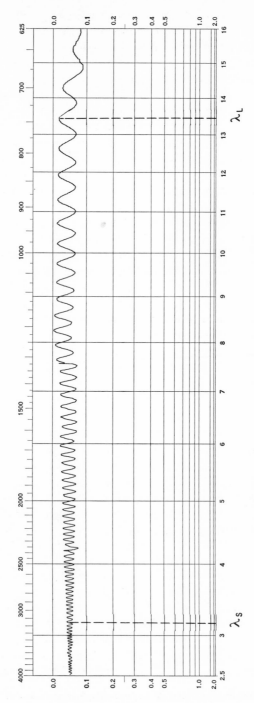

FIGURE 5-10   An "interference pattern" of an empty 0.1-mm cell.

120

divided by 1000:

$$b_{(mm)} = \frac{n}{2000} \frac{\lambda_L \lambda_S}{\lambda_L - \lambda_S}. \tag{5-2}$$

A similar equation may be obtained in terms of frequency ω:

$$n_S - n_L = n = 2b\omega_H - 2b\omega_L = 2b(\omega_H - \omega_L)$$

so that

$$b = \frac{n}{2(\omega_H - \omega_L)}, \tag{5-3}$$

where n has the same value as before, ω_H and ω_L are the high and low frequencies (corresponding to λ_S and λ_L, respectively) expressed in cm^{-1}, and b is the cell length in centimeters. If we wish the result in millimeters, we now multiply the equation by 10:

$$b = \frac{5n}{\omega_H - \omega_L}. \tag{5-4}$$

If a spectrometer whose presentation is linear in λ is used, equation 5-2 is more convenient, and the pattern will be similar to that shown in Figure 5-10. If its presentation is linear in frequency, equation 5-4 is more convenient; in this case the spectrum produced will have all the transmission maxima spaced at equal intervals along the chart. When determining a cell length, it is good practice to make the calculation two or three times, each time selecting different short-wave and long-wave maxima. Results should agree within 0.2%.

The appearance of the so-called "interference pattern" spectrum is an excellent indication of the quality of the cell. The greater the ordinate distance between transmission maxima and minima, the better the cell; barely detectable maxima and minima can result from foggy plates or may be the result of the inside cell faces not being parallel. Also, each transmission maximum or minimum should be a smooth and well-defined curve and should not have subsidiary maxima or minima; if this latter situation exists, it shows that the inside faces of the cell are not uniformly flat. If the cell has been properly made, according to the scheme we have outlined, with particular attention given to the fringes of visible light between the windows during assembly, it will produce an excellent "interference pattern" spectrum.

When in constant use, a cell should have its length checked by this method at least every two weeks. Salt plates, especially the very soft CsBr and CsI, and to a lesser extent NaCl and KBr, have some tendency to flow even under the slight pressure of clamping screws. A cell length determined just after cell assembly should not necessarily be regarded as a constant for the useful life of the cell, although the variation in cell length observed over a long period is usually small.

III. Vapor phase techniques

Infrared spectroscopic work in the vapor phase is of much more limited application than solution techniques because of the low volatility of most large molecules, hence the inability to obtain a partial pressure of the gas sufficient to produce a useful absorption spectrum. Spectra of materials of low volatility could be obtained if cells of long path length were employed, but simple gas cells longer than $\sim$10 cm will not fit in commercial spectrometers. To obtain longer path lengths, multiple reflection gas cells are necessary. Some of these cells and their applications are described in Chapter 7. We limit our discussion here to analytical applications of light molecules, that is, molecules with a vapor pressure of $\sim$25-mm Hg or greater at room temperature.

A. Uses and limitations of the vapor phase

In view of the foregoing discussion of the advisability of obtaining spectra under conditions of minimum complication and best reproducibility, on first thought the use of the vapor phase immediately suggests itself as the best way in which to obtain spectra, at least for volatile molecules. The vapor phase might well be universally employed for analytical spectroscopy of volatile molecules but for a fundamental complication: molecules in the vapor phase are free to undergo radiation-induced transitions between rotation states as well as vibration states, with the result that each vibrational absorption band now becomes a complex ensemble of rotation sub-bands. Figure 5-11 shows the vapor-phase absorption spectrum of the 715-cm^{-1} band of HCN obtained at reasonably high resolution ($\Delta\omega = \sim$1 cm^{-1}) with a fore-prism grating spectrometer and at somewhat lower resolution ($\Delta\omega = \sim$3 cm^{-1}) with an NaCl prism spectrometer.

Comparison of these spectra with the spectrum of HCN in solution (Figure 2-7) gives a good picture of the problem. Each of the individual maxima in the vapor-phase spectrum results from a different rotational transition accompanying the vibrational transition and constitutes a sharp absorption whose half-width is much smaller than

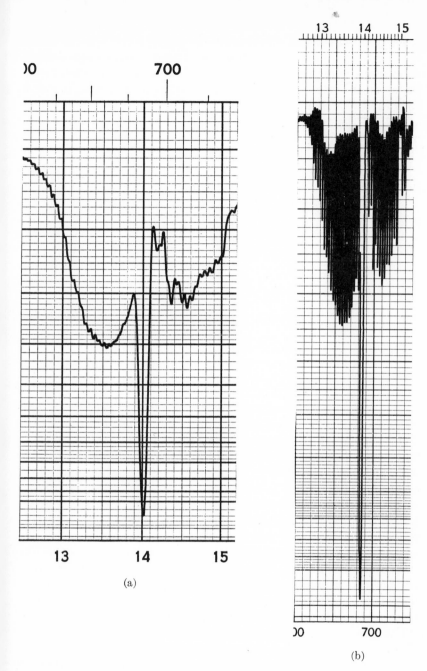

FIGURE 5-11   The 715 cm^{-1} band of HCN, obtained with (a) NaCl prism spectrometer; (b) fore-prism grating spectrometer.

123

$\sim$1 cm^{-1}, the spectral slit width of the spectrometer used to obtain the spectrum in Figure 5-11b. Because of the narrowness of these absorptions, the appearance of the whole contour will be sensitive to the spectral slit width of the spectrometer, as is apparent from comparison of a and b in Figure 5-11. On the other hand, the band shape as obtained in solution is more nearly independent of spectral slit width, and the entire band is not so wide, for rotational freedom of the absorbing molecule is severely limited in condensed phases.

The broadness of the absorptions resulting from these simultaneous rotation-vibration transitions, which can overlap in even slightly complex molecules, does not make them so well suited to the sort of qualitative chemical interpretation, discussed in great detail in later chapters, that is possible with absorption bands obtained in condensed phases. Qualitative analysis is therefore not usually so easily done with vapor-phase spectra as with condensed-phase spectra, although, strictly speaking, more information is available from the vapor-phase spectrum. However, a most useful qualitative application of vapor-phase spectra is derived from the fact that the form and shape of the rotation-vibration absorption depends on the space relation of the direction of dipole moment change during vibration to the moment of inertia axes of the molecule; these relations provide a great help in assigning specific absorptions to particular vibrational modes, as discussed further in Chapter 8.

The extreme sharpness of the individual rotation lines of a vapor-phase spectrum is often used as a demonstration or test of spectrometer resolving power. Favorite among the gases for this use is ammonia. Figure 5-12 shows the spectrum of ammonia vapor in the frequency region 800–1200 cm^{-1} as obtained on an NaCl-prism spectrometer and on a fore-prism grating spectrometer. These spectra were obtained under "standard" conditions of operation: scan rate $\sim$100 cm^{-1}/minute and slit width adjusted for a signal-to-noise ratio of 400–1 or better.

The exact frequencies of absorptions in vapor spectra of several light gases (H_2O, CO_2, CH_4, HCl, and NH_3) have been obtained precisely. Comparison of these frequencies with the published values provide perhaps the best means of precision frequency calibration of a spectrometer. References to highly accurate wavelength values for the rotation-vibration lines of these molecules can be found in Reference 4.

The fact that individual rotation lines in a rotation-vibration absorption band often have a half-width much smaller than the spectrometer spectral slit width leads to serious complications whenever

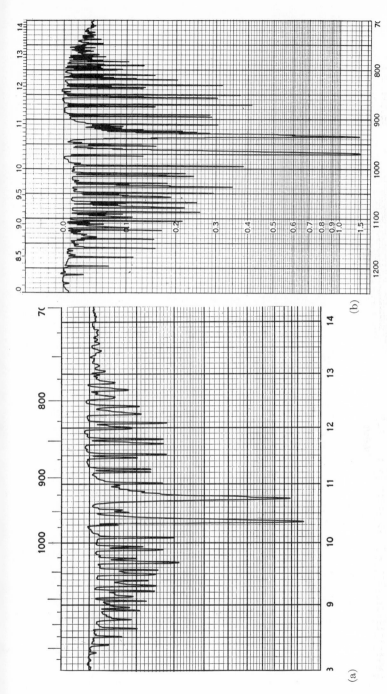

FIGURE 5-12 *A portion of the vapor spectrum of ammonia, obtained with* (a) *NaCl prism spectrometer;* (b) *fore-prism-grating spectrometer.*

125

quantitative analysis of vapors is attempted by infrared spectroscopy. At low pressure many individual rotation lines have half-widths of 0.01–0.1 cm^{-1}; the best resolution obtainable at present from commercial infrared spectrometers operated at reasonable signal-to-noise ratio and time constant is not much better than $\Delta\omega = {\sim}1$ cm^{-1}. As shown in Chapter 6, unless the spectrometer spectral slit width is essentially smaller than that of a band half-width, the absorption-concentration relation is not linear, nor is it known with any precision. Therefore quantitative analysis based on the measurement of light absorption by a single rotation line of a vapor band cannot be highly accurate.

Furthermore, the half-width of a single rotation line is a sensitive function of the total gas pressure; the higher the total pressure, the greater the half-width, the result of increased perturbation of the molecules by increased collision frequency and severity. As discussed in Chapter 6, the larger the fraction a band half-width is of the spectrometer spectral slit width, the greater the apparent light absorption by the vapor molecules. The result is that the observed absorption intensity of a rotation-vibration band is not only a function of the partial pressure of the absorbing gas, but it is also a function of the *total* gas pressure. To be meaningful, therefore, quantitative analysis in the vapor phase must always be done under conditions of constant total pressure. The constant total pressure is obtained by adding some inert, nonabsorbing gas such as nitrogen or argon to a convenient standard pressure, say 700 mm Hg. The effect is quite strikingly demonstrated by the spectra in Figure 5-13: *a* is the spectrum of HCl gas at a partial and total pressure of 10 mm Hg; *b* is the spectrum of HCl gas at a partial pressure of 10 mm Hg but at a total pressure of 700 mm Hg, attained by adding pure nitrogen gas to the absorption cell.

If gases are subjected to high pressures, say of the order of 100 atm, by the addition of an inert, nonabsorbing gas at high pressure, the molecules will be so strongly perturbed that each of the individual rotation lines of a vibration-rotation band will broaden to the point at which the whole band envelope will effectively become an absorption continuum. Under these conditions its half-width will be large compared to spectral slit width, hence the complication mentioned above may be avoided. This high-pressure technique has come into wide use for absolute intensity measurements in theoretical investigations, but it has not had serious investigation for analytical applications; the complications of using cells with NaCl or KBr windows at pressures of 100 atm is probably a factor.

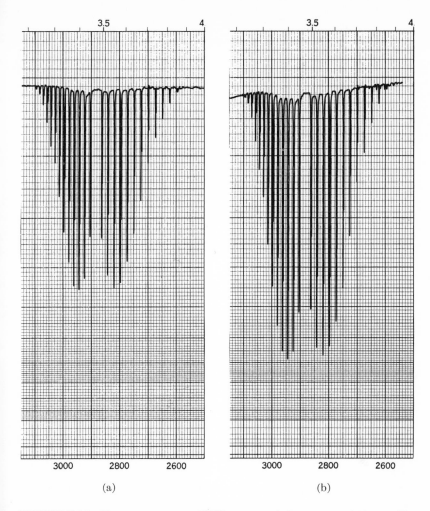

FIGURE 5-13 *Vapor spectrum of* HCl *at a partial pressure of 10 mm Hg,*
with total pressure: (a) *10 mm Hg;* (b) *760 mm Hg.*

B. Gas absorption cells and their use

Figure 5-14 sketches two simple gas cells with 5-cm path lengths.
The arm on the side of the cell is provided so that a small, convenient
amount of sample may be frozen out for later expansion into the cell
chamber.   The salt windows, prepared as described in the preceding
section, may be cemented onto the cell body with any convenient
wax or laboratory cement (due consideration being taken for possible
reaction with or solubility of the sample gas to be used).   An alternative way to attach the windows, shown in part *b* of Figure 5-14, is to

Vapor phase techniques   127

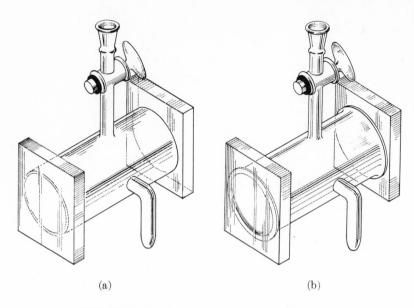

(a)   (b)

FIGURE 5-14   *Two simple gas absorption cells.*

make wide shoulders at the ends of the cell body, which are ground flat and coated lightly with stopcock grease; the cell window is stuck directly onto the greased surface by "wringing" it into place. The reduced pressure in the cell holds the windows tightly in place. This arrangement has the advantage that windows are easily removed for cleaning or replacement by windows of another material; but it is not quite so durable, hence not so useful, for repetitive or routine analytical work.

Vacuum lines for filling cells may be elaborate or simple, depending on the other functions they are to serve besides simple cell filling. Figure 5-15 shows a vacuum line of maximum simplicity for this purpose. The cell is filled as follows: the system, including the cell, is evacuated and the valve between manifold and pump is closed. Sample gas is introduced into the manifold through the sample inlet until the sample in the cell is at the desired pressure, as determined by the mercury (or other) manometer. In a 5-cm cell this value will be of the order of 20–200 mm Hg, depending on the strength of the absorption bands of the sample gas. The stopcock on the cell is closed, and the rest of the system is evacuated. Once again the pump valve is closed, and pressuring gas is slowly added to the manifold through its inlet until the manometer shows a higher gas pressure than the previously determined sample-gas pressure. At this point the cell stopcock is opened, and pressuring gas begins to flow into the cell. As long as the pressuring gas in the manifold is at greater pressure than that of the cell, no sample gas will diffuse out. When the total pressure in the system reaches the predetermined amount, as read from manometer or pressure gage, the pressuring gas inlet valve and cell stopcock are simultaneously closed, and the cell is ready to be disconnected and placed in the spectrometer.

If the gas is to be pressurized to some high total pressure, the techniques are modified somewhat: the cell must be designed to withstand whatever high pressures are to be used. Figure 5-16 shows the essentials of a high-pressure cell (after Crawford et al.).

All parts to the right of point A in Figure 5-15 must be of metal and designed to withstand the pressures to be used. When the pressuring gas is slowly added, the valve at A is closed at the time the cell valve is opened to admit pressuring gas, so that the glass vacuum system (to the left of A) is not subjected to high pressure.

Some provision must be made for mixing the sample gas with pressuring gas, for diffusion is slow at high pressures. Mixing can be accomplished by arranging the cell inlet arm tangentially to the cell body so that entering pressuring gas swirls the gas mixture. To aid further in mixing, a small Teflon bar can be placed in the cell; after pressuring gas is added, the cell is shaken well so that the Teflon bar acts as a stirrer.

Quantitative and qualitative analysis of light gaseous molecules

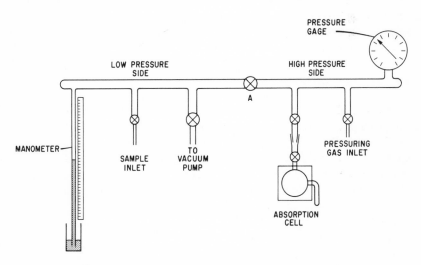

FIGURE 5-15 *Simple system for filling gas cells.*

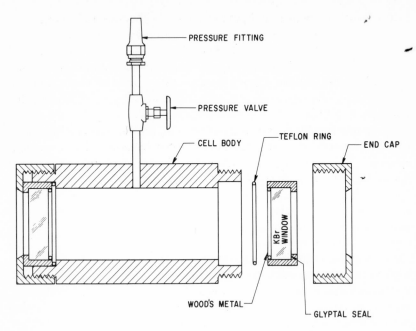

FIGURE 5-16   A high pressure gas cell.

by infrared spectroscopy has been reduced in importance because the techniques of mass spectrometry and vapor-phase chromatography (see Chapter 15, Volume II) have become well developed and universal and handle gas analyses with fewer complications than can infrared spectroscopy. However, analysis of gaseous samples by infrared methods is far from obsolete.

IV. Liquid and solid films

Spectra of materials which have little vapor pressure cannot be obtained in the gas phase; spectra useful for qualitative analysis (minimum of interfering solvent absorptions) cannot be obtained in CCl_4–CS_2 or other solution if the material is not reasonably soluble in these solvents. Clearly, then, other methods are necessary to obtain spectra of solids and liquids insoluble in CCl_4–CS_2 or other useful solvents.

A. Liquid capillary films

With a few exceptions, no helpful purpose is served if liquids are placed undiluted into sealed liquid infrared absorption cells of standard

130   Sample preparation techniques

($\sim$0.1-mm) length, for in a layer this thick most liquids have absorption bands far too intense to be at all useful.* On the other hand, sealed liquid cells of appropriately shorter path length, say 0.02 mm or shorter, are useless for all but the lowest viscosity liquids because most liquids cannot be forced into or out of cells of this thickness without difficulty nor can such cells be easily cleaned without great difficulty.

If a spectrum of a pure liquid suitable for use in qualitative analysis is to be obtained, the path length must be of the order of 0.01 mm; an average capillary film of the liquid will be just about this thickness. A capillary film is made by placing a drop or two of the liquid on a flat NaCl or KBr plate, then placing another flat plate on top of it, and squeezing the liquid out to cover the entire area of the plates. If the plates are flat, the liquid capillary will hold them together fairly tightly. If the plates are not flat (i.e., if one is concave or convex), the film will not be uniformly thick, the spectrum produced may be somewhat distorted, and the plates will not hold together well.

The two plates, between which is sandwiched the capillary film, are placed in a suitable holder (see Figure 5-17), which in turn is placed in the spectrometer sample beam, and the spectrum is scanned. When the spectrum has been obtained, the plates are conveniently cleaned by rubbing them on a flat soft cloth (such as a dish towel or a few layers of diaper), which has been wet on one spot with acetone, then on a dry spot to wipe the plate completely clean. Acetone will dissolve nearly all liquids that are likely to have their spectra obtained as capillary films.

If the liquid sample is observed to dissolve the NaCl plates rapidly, AgCl plates may be substituted. AgCl plates should be used only when NaCl will not serve, for they are so soft that they cannot be made so flat as is desirable, and they must be kept from strong visible or ultraviolet light or they will become blackened.

The capillary film technique has the advantage of being simple and easy and produces spectra free of any interfering solvent absorption. The technique is so simple, in fact, that many laboratories use it for *all liquids*, whether or not they are soluble in CCl_4–CS_2.

* One of the few exceptions is the detection and analysis of trace impurities in liquids. In this case the undiluted liquid is placed in a 0.1-mm or longer absorption cell so that the absorption bands of the trace impurities will be intense enough to be noted. But the types of liquids for which this can be done are obviously limited to those of high infrared transmission, such as small molecules with few functional groups or alkane hydrocarbons. In some cases the identification and analysis of alkane hydrocarbons themselves are most conveniently done by using undiluted liquids in a 0.1-mm cell.

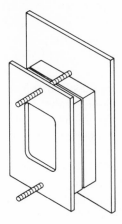

FIGURE 5-17 *A simple device for holding a capillary film between salt plates.*

A disadvantage of this technique is that the capillary film thickness cannot be made known or reproducible to an accuracy that allows quantitative analysis to be performed directly. If the sample consists of two or three materials only, it is possible to perform reasonably accurate quantitative analysis in some cases by *ratio methods* (discussed in Chapter 6), but no direct determination of a single component (as an assay) is possible.*

A second disadvantage of the capillary film technique is that intermolecular association effects, always present in undiluted polar liquids, tend to distort the spectrum and make its interpretation difficult. This is particularly disturbing with materials containing OH or NH groups; if these groups are highly acidic (as $-SO_3H$, for example), the spectra are often so poor as to be nearly useless.

For these reasons it would seem that regardless of the ease with which liquid capillary films are made the technique should be used only for liquids simply not soluble in CCl_4–CS_2.

B. Polymer films

Polymeric materials (including resins and plastics) are usually not soluble in CCl_4–CS_2. Many polymeric materials can be formed into

* Quantitative analysis can be performed directly on liquid samples by the technique of *attenuated total reflection* (see Chapter 7).

a thin (~0.01–0.03 mm), clear, coherent film, and in this form its spectrum may be obtained by placing the film directly in the spectrometer beam in a suitable holder (such as that shown in Figure 5-17). Forming the polymer into a thin, clear film is not always a simple process, however, for it usually requires a molding press or a microtome.

A more general technique for the preparation of polymer films for infrared analysis is to cast them from solution onto an NaCl or KBr plate. To do this the polymer is dissolved in any reasonably volatile solvent; the solution is then poured onto an NaCl or KBr plate and the solvent is evaporated by heating. A reasonably uniform polymer film is formed on the salt plate, and its spectrum is easily obtained by mounting the salt plate in the spectrometer with the holder shown in Figure 5-17. This simple technique gives a spectrum free from interfering absorptions so that qualitative identifications can be made. Quantitative analysis cannot be performed directly on polymer films with this technique, again for the reason that film thickness cannot be accurately known or controlled. However, ratio methods can be used to determine copolymer or even terpolymer ratios; this technique is described in Chapter 6.

A few precautions must be exercised in performing this technique. The polymer is more readily dissolved if the solvent is boiling, thereby supplying both heat and agitation. The salt plate should be preheated before hot solution is poured on it, or it is likely to crack. When solvent is being evaporated from the film on the plate, it is advisable to place the plate in an inert atmosphere (such as N_2), for thin polymer films when heated strongly in air show a tendency to oxidize. The last traces of solvent must be removed, or solvent absorptions will be superimposed on the polymer spectrum and may lead to possible misinterpretation. After the solvent has been removed, the plate should be cooled slowly to room temperature before being placed in the cold metal holder, or again it may crack. Furthermore, if the film is hot when its spectrum is obtained, it will emit radiation into the spectrometer in frequency regions in which it is a blackbody (i.e., regions of high absorption), with the result that absorption strengths will appear to be slightly low.

The criteria of solvents used for obtaining polymer films are that they are able to dissolve the polymer and be readily vaporized from the polymer film on gentle heating. The following solvents have been found to be generally useful for certain polymer types: acetone appears to be a good solvent for most polymers high in oxygen content, such as polyesters and phenolic resins. The simple vinyl-type

polymers $(—CH_2—CH—)_n$, where G may be H, R, phenyl, chlorine,
$$\mid$$
$$G$$
etc., are nearly always soluble in boiling *o*-dichlorobenzene; this class constitutes a large fraction of modern plastics. The boiling point of *o*-dichlorobenzene is high (178°C), which has the advantage that more heat can be applied in the solution process but the disadvantage that it is less easily completely removed from the plastic film. Since *o*-dichlorobenzene has several strong absorptions which might cause misinterpretation if superimposed on a spectrum, extra care is required with its use.

Polyvinyl cyanide is not soluble in *o*-dichlorobenzene but will dissolve in *N,N*-dimethyl formamide. This solvent is about the only one practical for the other highly insoluble nitrogen polymer types, especially the polyamides (nylons) or the nitrogen heterocyclic ring polymers. It is often difficult to remove dimethyl formamide completely from some polymers, and absorptions of this solvent should be anticipated in the spectra of polymer films prepared with it.

Finally, for polymers most conveniently soluble in water (methyl cellulose, polyacrylic acid, polyacrylamide, polyvinyl alcohol, and certain water-based gums and resins) or for polymers in the form of suspensions or emulsions in a water base (the latex paints) the techniques must be modified slightly. A film may be cast from water, but it must be cast on an AgCl plate rather than on an NaCl or KBr plate. Here the softness of AgCl is no disadvantage, for the plate need not be absolutely flat. However, as has been mentioned before, care must be taken to avoid exposure of the AgCl plate to strong visible or ultraviolet light or it will become blackened.

Copolymers may be prepared in the same way as polymers; normally the solvent will be chosen on the basis of the principal co-monomer constituent. When preparing films of copolymers by the film-casting technique, it is advisable to build up the film from successive thin layers, which helps to produce a more representative sample; often the constituents of a copolymer can fractionate to some extent as the solvent evaporates.

After the spectrum of a polymeric material has been obtained, the salt plate is easily cleaned with the same technique employed in cleaning plates used for liquid capillary films: the plates are rubbed on a flat cloth wet with acetone, then dried by rubbing on a dry portion of the cloth. Even though acetone may not be a solvent for the particular polymer, it will cause it to swell, and the slight abrasive action of the cloth, plus the fact that the polymer film is very thin and usually sticks poorly to NaCl or KBr, results in its ready removal with no damage to the plate.

Sometimes polymers that are insoluble in all volatile solvents must be analyzed. Highly cross-linked polymers or high molecular-weight poly-functional polymers, such as cellulose, and the fluorinated ethylene polymers are examples. Spectra of these materials are best obtained by reducing a portion of the polymer to fine particles and using the techniques normally applied to crystalline solids. Also, should a powdery material result from an attempt to prepare a clear, coherent film, its spectrum is best obtained by these techniques.

V. Crystalline state techniques

Obtaining spectra of crystalline solids insoluble in CCl_4–CS_2 presents a more difficult problem. A thin, single crystal would produce a satisfactory spectrum without further preparation, but to obtain a single crystal $\sim$0.01 mm thick and $\sim$2 cm square is an enormously difficult task. A film of a crystalline solid cannot be cast, as in the case of polymers, for a coherent film would not be produced, but instead a mass of many small crystals might form, which would scatter the light so badly that the mass would be opaque.

Two different techniques have been devised which allow solid crystalline materials to be prepared so that their infrared spectra may be obtained: the oil-mull technique and the pressed halide-disk technique. Both depend on (a) reducing most of the solid particles to a size well below that of the shortest wavelength of light to be used, so that reflections and refractions at the faces of the particles are minimized, and (b) surrounding the solid particles with a material whose refractive index is roughly the same as that of the particles, so that scattering by reflection and refraction is further reduced and Rayleigh scattering is also reduced (see later). In practice, however, the techniques are quite different.

A. Light transmission by small crystalline particles

In order to appreciate some of the difficulties encountered in working with crystalline solids, it is necessary to examine in some detail the mechanism by which light is transmitted by small solid particles. Figure 5-18 is a diagram of the transmission and reflection of an arbitrary light ray by a small particle. Not only will some of the light be lost by reflection off the face of the particle, but the ray refracted and transmitted by the particle will most likely emerge at such an angle that it will not reach the spectrometer entrance

Crystalline state techniques **135**

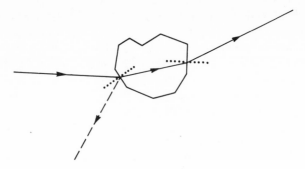

FIGURE 5-18 *Path of an arbitrary light ray through a solid particle.*

slit, and the few rays that might possibly get through the particle at an appropriate angle would undoubtedly be scattered by passage through other particles. Hence a collection of particles is essentially opaque to radiation of wavelength smaller than their diameters.

The angular deviation resulting from refraction is described by the familiar Snell Law,

$$\frac{\sin \theta_1}{\sin \theta_2} = \frac{n_2}{n_1}, \tag{5-5}$$

where θ_1 is the angle between the normal to the surface and the ray in phase 1 (air), θ_2 is the analogous angle for the ray in phase 2 (particle) and n_1 and n_2 are the refractive indices of air and particle, respectively. Also, the fraction of light reflected at the crystal face depends on the refractive indices of the phases:

$$r = \left(\frac{n_1 - n_2}{n_1 + n_2}\right)^2. \tag{5-6}$$

Now, when n_1 and n_2 are made more nearly equal, clearly the loss by reflection and the deviation by refraction will be reduced, and the loss of light intensity by scattering is thereby reduced. For this reason it is advantageous to surround the crystalline particles with, or imbed them in, some material whose refractive index is nearly the same as that of the solid particles. This material may be a liquid or a solid, but to be useful it must have little or no infrared absorption.

The mechanism just described concerns the scattering of light by particles that are large with respect to the wavelength of light being scattered. Because, in obtaining an infrared spectrum throughout the frequency region of interest to chemistry, a wavelength distribution of a factor of nearly 10 is employed, it is also necessary to consider the effect of particles that are small with respect to the radiation wavelength. Refraction and reflection cannot occur in this situation because a wavefront of coherent radiation cannot be formed from a surface that is smaller than the wavelength of the radiation. But at any phase boundary another phenomenon, known as Rayleigh scattering, is encountered. The scattering coefficient, a_s (analogous to the absorption coefficient a_A—see Chapter 6), is given by

$$a_s = \frac{(n_1 - n_2)^2}{\lambda^4} 4\pi^2 N, \tag{5-7}$$

where n_1 and n_2 are the refractive indices of the two phases, λ is wavelength, and N is number of particles per cubic centimeter.

This equation indicates that scattering by small particles increases as the number of particles per cubic centimeter increases, and on first consideration it would appear that making the particles very fine would defeat our purpose. Furthermore, the scattering is seen to be dependent on the inverse fourth power of wavelength, which would appear to make obtainment of transmission of a powder at short wavelength a hopeless undertaking. Fortunately, the scattering by this mechanism is far less severe than that by reflection and refraction of large particles, and good transmission can be achieved even at short wavelengths if the particles are reduced to a size effectively below 2 μ. Finally, the equation shows that the magnitude of Rayleigh scattering depends on the square of refractive-index *difference* of the two phases, and, if this is small, real benefit is obtained. Hence it is again seen to be desirable to suspend the particles in a medium whose refractive index is as similar as possible to that of the particles.

Because it is difficult to reduce absolutely *all* of the particles of a sample to a size below 2 μ, when a spectrum of a solid sample is obtained either by the mull or pressed halide-disk technique, it will often be found that the transmission of the sample falls off fairly rapidly below $\sim$4 μ and is at its lowest value (except for absorption bands) at the lowest wavelength light used in obtaining the spectrum. The finer the sample has been ground, the smaller this effect. But only by the most vigorous grinding can all transmission loss be eliminated at the shortest wavelength.

If the refractive indices of solid particle and surrounding medium differ appreciably, another difficulty, known as the Christiansen effect, is encountered. This effect develops because the refractive index of a material is a function of frequency that has a discontinuity in each frequency region of a strong absorption band. Figure 5-19*b* is a typical plot of refractive index as a function of frequency in the vicinity of a strong absorption band at ω_0. On the high frequency side of the absorption maximum the refractive index falls rapidly; on the low frequency side the refractive index rapidly falls from a high value to its value in regions of no absorption. This produces a peculiar distortion of absorption band shape if there are many large particles. At frequencies remote from the absorption band the transmission of the solid particle ensemble changes slowly, increasing as frequency decreases because there are fewer particles of a size comparable to the magnitude of wavelength and because of the factor $1/\lambda^4$ in the Rayleigh scattering equation. But as frequencies somewhat higher than the absorption maximum are reached, the refractive index begins to fall rapidly and more nearly equals the refractive index of the surroundings; the result is less scattering and a rapid rise in transmission. In the region of frequency slightly smaller than the absorption maximum the index of refraction of the particles is so high that it matches its surroundings very poorly. Therefore the transmission is much lower than would be caused by the absorption band

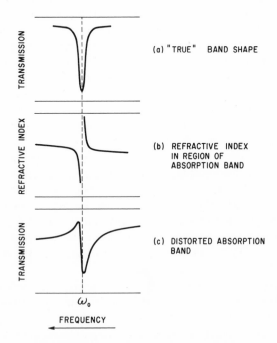

FIGURE 5-19   The Christiansen effect.

alone. The result is the shape shown in Figure 5-19c; clearly, neither the frequency of the absorption maximum nor the transmission value determined from such a band can be regarded as having high accuracy. The Christiansen effect will usually be more pronounced at short wavelengths, where a larger number of the solid particles will be a size comparable to radiation wavelength and the factor $1/\lambda^4$ becomes large; the effect will be less pronounced at long wavelength where opposite effects are encountered. The Christiansen effect is minimized by a reduction of as many as possible of the particles to a size smaller than ~ 2 μ, but it is never completely eliminated when obtaining spectra of powdered crystalline materials.

Still another complication is present when spectra of powdered samples containing large particles are obtained. Suppose we wished to measure the absorbance of an inherently intense absorption band; only a few particles can then be included in the sample preparation, or the light transmission will become so low that accurate absorbance measurement is impossible. (See Chapter 6.) Also, the larger the particles, the fewer that can be placed in the sampling area of the infrared beam for the same reason, and the fewer the particles, the poorer the statistical coverage of the infrared beam area, with the result that there will be small areas of the sample preparation in which no particles at all are encountered by the infrared beam. This situation is roughly equivalent to the case of bubbles in an absorption cell; strong bands will never be observed to be completely absorbing unless the particle size is so fine that the infrared beam area is uniformly covered.

Finally, attention must be given to the crystalline form of the sample. An infrared absorption spectrum depends not only on the identity of the molecule causing it, but when obtained in the crystalline state depends also on the exact nature of the arrangement of the molecules in the crystal lattice. Often one single chemical species can exist in more than one crystalline form, and spectra of the different forms can often be quite different. An example is shown by Figure 5-20; both spectra are of the same chemical species but are obtained from different polymorphic crystalline forms: they are quite different. (If the spectra of the two materials had been obtained in solution, they would have been identical.)

Now, in handling the solid crystals it is often possible to induce transformations from one form to another or to the amorphous (noncrystalline) form. Worse, these transformations may not be complete but may result in a mixture of two or more crystalline forms in the powder sample. Sometimes transformation occurs easily

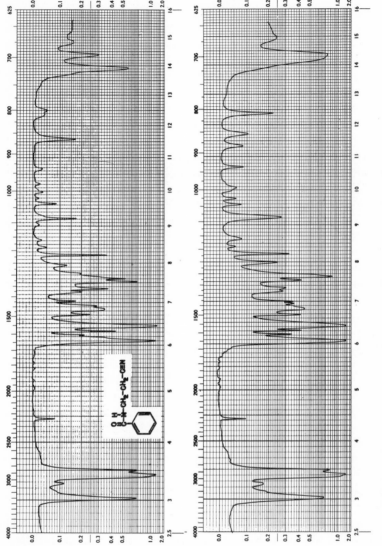

FIGURE 5-20 Infrared spectra of two different crystalline forms of the same material.

140

(grinding alone is sufficient); in other cases only more violent treatment will promote it. Obviously the possibility of different crystalline forms for the same compound is something that must be considered carefully when spectra of crystalline solids are being interpreted. Polymorphism appears to be the rule and not the exception with solid materials, especially the highly polar molecules.

In view of the foregoing considerations, it is the author's opinion that in the great majority of cases quantitative infrared analysis on powdered crystalline materials is not a fruitful undertaking. Light scattering by large particles is nearly impossible to eliminate completely or, at any rate, to make reproducible. Band shapes will *always* be distorted to a greater or lesser extent as a result of the Christiansen effect, again in a nonreproducible manner. Measurements of inherently strong absorption bands are likely to be inaccurate because the few particles required are arranged uniformly over the infrared beam area only with difficulty. In dealing with a solid sample it is difficult to be sure that only one polymorph is being measured; presence of a variety of polymorphic forms or of the amorphous form seems to be increasingly likely when the solid material is more impure, yet impure solids are just the sort on which it is most important to perform quantitative analysis. Finally, the absorption bands of pure crystalline solids are often extremely sharp—frequently much sharper than absorptions of materials in solution—and we have already noted, and will discuss further at length, the problem in quantitative analysis that arises when absorbance of a narrow absorption band is measured. For these reasons, then, quantitative analysis of polar materials is *best done in solution* wherever possible even if polar solvents and elaborate energy compensation methods are required.

However, spectra produced by powder techniques are *perfectly satisfactory for qualitative analysis* and even rough quantitative estimations, provided good technique in sample preparation is employed. We shall now discuss the practical points of these procedures.

B. The oil-mull techique

This is the older of the two principal techniques and has been used for many years. It is often referred to as a "Nujol mull," the name being derived from the trade mark, Nujol, for highly purified mineral oil. Nujol mineral oil is a mixture of alkane hydrocarbons in the range C_{20}–C_{30} which contains little, if any, olefinic or aromatic hydrocarbon, or other impurity, and has a convenient viscosity.

Briefly, an oil mull is made by grinding the solid sample to a fine particle size while the particles are suspended in Nujol. Grinding in a mortar is greatly facilitated when this mulling agent is used, the process being somewhat analogous to the use of cutting oil in machining operations or water in grinding operations. At the same time, the Nujol is the material in which the sample is suspended to produce a closer refractive index match between particles and surroundings. After the solid has been well ground and mixed with Nujol, the paste is spread between two flat NaCl or KBr plates, which are mounted in the spectrometer in the same fashion as are capillary films.

Probably no technique in infrared spectroscopy has been so horribly abused as the mull technique. Properly prepared mulls yield excellent spectra, but poorly prepared mulls yield spectra so inferior as to be nearly useless. Figure 5-21 compares the spectra of a well-prepared and a poorly prepared mull of the same material; unfortunately, examples of the latter are all too numerous in the infrared literature. Preparation of a good mull is somewhat of an art; hence we shall discuss this technique in some detail. The following procedure has been found to give consistently good results.

A small amount, usually 3–10 mg., and no more than necessary, of the solid is placed in a large wide mortar of some hard and smooth material, such as agate. The solid is ground vigorously with a hard pestle until it is spread out over the surface of the mortar and the particles are of such fineness that they become tightly "caked" to the mortar. This operation takes diligence and physical effort; it usually requires 1–5 minutes, or until the sample is so fine that its caked surface begins to acquire a "glossy" look. At this point *one small drop* of mulling agent is added. The vigorous grinding is continued, and as it proceeds the material caked onto the mortar will gradually be picked up and suspended by the oil, eventually forming a paste about the consistency of cold cream. If the paste appears drier than this, another small drop of mulling agent can be added. Vigorous grinding is continued somewhat beyond the point at which the last bit of material caked to the mortar goes into suspension in the paste. The paste is then scraped from the mortar and pestle with a rubber "policeman" and transferred to a flat NaCl or KBr plate. A second flat salt plate is placed on the paste, and the paste is squeezed into a thin uniform film between the plates by a gentle rotary motion. This ensemble is then placed in a holder, as illustrated in Figure 5-17, for mounting in the spectrometer.

A well-prepared mull should be semitransparent to visible light. When looking through the mull paste squeezed between the salt plates, the room lights should appear well outlined. If the mull as prepared is opaque to visible light or if it has a "frosty" or "grainy" appearance, it is almost certain to scatter the short wavelength infrared radiation

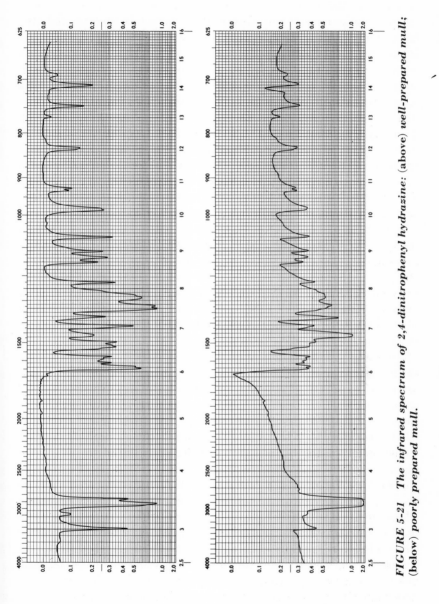

FIGURE 5-21 The infrared spectrum of 2,4-dinitrophenyl hydrazine: (above) well-prepared mull; (below) poorly prepared mull.

143

and should be scraped off the salt plates with the rubber policeman and returned to the mortar for further grinding. When scanned in the spectrometer, a well-prepared mull should have an essentially flat I_0 line, except possibly at the very shortest wavelengths.

The mortar used in mull preparation should be smooth and free from scratches or pits, for a smooth mortar easily scrapes clean with a rubber policeman, and a nearly quantitative recovery of the mull paste from the mortar is thus effected. The mortar and pestle should be large; the pestle should have a large wooden (or other) handle so that it may be firmly grasped with the full hand, and the mortar should be large enough to accommodate a pestle large enough for vigorous grinding. No sample is lost by use of a large mortar, for if smooth it can be scraped quite clean with a rubber policeman. Vigorous and effective grinding is simply not possible with a pestle so small that it can be grasped only with the fingers.

The opposing salt-plate faces must be flat. If one plate is concave or convex, the mull paste will not spread evenly between them and will be thick in some regions, thin in others. This will produce a somewhat distorted spectrum. The plates need not be free from scratches, however; the mull paste will fill the scratches and make the plates appear quite transparent. As the mull paste is spread between the plates, some scratches are often made in the soft NaCl or KBr plates, but this causes no difficulty, as just explained. Mull plates may be used many times before they require repolishing (by the methods described in Section II).

After the spectrum of a mull has been obtained, the plates are easily cleaned with the same technique employed for cleaning plates used with capillary or polymer films: the plates are rubbed on a flat cloth wetted with acetone, then dried by rubbing on a dry portion of the cloth.

The grinding operation, which is somewhat tedious, can be done with a mechanical vibrating ball mill (as described subsequently in the discussion of the pressed halide-disk technique). The use of a ball mill will yield results essentially comparable to the mulls prepared by hand grinding and may prove useful in routine examinations of materials whose identity is largely known. But use of the ball mill for mulls has two disadvantages: (a) often minute particles of the metal capsule containing the sample are abraded off and into suspension during the operation, which makes the mull considerably more opaque than one prepared by hand grinding. This is more likely to happen with a mull than with dry samples because the mulling agent acts as a cutting oil to some extent. (b) Since the preparation of a Nujol mull is somewhat of an art, it is often better to maintain a close watch on the grinding process, particularly with unknown samples, than to submit the sample to an automatic, high-energy grinding process over which neither close watch nor control can be kept. Experienced operators usually prefer the hand-grinding technique.

Once the art of making mulls is mastered, truly excellent spectra for qualitative uses can be obtained. There are, however, certain difficulties and disadvantages to the mull technique.

1. Although saturated aliphatic hydrocarbon oil (Nujol), if used sparingly, has little absorption throughout most of the 4000–400 cm^{-1} region, a very intense absorption does occur in the 3000–2800 cm^{-1} region, a fairly intense absorption is found at $\sim$1460 cm^{-1}, and a moderate absorption is produced at $\sim$1375 cm^{-1}. These absorptions result from hydrogenic stretching and deformation modes of the C—H groups in the Nujol. Obviously little use can be made of these regions and, should the substances being mulled have important absorptions at these frequencies, useful information is lost. However, this difficulty can be avoided by preparing a second mull, using a completely nonhydrogenic material as a mulling agent. A useful material for this purpose is a perhalocarbon oil, such as "Fluorolube," which is a polymer of —(CF$_2$—CFCl)— units with an average molecular weight of 775. If the spectrum is obtained from 4000 to $\sim$1330 cm^{-1}, with Fluorolube as a mulling agent, then from 1330 to 400 cm^{-1}, using Nujol, the spectrum will be essentially free of interfering bands from mulling agents. This scheme is analogous to the use of both CCl$_4$ and CS$_2$ as solvents above and below 1330 cm^{-1}, respectively, to minimize interferences from solvent absorptions. The spectra of capillary films of Nujol and Fluorolube are shown together in Figure 5-22. The disadvantage of this technique is, of course, that two mulls, rather than just one, must be prepared. Also, unless the two preparations are made in nearly the same thickness, the resultant spectrum can be misleading.

2. Quantitative analysis cannot be performed directly with this technique for the same reason that it cannot be done with liquid or solid capillary films: no accurate control over sample thickness or paste density is possible. Quantitative analysis may be performed indirectly by mixing a weighed amount of an "internal standard" into the mull preparation and using ratio methods (see Chapter 6), but the technique is rather tedious. However, as previously discussed, it is the author's opinion that quantitative infrared analysis in the crystalline state should be avoided.

Crystalline state techniques **145**

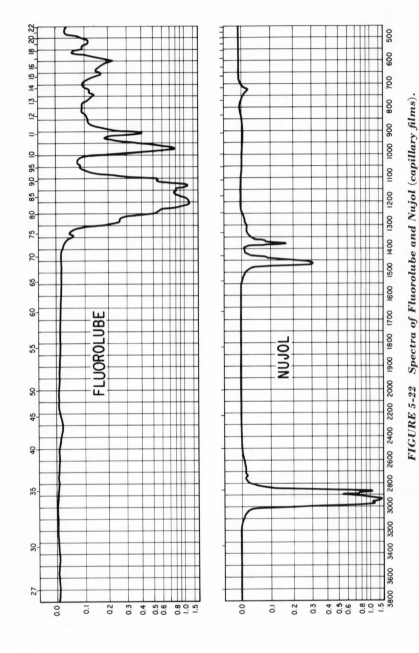

FIGURE 5-22 Spectra of Fluorolube and Nujol (capillary films).

146

3. Rubbery or plastic materials often grind up only with great difficulty. It is usually easier to obtain spectra of these materials by the polymer film-casting technique described in Section IV-B. But occasionally materials are found which are completely insoluble in all volatile solvents: cellulosic and proteinaceous materials and cross-linked polymers or resins are examples. To obtain mull spectra of these types requires a few "tricks." (a) A small amount of powdered NaCl may be added to the mortar during the grinding operation to act as an abrasive which is also transparent to infrared radiation. In using NaCl in this fashion it is necessary to reduce the NaCl particles below 2 μ in size or they will cause severe light scattering and low light transmission. (b) If the material is sufficiently hard, it may be powdered by scraping lightly with a fine file, such as a fingernail file, and collecting the resulting dust in the mortar. This technique is particularly useful on cross-linked resins and polymers. Once powdered, the material often mulls without difficulty. (c) Powdered solid CO_2 ("dry ice") may be added directly to the mortar. Most rubbery substances become brittle at low temperature and fracture easily, thus making grinding possible. The CO_2 readily evaporates as the grinding proceeds. This operation should be done in a dry box, however, since water from the air will condense into the mull at solid CO_2 temperature. In extreme cases liquid nitrogen can be used in place of solid CO_2 for this application.

4. Highly hygroscopic materials should be mulled in a dry box or they will become "mushy" during the grinding operation and give poor spectra that will show a great deal of absorption by water. For extremely hygroscopic samples the following technique has been shown to be useful: near the end of the mulling process excess 2,2-dimethoxypropane is added to the mull paste. This unique liquid reacts rapidly with water (if at pH < 7) according to the equation

$$
\begin{array}{c}
\quad\;\; \text{OCH}_3 \qquad\qquad\qquad\;\; \text{O} \\
\quad\;\; | \qquad\qquad\quad\;\; {}^{\text{H}^+} \quad\; \| \\
\text{CH}_3\text{—C—CH}_3 + \text{H}_2\text{O} \rightarrow \text{CH}_3\text{—C—CH}_3 + 2\text{CH}_3\text{OH} \\
\quad\;\; | \\
\quad\;\; \text{OCH}_3
\end{array}
$$

The excess dimethoxypropane and the methanol and acetone formed are all volatile and will evaporate as the grinding proceeds. As soon as the last of these liquids vanishes (noted by the somewhat abrupt increase in viscosity of the mull paste and by loss of odor), the mull is promptly placed between plates and scanned in the spectrometer.

Crystalline state techniques   147

5. Some solid materials have a disturbing tendency to convert themselves from one polymorphic form to another or to the amorphous form merely on grinding. When this occurs, the mull spectrum may be the result of one or more polymorphs, and this mixture will probably have a different composition each time it is prepared. Fortunately, apparently few crystalline solids are so sensitive to a simple grinding operation.

Some of the difficulties encountered in the mull technique are reduced in magnitude in the pressed-disk technique, the other common method for obtaining spectra of polar crystalline solids.

C. The pressed-disk technique

Briefly, this technique consists of grinding a few milligrams of the polar solid with about $\frac{1}{4}$–1 gm of a suitable powdered alkali halide, placing this mixture in a special die, and compressing it to a small disk about 1 mm thick under a pressure of 500–1000 atm. At this pressure many of the alkali halide crystals become quite plastic and flow together into a transparent disk. By this means the sample is imbedded in material of comparable refractive index, one of the requirements for reducing scattering. After the disk has been removed from the die, it is placed in a suitable holder in the spectrometer and scanned directly.

The pressed-disk technique has become very popular, perhaps partly because the technique for disk preparation appears to be more quickly learned than that for preparing mulls and perhaps partly because the physical labor of mull making is not involved. Contrary to opinions often expressed, however, it does not yield better solid-state spectra than mulls. Both techniques give good results if properly employed.

Before pressing the disk, a few milligrams of the solid sample must be intimately mixed with about 1 gm of an alkali halide. Just as in the mull technique, the particles must be reduced to a size smaller than $\sim2\,\mu$ if scattering is to be eliminated. Hand grinding of the alkali-halide sample mixture is not practical for all but the softest polar solids because a few hundred times more alkali halide than sample must be ground, and to reduce it all to particles below $2\,\mu$ in diameter by hand would be far too large a task to be practical. Various techniques have been employed to reduce the sample particles to appropriate size and to mix them with alkali-halide particles. The alkali-halide particles need not necessarily be made so small as $2\,\mu$ in size, for they will flow together under pressure and recoalesce, but they should be made reasonably fine in the interest of good mixing with the sample.

One technique used to reduce the particle size of the sample and to distribute it throughout the alkali halide consists of dissolving the polar solid in any polar volatile solvent, such as acetone, and spraying it on finely sieved alkali-halide powder. After the solvent evaporates, the powder mixture can be pressed to a disk. This technique apparently does not give the good results achieved with others subsequently described, probably because of the formation of large particles of sample upon evaporation of the solvent.

A technique that appears to give good results and is generally applicable is the grinding of both sample and alkali halide in a mechanical vibrating ball mill. In this device a motor-driven eccentric causes a small cylindrical capsule to be shaken vigorously several thousand times a minute. In the capsule are placed about 1 gm of powdered alkali halide and about 2 mg of powdered sample, along with a hardened-steel ball. The shaking action is vigorous enough to slam the ball against the ends of the container with sufficient force to fracture the solid particles. After about 5 minutes of this action (or about 50,000 ball-capsule impacts), the powder mixture is ready to be pressed to a disk. (Times shorter or longer than 5 minutes may be required, depending on the hardness of the sample.)

A third technique, reported to give satisfactory results, particularly on micro samples, is known as the lyophilization technique. The alkali halide is dissolved in water, and the solution is placed in a small tube whose opening is a male ground-glass joint. The tube is plunged into liquid nitrogen, and the contents swirled around, so that the solution is flash frozen and spread over the walls. A solution of the sample (in any volatile solvent that will dissolve it) is added to the tube, swirled about, and flash frozen on top of the water-halide layer. The tube is connected to a high vacuum system, and water and solvent are pumped off while the tube is kept in a liquid nitrogen bath. Removal of water and solvent in this way leaves both halide and sample in a finely divided form and well mixed. This technique is well suited to microsampling techniques (see Chapter 7), but it is not suited to general work because of the time required to remove the water and solvent by lyophilization (usually several hours).

After the sample halide mixture is prepared by one of the techniques just described, it is pressed into a disk in an evacuable die. There are many different designs for this equipment in use; all are probably equally effective in producing pellets that will yield satisfactory spectra, the principal differences being in ease or convenience of operation, assembly, and disk removal. A "standard" design is illustrated in Figure 5-23.

The parts of the die itself must be made of hardened steel, and the inner die faces are polished to a smooth mirror finish. An evacuation port is provided so that air can be removed from the powder before it is pressed; if this were not done, air pockets in the disk might render it cloudy. Hardened-steel plates cover the assembly on top and bottom in order to provide smooth surfaces on which the rubber evacuation chamber can rest, and thus effect a seal, and to distribute the force of the hardened-steel plungers over a larger area of the press faces so that they will not be deformed by the small hard plungers.

The disk is pressed as follows: The lower plunger is inserted in the cylinder, and the assembly is placed on the lower face of the hydraulic press. Sufficient mixed halide-sample powder to produce a disk about 1 mm thick is poured in and lightly tamped flat with the upper plunger. The rubber evacuation chamber is put in place, and enough pressure is applied to compress it sufficiently to produce a good air seal, but without pressing the upper plunger into the powder. A vacuum pump is attached, and the air is exhausted. A pressure of 10,000–15,000 psi is now applied with the press, and the assembly is left under pressure for several minutes (just how long depends largely on the diameter of the disk to be made, larger disks requiring longer pressing times than smaller disks). The pressure is released, and the disk is removed from the die by forcing the lower plunger up through the

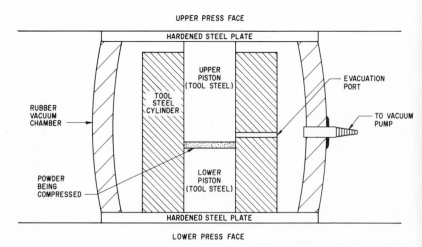

FIGURE 5-23   Die for pressing alkali halide disks.

die with an auxiliary rod.   Usually the force of the press is necessary in this operation, for the high pressure will have impacted the disk tightly against the die cylinder walls and it must be gently pressed out.

The dies supplied commercially offer certain convenience over the "standard" type just described.   Some have a longitudinally split cylinder which can be taken apart after pressing, thus facilitating removal of the disk.   Other types press the disk directly into a metal holder which slips into the spectrometer.

After pressing, the disk is placed in some simple mounting device that will hold it properly in the spectrometer sample beam.   When a spectrometer of large optics is employed, which is arranged so that the light beam area at the sampling point is large, it will be found that some compromise must be struck in choice of disk size.   It is difficult to prepare a disk of high clarity with a diameter much more than $\frac{3}{4}$ in.; disks larger than this are often cloudy.   On the other hand, although it is a simple matter to obtain a high clarity disk of $\frac{1}{2}$-in. diameter or less, when disks of this size are introduced into a spectrometer whose beam has a large area some light loss will be inevitable, thereby negating the advantage of large optics.   It is probably best to work with small disks and to tolerate the light loss in this case, for a cloudy disk may result in more light loss (plus other attendant disadvantages, as previously discussed) than the vignetting of the light beam by the small disk holder.

Various alkali halides have been used successfully for making disks. Perhaps KBr has had the widest use, although some spectroscopists prefer KCl and others prefer KI.   KI, the softest, flows most easily during the pressing operation; KCl, the hardest, facilitates fine grinding of the sample particles in a ball mill; KBr is the popular compromise.

The pressed halide disk has certain advantages over the mull technique.

1. Rubbery or plastic samples usually grind up without great difficulty in excess KBr in a vibrating ball mill.   This probably represents the most useful advantage of the pressed-disk technique over the mull technique, wherein these sorts of samples are prepared only with some difficulty.

2. Pure KBr (or KI or KCl) has no absorptions in the infrared region from 4000–400 cm^{-1} (however, see later).   Because Nujol and Fluorolube have, their combination is necessary to produce a spectrum essentially free from interfering absorptions.   No such duplication of effort is necessary with the pressed-halide-disk technique.

Crystalline state techniques   **151**

3. Quantitative analysis, when applicable, can be performed directly with the disk technique. Because all disks made from the same die will have identical cross section, the product of sample concentration and disk thickness is constant and independent of pressing time or technique for samples prepared from the same weight of sample, provided no sample is lost anywhere in the preparative process. Hence a pressed disk of a sample consisting of a mixture of different solids can, within limits, be analyzed quantitatively by comparison with spectra of disks prepared from pure materials by simple application of Beer's law (see Chapter 6) and without the use of any internal standard. Although this is usually cited as the principal advantage of pressed disks over mulls, it is the author's opinion that quantitative analysis attempted in the solid state can at best give only approximate results with general mixtures because of the complications of Christiansen effect, polymorphism and amorphism effects, and difficulty of uniform beam coverage. Therefore, if quantitative analysis in the solid state should be avoided as a matter of principle, this advantage seems small.

The pressed-disk technique also has certain difficulties.

1. Unless the most stringent precautions are taken to keep the alkali halide powder absolutely dry, an OH stretch absorption is almost always observed to a greater or lesser extent in the region of 3300 cm^{-1} as a result of trace amounts of moisture in the alkali halide powder. This is most annoying, for the spectroscopist cannot make confident statements regarding the presence or absence of OH or NH groups in unknown organic structures against a background of varying absorption in this characteristic region.

2. As mentioned in the discussion of mull techniques, it is possible to convert from one polymorphic form to another or to an amorphous form by abusing the crystals. Although this is seldom encountered in the mull technique, it appears to be somewhat more usual in the pressed-disk technique, for the abuse of the sample crystals is much more severe: the grinding operation is more violent, and the pressing operation is violent, indeed. Furthermore, this abuse is of an automatic, unobservable, and nonreproducible sort, for it is not possible to watch a material while it is being ground in a vibrating ball mill or while it is being pressed in a die. On the other hand, it is possible to observe what is happening during a hand-grinding operation and to make possible allowances or corrections before the material becomes degraded. Presumably this is why pressed disks in many cases seem to yield spectra of somewhat poorer quality than those that can

be produced by good mulling technique, particularly when an unfamiliar material is being prepared. Good spectra can be produced with the disk technique but usually only after a certain amount of experimentation with the vigor and duration of mixing, grinding, and pressing.

3. KBr is much less chemically inert than Nujol or Fluorolube and occasionally may react with the sample.

To summarize: the mull technique seems to be preferable for general qualitative analysis of polar solids. The disk technique requires less effort and skill and may well be better suited to routine examinations of materials whose identity is essentially known. The disk technique can perform quantitative analysis directly, without internal standards, but it is the author's opinion that quantitative analysis in the solid state is unreliable. Rubbery or plastic materials are usually handled more easily by the pressed-disk technique. Spectra prepared by the disk technique can never be completely relied on in the O—H stretch region. In order to eliminate interfering absorptions with the mull technique, two mulls (Nujol and Fluorolube) must be prepared.

Only the general techniques of sample preparation have been discussed in this chapter. Proper use of these techniques will enable a research chemist to obtain spectra of the great majority of materials in which he may be interested. But inevitably certain cases will develop which will require a combination of these techniques, coupled with some simple or complex chemical manipulations (determination of trace additives in a plastic, for example, or the identity of the emulsifying agent in an oil-water emulsion formulation). These problems are not different from the usual problems faced every day by the analytical chemist. It is assumed here that the organic or analytical chemist will be able to devise his own methods of extractions, concentrations, separations, and the like, in order to solve problems peculiar to his research.

Selected references

1. Lord, R., R. McDonald, and F. Miller, "Notes on the Practice of Infrared Spectroscopy," *J. Opt. Soc. Am.* **42,** 149 (1952).
2. Williams, V., "Infrared Instrumentation and Techniques," *Rev. Sci. Instr.* **19,** 135 (1948).
3. "Instruction Manual: Perkin-Elmer Infrared Equipment," Vol. 2: *Infrared Sampling and Techniques,* The Perkin-Elmer Corp., Norwalk, Conn., 1952.
4. "Tables of Wavenumbers for the Calibration of Infrared Spectrometers," International Union of Pure and Applied Chemistry Commission on Molecular Structure and Spectroscopy, Butterworths, Washington, D. C., 1961.

5. Dickson, A., I. Mills, and B. Crawford, "Vibrational Intensities," *J. Chem. Phys.* **27**, 445 (1957).
   Overend, J., M. Youngquist, E. Curtis, and B. Crawford, "Vibrational Intensities," *ibid.* **30**, 532 (1959).
6. Jenkins, F., and H. White, *Fundamentals of Optics* (Chapters 22 and 23), McGraw-Hill, New York, 1957.
7. Lecomte, J., "Spectroscopie dans l'infrarouge," *Handbuch der Physik*, Band XXVI (pp. 317 ff), Springer-Verlag, Berlin, 1958.
8. Brugel, W., *An Introduction to Infrared Spectroscopy*, Wiley, New York, 1962.
9. Bauman, R. P., *Absorption Spectroscopy*, Wiley, New York, 1962.

6

Quantitative analysis

Another of the great advantages of infrared spectroscopy is the nearly universal amenability of mixtures to quantitative analysis by this method. If a chemical substance is to be analyzed, all that is required is that it exhibit one or more unique, reasonably strong absorptions not grossly interfered with by absorptions of other compounds present and that it be soluble in a liquid having useful light transmission in a frequency region in which at least one of these unique absorptions occur. Nearly any material soluble in CCl_4 or CS_2 will meet these requirements. Many other organic materials are soluble in polar solvents, and analyses can be performed in them not only in regions of solvent transparency, but even where they are partially absorbing, if solvent compensation techniques can be employed. (See Chapter 7.)

Briefly, quantitative analysis is accomplished by comparison of the absorption strength of an infrared band exhibited by a component in the mixture to be analyzed with a corresponding absorption measured from a pure material under conditions of known concentration. If all the components in the mixture possess unique absorptions not highly overlapped by absorptions of the other components, all may be analyzed from the same scanned spectrum. As we have seen, only a few minutes are required to obtain an infrared spectrum when average compromises between time and signal-to-noise ratio have been made; hence rough quantitative analysis by infrared spectroscopy is rapid. Precise quantitative determinations are obtainable, but somewhat more time and care must be expended.

The Beer-Lambert law 155

Accuracy of a quantitative determination will ultimately be limited by noise level at which the spectrometer is operated. The factors contributing to noise have been discussed at some length in earlier chapters; how noise level relates to accuracy obtainable in quantitative analysis is discussed here.

I. The Beer-Lambert law and its application to quantitative analysis

Infrared photometric systems record the ordinate in terms of relative light intensity, or per cent of light transmission. This, of course, is a linear function of the number of light quanta arriving at the detector. However, the number of infrared light quanta absorbed by a chemical material is *not* a linear function of the number of its molecules placed in the infrared beam. The functional relationship is stated by the Beer-Lambert law, which we now derive.

A. The Beer-Lambert law

Consider a differential "slice" through the volume containing the absorbing molecules, as shown in Figure 6-1. Let I be the number of monochromatic light quanta passing through a square centimeter of

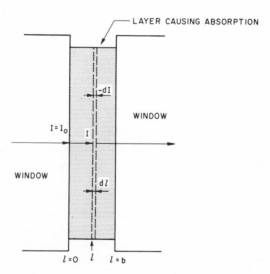

FIGURE 6-1   *Decrease of light intensity through a material as a result of absorption.*

beam area per second, at some distance l from the front boundary of the absorbing path. The decrease in number of light quanta per second per square centimeter across the differential "slice," $-dI$, will be proportional to the number of quanta per second per square centimeter available for absorption, I, and the number of absorbing molecules in a square centimeter of the differential "slice." The last number is equal to the product of the number of absorbing molecules per cubic centimeter and the differential length, dl, or proportional to concentration of absorbing molecules, c, and to dl. This is summarized by

$$-dI = a_A' Ic\, dl, \tag{6-1}$$

where a_A' is the proportionality factor,* whose magnitude depends on choice of units of c and l and is a constant for a given molecule at a fixed frequency. (Actually, an infrared absorption spectrum is a record of how this coefficient varies with radiation frequency.)

To find the total decrease in light intensity through the complete absorbing path, equation 6-1 is integrated:

$$\int_{I_0}^{I} \frac{dI}{I} = -\int_0^b a'c\, dl = -a'c \int_0^b dl,$$

so

$$\log_e \frac{I}{I_0} = -a'cb$$

or

$$\log_{10} \frac{I}{I_0} = -abc, \tag{6-2}$$

which is the usual symbolism for the Beer-Lambert law in application to quantitative analysis of solutions. Here I is the number of quanta per second (i.e., radiant power) per square centimeter of the beam

* This proportionality factor is variously known as *extinction coefficient, absorption coefficient,* or *absorptivity.* The symbol α is often used for absorption coefficient when discussing the vapor phase, in which case concentration is expressed as partial pressure. ϵ is the older symbol for absorption coefficient, and the symbol ϵ_{max} often appears in the literature in investigations concerned with the inherent strengths of absorption bands; subscript "max" designates the absorption coefficient which has been determined at the point of maximum absorption of a band or at its absorption peak; ω_{max} specifies the exact frequency at which this peak occurs.

The subscript A indicates that this is an *absorption,* not a scattering, coefficient; it is omitted in the discussion in the remainder of this book, it being understood that a is a pure absorption coefficient.

The Beer-Lambert law 157

transmitted by the solution, and I_0 is the number of quanta per second per square centimeter of the beam incident on the absorbing path. (See Figure 6-1.)   Logarithms to the base 10 are generally employed in analytical work, and a is defined as $a'/\log_e 10$.   Hereafter the subscript 10 will be dropped, with the understanding that common logarithms are being employed.   The cell length b is commonly expressed in centimeters, and the concentration c in moles per liter if absorption coefficient a is to be calculated.   However, as discussed in Chapter 5, it is usually more convenient to express concentration on a weight per volume basis and cell lengths in millimeters.   In practical analytical applications the absorption coefficient is usually not calculated (see later); hence *any* convenient units may be used.

Equation 6-2 may be written in various other ways for convenience. As $I/I_0 = T$, the per cent of light transmission by the absorbing material is given by

$$\log T = -abc \tag{6-3a}$$

or

$$\log \frac{1}{T} = abc. \tag{6-3b}$$

The important concept from the Beer-Lambert expression is that concentration of a solute is not proportional to $1 - T$, the linear displacement of an absorption maximum along the chart ordinate from 100% transmission, but to $\log 1/T$.   For small values of $\log 1/T$ (i.e., weak absorption bands) $1 - T$ is roughly proportional to $\log 1/T$, so that if a spectrum of one material has a weak band twice as deep as in another spectrum, the first material contains about twice as much of that component.   But no such approximation can be made for bands with large values of $\log 1/T$ (strong bands), for in this case a small change in $1 - T$ represents a large change in $\log 1/T$.   To use other words, equation 6-3b is the functional relationship between what the *spectrometer* measures ($\% \ T$) and what we wish to measure in quantitative analysis (c).   This relation must be borne in mind in order to have a proper understanding of the accuracy limitations imposed on quantitative analysis by inherent spectrometer accuracy, particularly when new or special quantitative techniques are developed.

B. The absorbance

In actual quantitative analytical calculations relations such as equation 6-3 are not employed because a somewhat unwieldy logarithmic manipulation is required, which can be avoided.   We do this by measuring a quantity called the *absorbance,* or, as it is often called, the *optical density.* Absorbance, A, is defined by

$$A = - \log \frac{I}{I_0} = - \log T = \log \frac{1}{T}. \qquad (6\text{-}4)$$

The Beer-Lambert law, in terms of absorbance, becomes simply

$$A = abc. \qquad (6\text{-}5)$$

Obviously, if absorbance of an analytical absorption band can be determined easily, quantitative analysis is reduced to the simplest possible arithmetic procedure.

Absorbance can be measured directly from a spectrometer chart in three different ways. The first consists of placing a logarithmic cam in the recorder-pen servo system between light attenuator and pen, so that the pen records linearly in absorbance. This is normally the system employed in ultraviolet recording spectrometers, but it is not practical with infrared spectrometers because of the high noise level at which they must operate: as the noise level is a constant number on the transmission scale, consideration of equation 6-4 shows that a $\frac{1}{2}\%$ noise level would become an unmanageably awkward distance on a linear absorbance chart at high absorbance levels.

The second method is to print the ordinate scale of the spectrometer chart so that a reading from this scale is in units of absorbance rather than per cent transmission. This sort of scale, of course, will be nonlinear; such a scale, together with a linear transmission scale, is shown in Figure 6-2. The pen servo system still records linearly in transmission, which is mechanically most convenient. Most infrared spectrometer charts are now printed with absorbance units as the ordinate scale.

The third method is essentially the same as the second: an absorbance scale is made into the form of a transparent plastic ruler. This scale, jocularly known as a "Beer glass," has certain advantages. (*a*) It can be used with older spectrometer charts whose ordinate scale is per cent transmission. In this application the ∞ absorbance mark is placed at 0% transmission on the chart, and absorbance values of bands read on the plastic scale. (*b*) If made large enough, it can be used with *any* size spectrometer chart, for what is normally measured is an *absorbance difference* (see below), and this is independent of the actual expansion of the scale. (*c*) Because it is movable on the chart, it can easily be used to give correct absorbance values even though the spectrometer has scattered light: the ∞ absorbance

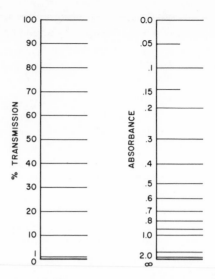

FIGURE 6-2 *Absorbance and transmission scales compared.*

mark is placed on the chart at a transmission value equal to the known amount of scattered light, and the absorbances then read from the chart will be corrected for scattered light.

Another great convenience of working in units of absorbance rather than per cent transmission is that absorbances are additive. If two (or more) different materials absorb infrared radiation at the same frequency, the total absorbance at this frequency is the simple sum of the individual absorbances. If desired, the total absorbance can be converted to per cent transmission. The individual transmission values, of course, are not additive. Additivity of absorbances forms the basis of multicomponent analyses, discussed in Section IV.

II. Elements of quantitative analysis

Nearly all quantitative analysis is done with the absorbance measured at the absorption maximum, or transmission minimum, of an appropriate absorption band. Reflection shows that this is the natural point on the band contour to employ, for it is located easily and accurately (i.e., it can be found independently of absolute wavelength accuracy); being the highest value of absorbance of the band, its use results in greater sensitivity; and at the absorption maximum the spectrometer's recording servo system is much more likely to be

160 *Quantitative analysis*

at equilibrium and therefore to render a true reading than it would be on the side of a steep absorption. This method is commonly known as the method of "peak height"; the other method used in quantitative analysis—the method of integrated absorption bands—is discussed in Section VII.

Simple quantitative determinations, using absorption maxima, or peak heights, are made by two principal methods: (a) the "cell-in-cell-out" method, done at fixed frequency, usually on a single-beam spectrometer, and (b) the "base-line" method, performed with a scanned spectrum obtained from either a single-beam or a double-beam spectrometer. Each has its own advantages.

A. "Cell-in-cell-out" method

In performing this method the spectrometer is set at a previously determined fixed frequency and fixed slit width. When no scan is being made, hence no need exists for a flat I_0 line, the best transmission reproducibility is provided by the single-beam spectrometer, as discussed in Chapter 4. For this reason single-beam spectrometers now find this one of their principal uses in analytical infrared spectroscopic laboratories. As already mentioned, the analysis is made by comparison of an absorbance resulting from a component in the mixture of unknown composition with a corresponding absorbance of a pure material obtained under known conditions, usually referred to as a "standard" or "reference" material.

To illustrate the method, let us say that we seek the per cent of material M in a mixture of unknown composition. Absorbances are determined as follows:

1. A solution prepared by placing a known weight of the mixture containing material M into a suitable solvent is inserted into a cell of known path length. The transmission is measured at a predetermined frequency; this will be a frequency at which the material is known to have a well-defined absorption band maximum and at which the solvent has little or no absorption. Because this analytical method is rapid, time can be afforded in making the measurement; as the spectrometer is already at the appropriate frequency, the only time interval required is for the detecting and recording systems to come to equilibrium. Hence, if the time constant is set at a high value and ample time, consistent with this value, is allotted to making the measurement, the signal-to-noise ratio can be increased (as square root of time constant) and a highly accurate transmission value determined. Further, if generous time is allowed for the transmission

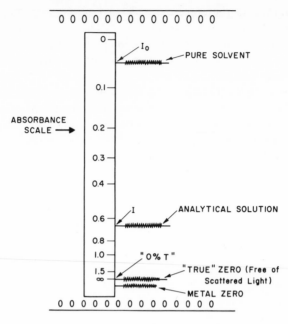

FIGURE 6-3 *Absorbance measurement by "cell-in-cell-out" method.*

measurement and a time versus transmission recording is made of it, the remaining noise may be neatly averaged to increase the precision further. The point measured represents I, the transmitted intensity. A sketch of this and subsequent measurements is given in Figure 6-3.

2. A similar measurement is made with the same cell filled with pure solvent. This is I_0, the value of light intensity transmitted by cell and solvent when the absorbing molecule of interest is not present.

3. A "0% transmission" is determined. This is presumed to denote the point on the chart which represents no light transmission at the analytical wavelength. It could be obtained simply by placing an opaque object (such as a metal shutter) in the beam and determining the resulting chart deflection. However, if scattered light (see Chapter 3) is present at the analytical frequency, the wrong zero would result. A more sophisticated way to make this determination is to place in the radiation beam some material that is known to be opaque at the analytical frequency but transparent at higher frequencies, thus resulting in a value which represents "0% transmission" for the analytical wavelength alone. (See Figure 6-3.) If the analytical frequency is 1000 cm^{-1}, for example, a CaF$_2$ plate serves nicely; if

162 *Quantitative analysis*

it is 700 cm^{-1}, a BaF$_2$ plate is best.   (Other plates for other regions can be found by reference to Table 1-1.)

The actual absorbance of material M in this unknown mixture is now determined.   By equation 6-4 absorbance is equal to the logarithm of the quotient: distance between I_0 and 0% T divided by distance between I and 0% T.   Rather than measure these distances linearly, however, we measure the absorbance directly by use of the absorbance scale previously described: the ∞ mark is placed on the *true* 0% T reading, thereby correcting for scattered light, and absorbance is found by subtracting the reading at I_0 from the reading at I.

Clearly, this scale will give the same result for any setting of slit or gain control (on the single-beam spectrometer), provided the band shape is not distorted by widening the slit (see next section).   Widening the slit or increasing the amplifier gain simply expands the entire transmission scale across the chart; the individual values of I and I_0 determined by the absorbance scale will vary, but the *difference* between them is still the same on the scale.   Obviously, then, such a scale, if long enough, may be used on any chart size; or, conversely, any arbitrary scale length laid off as the logarithm of the reciprocal will serve.

When the slit aperture is increased in operating a single-beam spectrometer, the chart transmission scale is expanded; when gain control setting is decreased, the scale is compressed.   As noise level decreases with decrease of amplifier gain, it is therefore advantageous to widen the slits and reduce the gain in order to increase the signal-to-noise ratio.   If the increase of slit and decrease of amplifier gain has been continued past the point at which noise level is so small that it is no longer visible in the recorded spectrum (possible when a long time constant is employed), the scale should be expanded to take full advantage of the increased accuracy that becomes available, if such scale expansion facility is available on the spectrometer being employed.

After the measurement of the absorbance of material M in the unknown mixture has been made, a similar measurement of the corresponding band in a "reference" solution of pure M is taken.   The per cent of material M is the unknown mixture can now be calculated. By equation 6-5,

$$A_{M,\text{un}} = a_M b_{\text{un}} c_{M,\text{un}},$$

and an analogous equation exists for the reference solution:

$$A_{M,\text{ref}} = a_M b_{\text{ref}} c_{M,\text{ref}}.$$

Elements of quantitative analysis   **163**

Because the absorption coefficient is a constant, it can be eliminated between these expressions:

$$\frac{A_{M,U}}{A_{M,R}} = \frac{b_U c_{M,U}}{b_R c_{M,R}}, \tag{6-6}$$

and, because a_M is eliminated from the equation, leaving ratios of b's and c's, we can express cell length and concentration in any convenient units. As discussed in Chapter 5, cell length is usually conveniently expressed in millimeters, whereas concentration is usually expressed as a weight per volume per cent ($10\% = 100$ mg/ml solution).

Now, $c_{M,U}$, the weight per volume per cent of material M in the solution prepared from the unknown for spectroscopic analysis, is not being sought. Rather we wish to determine the per cent of M contained in the unknown mixture. Clearly

$$\% M_{\text{by weight}} = \frac{c_{M,U}}{c_{\text{total unknown}}}, \tag{6-7}$$

where $c_{\text{total unknown}}$ as a weight per volume per cent is the expression of the weight of sample of unknown composition per volume of its solution. Combining 6-6 and 6-7 yields

$$\% M_{\text{by weight}} = \frac{A_{M,U}}{A_{M,R}} \frac{b_R}{b_U} \frac{c_{M,R}}{c_{TU}}, \tag{6-8}$$

whose evaluation on a slide rule can obviously be done rapidly. The simple equation 6-8 is the essence of all quantitative analysis by light absorption methods.

The cell-in-cell-out method has the advantage of being simple and precise. Because no time is spent obtaining spectral data at other frequencies, all available time can be devoted to the measurement at the analytical frequency, with attendant increase in accuracy (see later). But, although the *precision* is high, in many cases there is likely to be a serious systematic error which results from inability to measure the I_0 value correctly.

If the unknown mixture contains only a small number of components, each having but few sharp, unique absorptions but showing no appreciable absorption from electronic transitions (usually occurring in the ultraviolet and visible region but sometimes extending weakly but finitely well into the infrared region, especially in samples containing graphite or carbon-black structures resulting from highly degraded organic material), and if the solution prepared is free of suspended solids, so that no Rayleigh scattering occurs, then, perhaps, the I_0

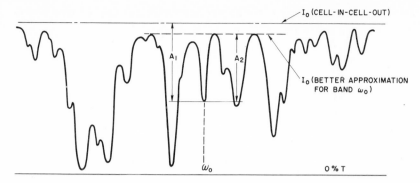

FIGURE 6-4 *Difficulties of the "cell-in-cell-out" method in complex mixtures.*

measured by cell-in-cell-out procedure will be essentially free of error. Such ideal conditions, of course, are not often the case in laboratory or industrial chemistry. Figure 6-4 illustrates with somewhat more realism the situation usually encountered. Here A_1 is the sort of absorbance that would be determined by the cell-in-cell-out method, which, although precise, is clearly too large. A_2 is certainly a better value, although it cannot be determined with the same precision. In order to determine A_2, a scanned spectrum is necessary and the "base-line" technique is used.

B. "Base-line" method

This method is an attempt to circumvent the difficulties just described so that a closer approximation to the true absorbance of a band may be determined. As discussed later, it has certain disadvantages, but it does avoid the systematic error likely to occur in the cell-in-cell-out method. A scanned spectrum (obtained with a double-beam spectrometer or a single-beam spectrometer whose slits have been programmed for constant energy—see Chapter 3) is used for analysis by this method.

The I_0 of an absorption band is determined by asking the question: "how would the spectrum appear if this absorption band were not a part of it?" Clearly, for the case illustrated in Figure 6-5a, the dashed line represents with high probability of correctness how the spectrum would appear if the band had not occurred; this line is called the *base line*. The absorbance of this band, then, is determined by reading the value on the absorbance scale at the absorption maximum

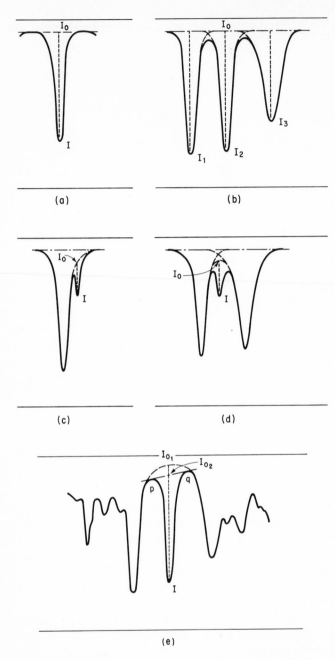

FIGURE 6-5 *Various base-line constructions.*

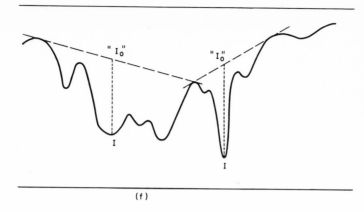

(f)

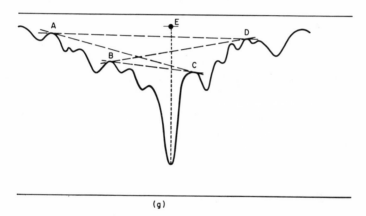

(g)

FIGURE 6-5 (continued)

(I) and subtracting from this value the reading at the intersection of dashed and dotted lines (I_0).

When two or more bands are fairly close together so that there is some doubt just where the I_0 (base line) should be drawn, it is useful to assume that absorption bands have symmetrical, or "Lorentzian," shape. (See equation 6-11.) In Figure 6-5b the dashed lines appear to describe in a reasonable manner how each band would appear if it were alone. Because these extrapolations meet the dot-dashed I_0 line in such a way that they do not cross the dotted lines, it can be assumed that the dot-dashed line is a good approximation to the true I_0 and can be considered a good base line. In this case, and in that illustrated

Elements of quantitative analysis   **167**

by Figure 6-5a, the I_0 determined by the base lines would be essentially the same as that found by the cell-in-cell-out method.

Often neighboring bands are so closely situated that the extrapolations of the Lorenztian shapes overlap neighboring absorption bands, thereby complicating the determination of I_0. In these cases the extrapolations themselves become perhaps the best base lines, as shown in Figures 6-5c and 6-5d. Obviously construction of the heavy dashed I_0 line of Figure 6-5d is subject to some uncertainty and cannot be reproduced with precision. The limits outside which it can reasonably fall are not far apart, however; furthermore, inspection of Figure 6-2 will show that the absorbance scale moves but slowly in this region of high transmission, so that errors in this sort of base-line construction are not too serious.

Although careful extrapolations of Lorentzian shaped bands often provide an accurate I_0 line, in many cases a more convenient and sometimes even more reproducible method can be used. Consider the band in Figure 6-5e. Probably the curved dashed line will be the closest approximation to the "true" I_0, but construction of this sort of curve, as we have noted, is subject to some nonreproducibility. A line drawn tangent to the transmission maxima at p and q on either side of the band will be quite reproducible, however. Although the value I_{0_2} subtracted from I will not yield the true absorbance, it will yield a number proportional to it; the proportionality will be the same when the measurement is made on other similar bands for comparison, provided any small absorbance at the tangent points p and q also results from the same material in the mixture which produces the absorption band being measured. This tangent-line technique is probably the most common application of base-line methods because it is so convenient to construct.

The tangent-line method could have been used to determine the I_0 of the central band in Figure 6-5b, probably with as much accuracy as the I_0 actually shown. Application of the tangent-line method to the central band in Figure 6-5d might lead to gross errors, however: if the strong bands on either side of this weaker band resulted from different materials in the mixture than the weaker central band we wish to measure, the transmission maxima to which the base line is drawn tangent would vary with composition of the mixture; this would result in measured absorbances that would no longer bear the same proportionality to true absorbance, hence would have little usefulness in analysis. In cases intermediate between those shown by Figures 6-5b and 6-5d individual judgment and experience is perhaps the best guide in making the choice between a sketched base line or a

168 *Quantitative analysis*

tangent base line. The tangent base-line method is good only if the points to which the base line is tangent remain reasonably well fixed with changing composition.

The tangent-line method suffers from a further difficulty. This straight line is, of course, an attempt to estimate a reproducible average background absorbance at the analytical frequency. But when this construction is made on a spectrometer chart, the result is *not* an average of background *absorbance* but an average of *transmission*. Hence absorbances obtained with tangent-line base lines will not be strictly linear functions of concentration unless the tangent line is horizontal. However, since $\log 1/T$ is essentially directly proportional to $1 - T$ at high transmission values (see Figure 6-2), the departure from nonlinearity can be neglected if the base line is drawn at high transmission values and is not too far from horizontal, as is usually the case.

With spectra having broad, badly overlapping bands (common with molecules containing oxygen functional groups, for example), it often becomes a hopeless task to sketch in a base line (see Figure 6-5d), and the tangent-line method, although clearly not accurate, must be used. A situation of this sort is illustrated in Figure 6-5f. The two tangent lines shown are probably the best reasonably *reproducible* approximations that can be made to I_0 values of the two bands indicated. Although the absorbances resulting from these measurements are probably not good approximations to the "true" values, nevertheless, if comparisons are being made to other mixtures of similar composition, these absorbances will be sufficiently reproducible and constantly proportional to the "true" values to allow at least fairly approximate quantitative analyses to be made with simplicity and confidence. If a series of reference spectra is produced from known mixtures, using compositions similar to those expected in the unknowns, respectable quantitative analyses can be performed even with the base lines shown in Figure 6-5f.

Finally, it often occurs in dealing with a complex spectrum that several different base-line constructions are possible (see Figure 6-5g). All four of the base lines indicated have the requirement that they be drawn tangent to prominent minima on either side of the band, and all seem to be about equally logical. Obviously, all four give different I_0's hence different absorbances. But, as we have seen, the choice is not critical, provided the spectrum to which a comparison is being made has this base line drawn in a similar manner. The choice of base line is made on the basis of the relative reproducibility of points A, B, C, and D in the comparison spectra, tangent points which are most reproducible among the spectra to be compared being selected.

It is in cases such as these that the base-line technique shows its greatest advantage over the cell-in-cell-out method. Had the latter method been used in the case in Figure 6-5g, the I_0 determined would have been something like point E in the figure. In a comparison of a series of mixtures of this type it is often found that the distance between point E and the line tangent at A and D, for example, varies to a surprising degree. When this occurs, clearly point E is a poor I_0 to use, whereas any of the base line I_0's we have described are satisfactory. For this reason, when making an assay of the major constituent in a complex or "dirty" mixture, the experienced analyst uses a scan (either single-beam or double-beam spectrometer) over a short frequency region and applies the *base-line* method for best results.

In some cases, such as those illustrated by Figures 6-5c and 6-5d, it is quite obvious that the base-line method will give better accuracy. However, for the cases illustrated by Figures 6-5a and 6-5b the cell-in-cell-out method is perhaps best because single-beam spectrometry is capable of greater precision. For each different quantitative analytical problem a "best" method can usually be found by a little experimentation if these considerations are kept in mind.

A final point, in the nature of a reminder, should be made before leaving the discussion of cell-in-cell-out versus base-line methods. When a scanned spectrum is obtained for the purpose of qualitative analysis, quantitative analysis can be done by the base-line method on this same spectrum, whereas the techniques by which cell-in-cell-out information is produced must be separately set up. The ultimate in quantitative analytical accuracy will always require a special set up, whether it is the cell-in-cell-out method on a single-beam spectrometer or differential scans on a double-beam spectrometer. But if reasonably approximate quantitative data are all that is required, they are easily obtained from the same spectrum by which qualitative information is best supplied, namely a spectrum scanned on a double-beam spectrometer. Furthermore, no quantitative analysis, except the most routine, should *ever* be done without first having obtained a scanned spectrum to ensure that the material being analyzed and the band being measured are really what have been supposed. When a method as powerful as infrared spectroscopy is available, it is foolish to overlook such an excellent method of check.

C. Accuracy of quantitative analysis

As implied in Chapter 4, casual use of infrared spectrometry does not yield high precision results. How accurate, then, are the results of quantitative analysis obtained by these methods? We shall attempt an answer. (In the discussion that follows it is assumed that errors of weighing, preparation of solutions, cell length measurement, etc., will be small compared to spectrometric errors.)

Because the spectrometer measures light transmission, but the concentration of an unknown solution to be measured is proportional to absorbance, it is necessary to determine at what point on the transmission scale the uncertainty of a transmission measurement provides the smallest value of uncertainty of absorbance. This will occur when the absorbance value is such that a small change in it will produce the greatest change in chart deflection $(1 - T)$. From equation 6-4 we have

$$1 - T = 1 - 10^{-A}$$

The change in chart deflection ΔT, produced by increasing A to αA (α is a number slightly greater than unity), is then

$$(1 - T_{\alpha A}) - (1 - T_A) = (1 - 10^{-\alpha A}) - (1 - 10^{-A})$$

or

$$\Delta T = T_A - T_{\alpha A} = 10^{-A} - 10^{-\alpha A}. \quad (6\text{-}9)$$

Figure 6-6 illustrates ΔT as a function of A for $\alpha = 1.01$ (or 1%

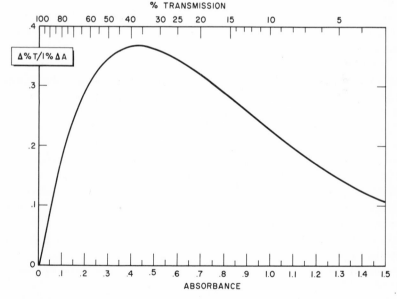

FIGURE 6-6 *Change in transmission produced by a 1 % change in absorbance as a function of absorbance.*

increase of A). The curve has its maximum at $A \approx 0.43$,* $T \approx 37\%$, although the maximum is a broad one.

From inspection of the curve it is seen that in the region $A \sim 0.3$ to $A \sim 0.6$ (or $T \sim 50\%$ to $T \sim 25\%$) uncertainty in A as a result of uncertainty in T is roughly constant. Obviously the best precision will result when quantitative determinations are made in this transmission range. To do this, the value of A ($= abc$) is placed in the range 0.3–0.6 by adjustment of cell length or concentration, as solvent absorption or convenience dictate. In our discussion it is assumed that this has been done.

As noted, the most favorable relation between absorbance uncertainty and transmission uncertainty is the maximum of the curve of Figure 6-6:

$$\Delta T \sim 0.37 \, \Delta A$$

or

$$\Delta A \sim 2.7 \, \Delta T. \tag{6-10}$$

Therefore an uncertainty of $\pm \frac{1}{3}\%$ in T results in an uncertainty of $\sim \pm 1\%$ in A, or $\pm 1\%$ of the amount present of the material being analyzed.

In theory it should be the noise level of the spectrometer that sets the ultimate limit on the precision with which quantitative analysis can be performed. This limit is probably realized in measurement of absorbance with a single-beam spectrometer under ideal conditions, for the amplification and recording systems are of maximum simplicity, as discussed in Chapter 4. Therefore, in the cases in which the precision of absorbance measurement depends only on the precision of transmission measurement (namely, in the cases in which the cell-in-cell-out method is applicable), a noise level of $\sim \frac{1}{3}\%$ should result in analytical precision of $\sim \pm 1\%$. If this noise level can be decreased by increasing slit aperture or increasing time constant, an increase in precision will result, provided (a) that all the noise visible on the recorder chart originates at the detector, as is usually assumed, and (b) that the physical dimensions of the recorder chart, the pen line width, the back-lash in pen drive gears, etc., are such that the noise level, even though reduced, is still observable as detector noise. If transmission is recorded over a reasonable time interval, as illustrated in Figure 6-3, then the noise can be "averaged," as discussed on p. 162 and illustrated in Figure 6-3, and the transmis-

---

* This is easily shown analytically by differentiating equation 6-9 with respect to A, setting the expression equal to 0, and solving for A as a function of α. In the limit $\alpha = 1$, A has the value $\log_{10} e = 0.4343$, T has the value $e^{-1} = 36.79\%$.

sion uncertainty can be at least halved. Therefore a noise level of $\sim 0.15\%$ (not unreasonable with wide slits and long time constant) can result in absorbance precision of $\sim \pm\frac{1}{4}\%$.

The *accuracy* of the quantitative analytical result obtained by the cell-in-cell-out method with a single-beam spectrometer also depends on the long-range reproducibility of source output, detector and amplifier stability, etc., between the time that the reference material and the unknown are measured. If this time can be kept as short as possible, the accuracy will approach the precision $\pm\frac{1}{4}\%$ with careful work under favorable spectrometer conditions.

When the base-line (scan) method is employed with a single-beam spectrometer, the continuous, slowly moving recorded line can be used to average out noise level in much the same way that obtaining a time average of transmission can be used to increase precision when measuring absorbance at fixed wavelength by the cell-in-cell-out method. However, the precision of the absorbance may be poorer than the precision of transmission if the base line (I_0) is not reproducible to this same precision. In cases in which base-line reproducibility is good (see preceding discussion) and a spectrometer noise level of $\sim \pm\frac{1}{3}\%$ is obtainable, $\sim \pm\frac{1}{2}\%$ accuracy of absorbance measurement is possible. Under these conditions it is worthwhile to obtain spectra of reference and unknown materials as close together as practical so that accuracy will approach precision.

The precision of absorbance measurements made from scanned spectra obtained with a double-beam optical-null spectrometer does not appear to reach the level set by noise limitations, falling somewhat short of it. Just why this is true of optical-null spectrometers does not appear to be known exactly; it is still a subject under investigation and debate. It has been the observation of the author that the short-term precision of absorbance measurement is probably near the limit set by base-line approximations or noise level but that the long-term precision of a well-cared-for optical-null spectrometer is somewhat poorer than that displayed by a well-cared-for single-beam spectrometer. Therefore, if precision (within 1%) quantitative analysis is to be performed with an optical-null spectrometer, it is suggested that spectra of unknown and reference materials be obtained in succession, using the same absorption cell.

The ultimate accuracy possible with infrared spectrometers now available is attained by the *differential comparison method*, using a double-beam spectrometer. Simultaneously this method (*a*) can be used with wide slits and long time constant; (*b*) it virtually eliminates the uncertainty in base-line approximations; (*c*) it effectively expands

Elements of quantitative analysis   173

the chart ordinate so that full advantage can be taken of lower noise level; and (d) it compares the unknown *directly* against the reference material so that long-term variation of absorbance measurement is essentially eliminated. The use of this panacea, unfortunately, is somewhat tedious and is not applicable to all quantitative analytical situations. But, wherever applicable, thè resulting accuracy is worth the effort. The method is described in detail in Chapter 7.

III. Deviations from Beer's law

The foregoing discussion has assumed that absorbance $(- \log I/I_0)$ is a linear function of the product of cell length and concentration. This is not always so. When deviations from linearity do occur, approximate corrections can often be made, as discussed in this section.

Deviations from Beer's law result from two principal causes: (a) variation of certain absorption band frequencies, shapes, or intensities brought on by association effects between solute molecules, which effects vary as concentration varies, and (b) false measurement by the spectrometer of the transmission of absorption bands which are narrower in frequency range than the distribution of frequencies emerging from the exit slit of the spectrometer. These effects might be conveniently described as chemical and spectrometer.

A. Beer's law deviations: chemical effects

The problem of Beer's law deviations stemming from intermolecular association effects is relatively simple because it is usually predictable from chemical knowledge of the molecule, only a few types of vibrational modes are thus affected to large extent, and when it does occur this difficulty can either be easily circumvented or cannot be corrected for at all.

A common example of the problem is that of intermolecular hydrogen bonding in alcohols and phenols. As discussed in some detail in Chapter 10, the absorption band resulting from the stretching motion of the O—H bond in an unassociated OH group is at relatively high frequency, sharp, and not highly intense; on the other hand, the stretch absorption of a hydrogen-bonded O—H group is some 300 cm^{-1} lower in frequency, broad, and intense. (See Figure 10-1d, Volume II.) In solution an equilibrium will always exist between the associated and unassociated forms, the amount of each form depending on the gross concentration, dilute solutions naturally favoring the unassociated form. Hence, in concentration ranges in which both forms exist to appreciable extent, any absorption band unique to one form and not the other, particularly O—H stretch, will not obey Beer's law, for absorbance of one species is not a linear function of over-all concentration, presumably the quantity to be analyzed.

This difficulty can be eliminated if the absorption band is in a frequency region in which solvent absorption is low. If this is the case, a much more dilute solution may be used in an appropriately longer cell, such that the product of cell length and concentration still results in a useful absorbance. In the very dilute solution essentially all alcohol or phenol molecules will be in the unassociated form; in this situation all absorptions, whether or not they are unique to the unassociated form, will follow Beer's law.

If the absorption band of interest occurs in a region in which there is solvent absorption, then the latter approach cannot be adopted, for the use of a cell length many times as long as before may make the solvent absorption prohibitively large so that little or no infrared radiation of this frequency will be available for analysis. In these cases such an absorption band must be dismissed as a candidate for use in quantitative determinations.

O—H stretching absorption bands are not the only absorptions of alcohols or phenols that do not obey Beer's law. Any other type of vibration that changes in frequency or intensity as the molecule changes from associated to unassociated form will show this behavior. Usually it is possible to predict which sorts of vibrations are affected, and which are not, as the result of association effects. How these predictions are made will become clear after the natures of specific group absorptions have been discussed in some detail in later chapters (Volume II).

The types of molecules showing association effects are those that have both acidic and basic sites in them; hydrogen bonding in alcohols and phenols is perhaps the most common example. However, when quantitative analyses of *mixtures* are performed, it must be remembered that both acidic and basic sites need not be in the same molecule in order for association effects to exist, for one molecule might well supply the acidic site, another the basic site. An example is the association of diphenylamine (acid) and pyridine (base); the spectrum of a mixture of the two, each at 5% concentration in CCl_4–CS_2 solution, is not a simple superposition of their spectra as obtained alone in 5% solution (see Figure 6-7); the absorption bands which are not the same when in the mixture as when alone in solution clearly will not obey Beer's law.

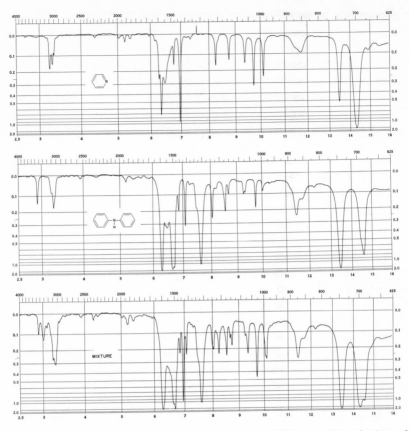

FIGURE 6-7 Intermolecular association effects: (Above) *5% solution of pyridine in* CCl_4*–*CS_2 *solutions;* (Middle) *5% solution of diphenyl amine in* CCl_4*–*CS_2 *solutions;* (Below) *5% of both pyridine and diphenyl amine in same* CCl_4*–*CS_2 *solutions.*

Nearly any strong base in the Lewis sense (electron donor) can cause association effects to some extent even with the weakest acids; strong acids (electron acceptors) may well cause association effects with substances that might normally be regarded as only weakly basic. The possibility of these effects must always be considered in quantitative analysis; as greater familiarity with the group frequencies is attained it is not difficult to predict in many cases when association effects will occur and which vibrations of the molecules associated will be strongly affected.

176   *Quantitative analysis*

B. Beer's law deviations: spectrometer effects

The second cause of deviations from Beer's law is far more serious, for it occurs to a greater or lesser extent with all except the broadest absorption bands in all materials when using the spectrometers commercially available today. Briefly, Beer's law is not obeyed unless the distribution of radiation passed by the spectrometer exit slit is considerably narrower than the absorption band being measured. In order to gain a realization of the situation so that corrections can be made most effectively, some understanding of just why this occurs is necessary.

It can be shown that over a single symmetrical absorption band $a(\omega)$, the absorption coefficient as a function of frequency, is closely approximated by

$$a(\omega) = \frac{\alpha}{\pi} \frac{\gamma}{(\omega - \omega_0)^2 + \gamma^2}, \tag{6-11}$$

where α is the integrated intensity (see Section VII), ω_0 is the frequency of the absorption maximum, and γ is an important constant known as band "half-width." It is easily seen that when $\omega - \omega_0 = \gamma$ the absorption coefficient has just half the value it has at the maximum $(\omega = \omega_0)$; also 2γ is the width of the band in cm^{-1} measured at the point of half the value of maximum absorbance; γ, it should be noted, is *independent* of the inherent strength of the absorption band. An absorption band having the shape described by the function of equation 6-11 is said to be *Lorentzian*.

In order to consider transmission, the actual quantity measured by the spectrometer, we express the Lorentzian band-shape function in terms of transmission. Remembering that $\log_{10} T = -abc$, we have

$$T(\omega) = \exp\left[-\frac{\alpha bc}{\pi} \frac{\gamma}{(\omega - \omega_0)^2 + \gamma^2} \log_e 10 \right]. \tag{6-12}$$

The solid curves of Figure 6-8 show the form of this function for a few values of the product bc for an arbitrary half-width γ.

Now, as we saw in Chapter 3, a finite spectral slit width allows a *distribution* of frequencies to pass through the monochromator and reach the detector when the spectrometer is set at fixed frequency. Certainly the nature of this function will be such that it will peak more or less sharply at ω_0 (as the slits are made narrow or wide) and will fall to a small value at frequencies far removed from ω_0. A function having these properties is the well-known Gaussian or error function, which is probably a close approximation to the actual slit function

$$P(\omega) = P_0 \exp\left[-\frac{(\omega - \omega_0)^2}{(\Delta\omega)^2} \right].$$ (6-13)

where $P(\omega)$ is the monochromator output power at frequency ω, P_0 is the output power at ω_0, the frequency of transmission, and $\Delta\omega$ is the spectral slit width, as defined in Chapter 3 (when $\omega - \omega_0 = \Delta\omega$, the power transmitted by the monochromator is $1/e$ of its maximum value). The dashed curves of Figure 6-8 illustrate this function. In the three sections of the figure a curve of different width has been superimposed on the Lorentzian transmission function, representing small, medium, and large values of $\Delta\omega$ with respect to γ.

Clearly the various transmission values of the absorption maxima of Figure 6-8a will be measured by the spectrometer as very nearly the values shown, and a plot of absorbance, $A = \log 1/T$, versus product of cell length and concentration, bc, will be essentially linear, commensurate with Beer's law. However, Figure 6-8c hardly suggests that either the correct values of transmission will be measured by the spectrometer or that the resultant plot of A versus bc will be a

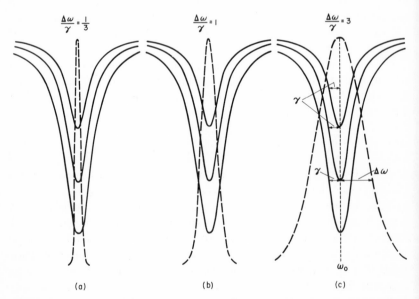

FIGURE 6-8 *Bandwidths and slit widths compared for various values of* $\Delta\omega/\gamma$.

178 *Quantitative analysis*

straight line. The situation in Figure 6-8*b* presumably will be intermediate between the two extremes.

In order to determine the exact nature of the deviations from Beer's law produced by this situation, it is necessary to calculate the total amount of radiant power that will reach the detector when a monochromator with finite spectral slit width is set at ω_0 and a material having a Lorentzian shaped band at ω_0 is placed in the beam. The power at any frequency ω will be the product of the appropriate solid and the dashed curves of Figure 6-8; or, from the combination of equations 6-12 and 6-13,

$$P(\omega)\ T(\omega)\ =\ P_0 \exp\left[-\frac{(\omega - \omega_0)^2}{(\Delta\omega)^2} \right]$$

$$\exp\left[-\frac{\alpha bc}{\pi}\ \frac{\gamma}{(\omega - \omega_0)^2 + \gamma^2}\ \log_e 10 \right].$$

The total power reaching the detector is just the integral of this function over the frequency range in which the detectable level of this power is larger than the Johnson noise level. Finally, the transmission measured by the spectrometer set at frequency ω_0 is this integral divided by the total power that would reach the detector if no absorbing material were placed in the beam. The result is

$$\bar{T}_{\omega_0} = \frac{\int P_0 \exp\left[-(\omega - \omega_0)^2/(\Delta\omega)^2 \right] \exp\left\{ -(\alpha bc/\pi)[\gamma/(\omega - \omega_0)^2 + \gamma^2] \log_e 10 \right\}\ d\omega}{\int P_0 \exp\left[-(\omega - \omega_0)^2/(\Delta\omega)^2 \right]\ d\omega}. \quad (6\text{-}14)$$

The integrals in equation 6-14 have been evaluated numerically, and the results have been plotted in Figure 6-9 as a function of A $(= \log 1/T_{\omega_0})$ versus the product bc. The dashed straight line results from an infinitesimal value of $\Delta\omega/\gamma$; this is the ideal situation in which the spectral slit width is much smaller than the absorption band width, with the result that the true transmission (hence absorbance) is measured, and the relation between the cell length-concentration product and absorbance is strictly linear. The other curves, however, are the result of successively higher values of $\Delta\omega/\gamma$, ranging from 0.1 to 10.0.

Not only is the correct value of absorption coefficient not measured by the slope of the line, but, worse from the standpoint of quantitative analysis, the curves depart further from linearity as the value of $\Delta\omega/\gamma$ increases.

Because these difficulties cannot be eliminated, a correction for them must be made. Although, as shown in Figure 6-9, the relation

Deviations from Beer's law   **179**

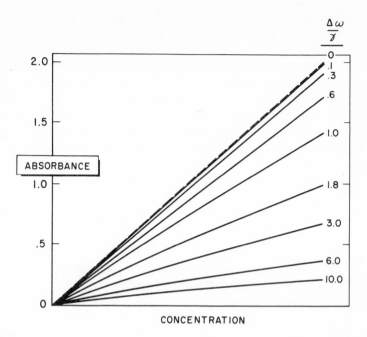

FIGURE 6-9 *The effect of spectral slit width on absorbtivity and Beer's law relation.*

between absorbance and transmission is not a straight line, it is nearly so over short ranges.   If analytical applications are restricted to a relatively narrow concentration range, as is often the case in practice, the curve may be assumed to be linear in the corresponding absorbance range, and reference spectra may be established in this region on the assumption that this is the true Beer's law relation.   The analytical results obtained will show only a small error.

However, as is also obvious from Figure 6-9, careful attention must be given to the spectral slit function of the spectrometer, and it *must remain strictly unchanged* when absorbances for quantitative analysis are compared, for the slope of these absorbance versus concentration curves is seen to be fairly sensitive to spectral slit width.   It is this unfortunate situation that makes it nearly impossible to transfer accurate absorbance data from one infrared spectrometer to another when $\Delta\omega/\gamma$ is 1.0 or more.   It appears to be difficult to reproduce the shape and width of the spectral slit function accurately among different spectrometers, even though they be made as nearly identical as possible.   Just why this is so does not appear to be known exactly,

180   *Quantitative analysis*

and it is still a point under investigation and argument among many spectroscopists. The newer grating spectrometers, which allow $\Delta\omega/\gamma$ to be a small number for all but the narrowest absorptions in solution, yet can be operated at reasonable signal-to-noise ratio, offer some hope in transference of quantitative data among instruments.

If the departure from linearity over a region of an absorbance *versus* concentration curve is too great to give results within the required accuracy by simple application of equation 6-8, direct plots from experimental values of concentration and absorbance must be made. Once this curve is obtained, the analysis is done by reading the concentration from the curve corresponding to the measured absorbance value. This sort of curve, similar to those shown in Figure 6-9, is very useful, for when constructed it not only corrects for Beer's law deviations resulting from finite spectral slit width but also for any other systematic and *reproducible* error, such as scattered light, (unavoidable) poor choice of base line, small constant absorption interferences by other materials in the analytical mixture, and, within limits, chemical association effects as previously described. It is these difficulties that often make the experimental plots more curved than those of Figure 6-9. Curves of this sort are particularly effective in analysis of complex mixtures where these sources of error are known to be present.

Furthermore, if this sort of curve must be obtained in any event, it is best to obtain it for a relatively large spectrometer slit width, for $\Delta\omega$ is proportional to slit width, whereas signal-to-noise ratio is proportional to the *square* of the slit width (see Chapter 3).

Because the construction of such curves is somewhat time consuming, it will probably be done only when a large number of similar analyses are to be made, such as in analytical control work or in studies involving many similar quantitative determinations over a rather wide range of concentration.

IV. Multicomponent analysis

So far our discussion of quantitative analysis has assumed that an absorbance determined at a given frequency results from absorption of radiation by but one chemical species. When all components of a mixture have at least one absorption band each in a region in which no absorption by any of the other components occurs, all can be determined quantitatively by use of equation 6-8. However, it often occurs that a component in a mixture possesses no absorption band that is free from interference by absorption of another material in a mixture. Now, because absorbance is proportional to concentration, a measured absorbance resulting from more than one chemical species is the sum of their individual absorbances. Therefore it is still possible to make quantitative determinations of all components in a mixture, provided that their absorbances are overlapped in a way that can be determined accurately. In the general case, in which the analytical absorption band of each component of a mixture is over-lapped by absorption of every other component in the mixture, linear simultaneous equations, graphical methods, or successive approxima-tions must be used. We shall discuss first some simple cases of absorp-tion interferences, then proceed to the more general cases of multi-component analyses with general overlapping of absorption bands.

A. Simple absorption coincidences

Suppose that a mixture of two components, X and Y, yields the spectrum shown in Figure 6-10a, and pure X and pure Y yield the spectra shown in Figure 6-10b and 6-10c, respectively. (Let us pre-sume that these materials, for some reason, have no absorptions satis-factory for analytical determinations in any other accessible region of the spectrum.) Determination of component X is a simple matter easily achieved by comparison of the absorption at 1000 cm^{-1} in the spectra of the mixture and pure X by use of equation 6-8, with either the base-line or cell-in-cell-out method. However, there is a compli-cation in the determination of component Y, for the spectra of the pure components show that both X and Y have an absorption at 900 cm^{-1}.

If ω_{max} of the 900-cm^{-1} absorption of both components occurs at the same frequency (reasonably well within the spectral slit width of the spectrometer), the absorbances are directly additive. Because the amount of component X in the mixture has been determined from an independent frequency, the absorbance at 900 cm^{-1} resulting from component X is readily obtained by use of equation 6-8. This absorbance, when subtracted from the measured absorbance at 900 cm^{-1} in the spectrum of the mixture, yields an absorbance that is directly proportional to the content of component Y, which may now be calculated in the usual way with equation 6-8. The errors in computing component Y will naturally be somewhat larger than those of component X because of the cumulative nature of the calculation.

This simple method can be extended to the simultaneous analysis of several components, provided that one or more components can be determined independently. The net absorbance of a component may be calculated by subtraction of more than one interfering absorbance from the measured absorbance, but each such correction increases the

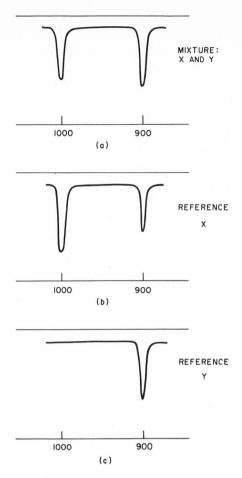

FIGURE 6-10 *Simple overlap of absorption bands in a mixture.*

uncertainty of the result, hence the accuracy of the analytical determination. If no component possesses an interference-free absorption band, simultaneous equations or other methods are necessary.

B. Multicomponent analyses: general case

Consider a mixture of n components in which each has at least one reasonably prominent absorption band at whose frequency there is some absorption by each of the other components. Now, if each absorption of all the components can be assumed to obey Beer's law

Multicomponent analysis **183**

reasonably well and the absorbances are additive, the total absorbance at frequency 1, say, can be expressed as

$$\bar{A}_1 = A_{11} + A_{12} + \cdots + A_{1n}$$
$$= a_{11}c_1 + a_{12}c_2 + \cdots + a_{1n}c_n, \tag{6-15a}$$

where A_{12}, say, is the absorbance of component 2 at frequency 1; $\bar{A}_1$ is the total of these absorbances at frequency 1, $c_1 \cdots c_n$ are the concentrations of each of the n components of the mixture (their sum may be equal to or less than 100%, depending on whether all or only some of the components are to be determined); and a_{12}, for example, is the coefficient which converts c_2 to A_{12}.

Similar equations can be written for the absorbances produced at other frequencies:

$$\bar{A}_2 = a_{21}c_1 + a_{22}c_2 + \cdots a_{2n}c_n$$
$$\cdot$$
$$\cdot \tag{6-15b}$$
$$\cdot$$
$$\bar{A}_n = a_{n1}c_1 + a_{n2}c_2 + \cdots a_{nn}c_n.$$

These n equations in n unknowns can be solved to determine the concentrations of the components of the mixture. Results of useful accuracy will be obtained only if the diagonal elements of the matrix (i.e., $a_{11}, a_{22} \cdots a_{nn}$) are large with respect to the off-diagonal elements; accuracy will be lost as the size of the off-diagonal elements increases in relation to the diagonal elements.

Each of the n^2 different a_{ij}'s must be determined from reference spectra of pure samples of the various n components and is given by

$$a_{ij} = \frac{c_{TU}b_U}{c_{R,j}b_{R,j}} A_{R,ij}, \tag{6-16}$$

where c_{TU} is the concentration of the total unknown mixture in its solvent, $c_{R,j}$ is the concentration of pure component j in the reference spectrum, b's are appropriate cell lengths, and $A_{R,ij}$ is the absorbance produced in the reference spectrum of component j at frequency i. This equation is derived in the same manner as equation 6-8. The labor involved in determining n^2 different a_{ij}'s is usually warranted only if equations 6-15a,b are to be used for many repetitive analyses. If this application is to be made, the solution of these equations is facilitated by transforming them to a more convenient form (usually called inversion of the matrix):*

$$c_1 = a_{11}^{-1}\bar{A}_1 + a_{21}^{-1}\bar{A}_2 + \cdots + a_{n1}^{-1}\bar{A}_n$$
$$c_2 = a_{12}^{-1}\bar{A}_1 + a_{22}^{-1}\bar{A}_2 + \cdots + a_{n2}^{-1}\bar{A}_n$$
$$\vdots \qquad\qquad\qquad\qquad\qquad (6\text{-}17)$$
$$c_n = a_{1n}^{-1}\bar{A}_1 + a_{2n}^{-1}\bar{A}_2 + \cdots + a_{nn}^{-1}\bar{A}_n$$

where

$$a_{ij}^{-1} = \frac{\text{cofactor } a_{ij}}{|\det a|}\,(-1)^{i+j}. \qquad (6\text{-}18)$$

After the individual a_{ij} coefficients have been determined from standard spectra with equation 6-16 and the various a_{ij}^{-1} coefficients have been determined by equation 6-18, it becomes a simple matter to calculate the concentrations of the n components from the n absorbances with equations 6-17.

In some instances it happens that a series of simultaneous equations must be solved only once or, at any rate, only a few times. Rather than invert the matrix, a rather tedious chore, a system of equations such as (6-15) may be solved by successive approximations. This is probably most easily done by assuming all off-diagonal elements to be zero (i.e., $a_{ij} = 0$, $i \neq j$ or $\bar{A}_i = A_{ij}^0$, $i = j$) as a first approximation, thereby obtaining the first order c_j's: $A_{ij}^0 = a_{ij}c_j'$ $(i = j)$. Clearly this method will not be useful unless the diagonal elements $(a_{ij}, i = j)$ are considerably larger than the off-diagonal elements. Having now obtained an approximation to each c_j, we calculate a new value of each A_{ij} $(i = j)$ by subtracting from each $\bar{A}_i$ the sum of the appropriate products, $a_{ij}c_j'$ $(i \neq j)$, to yield A_{ij}' $(i = j)$. From these values of A_{ij}' are calculated the second approximation c_j concentrations: $A_{ij}' = a_{ij}c_j''$ $(i = j)$. This process is repeated until the change between successive approximations is of the order of the expected analytical error.

If the analytical absorptions chosen for the analysis do not follow Beer's law over the region in which they will be employed, then linear equations cannot be used. As in the case of single-component analysis, empirical curves of the sort illustrated in Figure 6-9 can

* See any standard treatise on theory of linear equations; for example, H. Margenau and G. M. Murphy, *The Mathematics of Physics and Chemistry*, Chapter 10, Van Nostrand, Princeton, New Jersey, 1943.

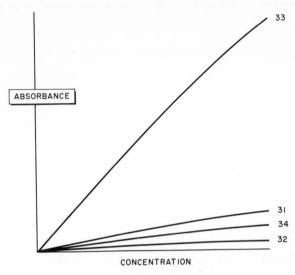

FIGURE 6-11 *Calibration curves for four substances, obtained at one of the analytical frequencies, for use in multicomponent analysis.*

circumvent this difficulty. A series of n^2 different curves must be obtained, corresponding to all of the various a_{ij} coefficients, and the determination of each curve will require that several absorbance measurements of each pure reference substance (rather than just one) be obtained over a wide concentration range. Presumably, among each set of n curves obtained at one of the analytical frequencies one curve will have a much steeper slope than the others (analogous to the situation that the diagonal a_{ij} coefficients of equations 6-15a,b are much larger than off-diagonal a_{ij} coefficients). A typical family of curves for $n = 4$ (obtained at, say, frequency 3) is shown in Figure 6-11.

The analysis is performed graphically as follows: a first approximation, c_3', is read off curve 33 at absorbance $\bar{A}_3$ (in first approximation equal to $A_{33}{}^0$), which was the absorbance measured at frequency 3 in the spectrum of the unknown mixture. Off similar curves first approximations c_1', c_2', and c_4' are found. Returning now to the curves of Figure 6-11, absorbances A_{31}', A_{32}', and A_{34}' are found by curves 31, 32, and 34 from the first approximations c_1', c_2', and c_4', respectively. Their sum is subtracted from $\bar{A}_3$, and the new value of A_{33}' is used to find c_3'' from curve 33. This process, clearly exactly analogous to the system of successive approximations previously described, is repeated until the difference between successive values is of the order of the expected analytical error.

C. Limitations in multicomponent analysis

The limitation on the number of components that can be determined in a mixture or the accuracy with which they can be determined depends on the accuracy with which the coefficients a_{ij} of equations 6-15 can be measured and the magnitude of the values a_{ij} $(i \neq j)$ with respect to those of a_{ij} $(i = j)$.

The effects of the latter limitation are quite obvious from consideration of the methods of solving equations 6-15a,b just described: our statement that the diagonal elements of the matrix of the equations must be large with respect to the off-diagonal elements is equivalent to saying that the pertinent portion of any measurement should be as large as possible with respect to the corrections that must be imposed on it. Clearly, if the corrections become the larger part of a measurement, the accuracy decreases. This factor probably most often sets the practical limit on the number of components that can be determined simultaneously. If all (or at least the majority) of the components of a mixture have just a few strong, rather sharp absorptions, several such components may be determined simultaneously. However, if the only available absorption bands of most of the components are very broad, then the overlap of absorptions will be such that the off-diagonal coefficients will be nearly as large as the diagonal coefficients, no matter what frequencies are chosen for analysis. In these cases infrared spectroscopy is probably not the method to use for quantitative analysis.*

If all of the a_{ij} coefficients can be determined accurately, the uncertainty of each determination in an n-component mixture is probably something less than n times the uncertainty of a single determination made in a case in which the absorption band measured is free from interference from other absorptions. In ideal situations (wide slits, long time constant, favorable absorption bands) the precision of determination of each component should be somewhat better than $n \times \frac{1}{4}\%$. (See Section II-C.) However, accurate determination of the a_{ij} coefficients is not always simple, as we shall now show.

The diagonal a_{ij} coefficients are presumably determined accurately

---

* The technique of integrating one or more absorption bands for each component has shown some promise, but equipment for doing so automatically is still in development stages. The uses of integration of absorption bands is discussed in Section VII. Also, in certain cases the techniques of compensated spectra, as described in Chapter 7, will help to unravel such mixtures.

and easily from measurement of absorption-band maxima of well-chosen bands in spectra of pure reference, or standard, materials. However, the determination of the off-diagonal a_{ij} coefficients may be much less accurate, for they depend on measurement of absorbances from reference spectra which are *not necessarily absorption maxima.* In the least favorable cases off-diagonal a_{ij} coefficients must sometimes be obtained from an absorbance measurement at a frequency on the side of a steep absorption band. Here there is virtually no margin for frequency inaccuracy of the spectrometer, as there is in measuring absorption-band maxima, and determination of the correct absorbance will be sensitive to just how accurately the spectrometer can be set to a predetermined frequency. Furthermore, measurement of this absorbance value from a scanned record will lead to further inaccuracies, for the servo system is out of balance and moving fairly rapidly when on the side of a steep absorption; hence it will not reproduce any given point on the side of the band with much accuracy. In these cases the a_{ij} coefficients are probably best determined by stopping the scan at the predetermined analytical frequency and measuring absorbance with the servo system at equilibrium. Such determinations make the whole operation still more tedious, of course.

The use of a grating spectrometer and expansion of the abscissa (frequency) scale of the recorder should prove helpful in increasing the accuracy with which off-diagonal a_{ij} coefficients can be obtained. At the present writing grating spectrometers are still too new for much experience to have been acquired in this application.

The possibility of combining infrared methods with other analytical methods in order to solve difficult cases of multicomponent analysis must not be overlooked. Often the determination of some of the components of a mixture by, say, titration, ultraviolet spectrometry, mass spectrometry, or polarography makes the determination of the remaining components by infrared spectroscopy a simple task, which otherwise might have been nearly hopeless. In many cases a simple chemical or physical separation of the components will render an otherwise intractable mixture amenable to multicomponent analysis by infrared methods. Presumably these possibilities will have been given careful consideration before the rather tedious determination of n^2 different a_{ij} coefficients is undertaken.

V. Quantitative analysis without use of reference spectra

In certain cases it is possible to make fairly accurate estimations of the composition of simple mixtures without reference to standard spectra of the pure components. This can be done only under rather special limiting circumstances, as subsequently described. Situations in which these methods are applicable occur not infrequently in examination of mixtures resulting from successive distillation cuts or successive fractions of a crystallization.

To illustrate with an example, suppose that two successive distillation cuts yield the spectra shown in Figure 6-12. Let us assume that only component X has appreciable absorption at 1000 cm^{-1}, only component Y has appreciable absorption at 900 cm^{-1}, and both cuts are known to contain only materials X and Y. We may write

$$A_{1000,1} = a_{1000,x}c_{x,1}$$
$$A_{900,1} = a_{900,y}c_{y,1}$$
$$A_{1000,2} = a_{1000,x}c_{x,2}$$
$$A_{900,2} = a_{900,y}c_{y,2},$$

(6-19a)

where $A_{1000,1}$ is the absorbance measured at 1000 cm^{-1} in cut 1, $a_{1000,x}$ is the coefficient relating the concentration of component x to the absorbance at 1000 cm^{-1}, $c_{x,1}$ is the concentration of x in cut 1,

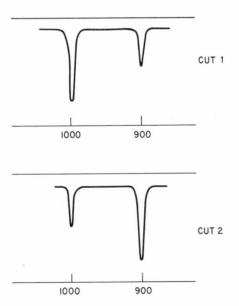

FIGURE 6-12 *Hypothetical spectra of two successive distillation cuts in the region near 1000 cm^{-1}.*

Quantitative analysis without use of reference spectra **189**

etc. This is a system of four equations in six unknowns. But we also have (by assumption)

$$c_{x,1} + c_{y,1} = 1 \quad \text{(or } 100\%\text{)}$$
$$c_{x,2} + c_{y,2} = 1 \quad \text{(or } 100\%\text{)},$$

$$(6\text{-}19b)$$

so that these six equations, being very simple, are easily solvable for the concentrations of X and Y in cuts 1 and 2 and also for the absorption coefficients, should they be desired.

This method could easily be extended to three components, but would require three successive distillation cuts (or other mixtures of varying composition) and would result in six equations analogous to (6-19a) and three equations analogous to (6-19b), or nine equations in nine unknowns. Because the equations are almost trivially simple, their solution is not at all difficult.

As is obvious, the compositions in the two (or three) mixtures must differ as much as possible in order that two similar equations avoid near redundancy. This puts an upper limitation on the number of components that can be practically analyzed in this manner, for as the number of components grows the increased number of mixtures of different composition required will force some compositions too close to similarity, with resulting loss in accuracy in solution of the equations.

In the general case, in which each of the components absorbs at both frequencies, the analysis is more complex. Consider again the case of binary mixtures of X and Y, but now assume that although there are well-defined absorption maxima at, say, 1000 cm^{-1} and 900 cm^{-1} both components contribute to each absorption. We then write

$$A_{1000,1} = a_{1000,x}c_{x,1} + a_{1000,y}c_{y,1}$$

$$A_{900,1} = a_{900,x}c_{x,1} + a_{900,y}c_{y,1}$$

$$A_{1000,2} = a_{1000,x}c_{x,2} + a_{1000,y}c_{y,2}$$

$$A_{900,2} = a_{900,x}c_{x,2} + a_{900,y}c_{y,2},$$

$$(6\text{-}20a)$$

and again we must assume that

$$c_{x,1} + c_{y,1} = 1 \quad \text{(or } 100\%\text{)}$$
$$c_{x,2} + c_{y,2} = 1 \quad \text{(or } 100\%\text{)},$$

$$(6\text{-}20b)$$

where the meaning of the symbols and their subscripts is the obvious extension of the notation used. Here, however, equations 6-20a,b are a system of *six equations in eight unknowns* and cannot be solved without further information.

Now let us further suppose that two more successive cuts, each of composition differing as widely as possible from cuts 1 and 2 and from each other, are available. Their spectra will then yield

$$A_{1000,3} = a_{1000,x}c_{x,3} + a_{1000,y}c_{y,3}$$

$$A_{900,3} = a_{900,x}c_{x,3} + a_{900,y}c_{y,3}$$

$$A_{1000,4} = a_{1000,x}c_{x,4} + a_{1000,y}c_{y,4}$$

$$A_{900,4} = a_{900,x}c_{x,4} + a_{900,y}c_{y,4}$$

$$c_{x,3} + c_{y,3} = 1 \quad (\text{or } 100\%)$$

$$c_{x,4} + c_{y,4} = 1 \quad (\text{or } 100\%). \tag{6-20c}$$

Equations 6-20a,b,c are now 12 equations in 12 unknowns but are not so simple as equations 6-19, hence not so readily solvable. In the rare case in which this situation is encountered it is probably easiest to solve these equations by successive approximations as follows: Assume reasonable values for the four absorption coefficients $a_{1000,x}$, $a_{900,x}$, $a_{1000,y}$, and $a_{900,y}$; then proceed to solve equations such as 6-20a in pairs (there are four such pairs). The discrepancies produced when the resulting values of concentrations are substituted into equations of form 6-20b can be used as a guide to reapproximate the absorption coefficients. This process, in practice, is not so difficult as it appears algebraically.

The extension of this method to mixtures of three components (now requiring *nine* different mixtures of differing composition, yielding 36 equations in 36 unknowns) is obviously not practical.

VI. Ratio methods of analysis

Often the spectra of certain sample types cannot be obtained in solution because of solubility limitations, as discussed in Chapter 5. Spectra of these materials must be obtained as films, or as pressed disks or mulls if they are crystalline solids. These methods (except pressed disks) have the undesirable feature that the absorption-path length cannot be known or reproduced accurately enough to allow quantitative analysis to be performed directly. However, quantitative determinations may still be made, not on an absolute basis, but on a relative basis, by measuring absorbance *ratios*.

A. The method of the indeterminant optical path

Suppose that a spectrum of a mixture of two (or more) components, X and Y (etc.), is obtained from a film of indefinite and unknown thickness. Such a film might be a capillary liquid film, or a uniform solid film, such as a copolymer. If each of the two components produces in the spectrum at least one uninterfered absorption that obeys Beer's law, we may write

$$A_x = a_x b_x c_x$$

$$A_y = a_y b_y c_y,$$

where the symbols have the usual meaning. Concentration can be expressed here as a weight fraction or as a mole fraction, whichever is convenient, but once the choice is made it must be adhered to, of course. Because both absorptions result from the same film, $b_x = b_y$, although this value is not known. Therefore

$$R = \frac{A_x}{A_y} = \frac{a_x}{a_y} \frac{c_x}{c_y} = k \frac{c_x}{c_y}. \qquad (6\text{-}21)$$

If one or more similar mixtures of known composition can be prepared (i.e., a liquid mixture of known composition, a mull made from known amounts of two solids, or a copolymer of known polymer ratio), its spectrum can be obtained, and from the known composition and determination of the ratio of absorbances of the appropriate absorption bands k is easily calculated. With k determined, equation 6-21 can be used to determine the *ratio* of the two components in an unknown mixture by measurement of these same absorption bands from the film spectrum of the unknown. The accuracy of this ratio of component concentrations so determined depends only on the accuracy with which the absorptions obey Beer's law (see later) and the accuracy to which the composition of the standardizing mixture is known.

If the sum of the concentrations of the two components is known, then they may be determined specifically. The usual case is a mixture of only two components, so that $c_x + c_y = 1$. If this relation is combined with equation 6-21, it is easily shown that

$$c_x = \frac{R}{k + R} \qquad c_y = \frac{k}{k + R}, \qquad (6\text{-}22)$$

where R and k are defined as in equation 6-21.

Ratio methods of this sort must be used with some caution, however. Equations 6-22 are not valid in any composition range far removed from that at which k was determined from known compositions. Deviations from equations 6-22 are not so much the result of Beer's law deviations because of "spectrometer effects" but are more properly described as Beer's law deviations resulting from "chemical

192 *Quantitative analysis*

effects," as discussed in Section III-A. An absorption coefficient, a, depends not only on the particular vibrational mode causing absorption but also, to a lesser extent, on the nature of the surroundings of the molecule; when the composition of a two-component mixture varies over a wide range, the effective surroundings and the absorption coefficients change; hence k is not constant over a wide range of composition.

This difficulty can be circumvented in a manner similar to that employed in the more common cases of Beer's law failure. A plot is made of the ratio of absorbances, R, versus the ratio of component concentrations; if there were no difficulties, equation 6-21 would show this as a straight line, but in practice the nonconstancy of k just discussed would cause it to be somewhat curved. A typical plot is shown in Figure 6-13. Several known compositions are required in order to prepare such a curve, but once done the concentration ratio of components in an unknown mixture is easily found by reading from the curve its value as indicated by the absorbance ratio measured from the spectrum. In this application accuracy is limited only by the precision to which the concentration ratios are known in the reference mixtures and, of course, the noise level of the spectrometer.

These methods of component-ratio determination are most useful in copolymer analysis; in fact, they constitute the only *general* method

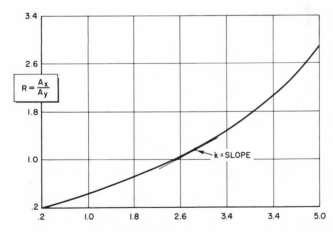

FIGURE 6-13 *A typical relation between absorbance ratios and concentration ratios over a wide composition range.*

Ratio methods of analysis **193**

of any sort by which copolymer analysis can be performed at the present time. The method is rather sensitive to small errors of experimental procedure; the nature and avoidance of these errors were discussed in Chapter 5.

Ratio methods can be extended to three or more components. An equation such as (6-21) will relate any two components; only two such equations are necessary, of course, to determine the composition of a three-component mixture. Equations analogous to (6-22) can be derived, but they become a bit more complicated; it is probably much easier to determine composition from ratios (when the components total 100%) by successive approximations and clever manipulation on a slide rule than by algebraic equations. If analysis must be done over a broad composition range, over which the k's of equations like (6-21) are not constant, then for a three-component mixture two curves (see Figure 6-13) must be constructed. In the application of these methods to terpolymer systems perhaps the most difficult task is to obtain several terpolymers of known composition from which to obtain data for the curves, but this is not our concern here.

B. Internal standards

The ratio methods just described do not make possible a direct assay of a component in a mixture. However, by a modification of ratio techniques assays can be performed in applications in which the absorbing path length is unknown. This is accomplished by adding to the mixture a known amount of a compound which has one or more absorptions at frequencies not interfered with by components of the mixture. This added compound is usually known as an *internal standard*.

To perform analyses with the internal standard technique, a reference spectrum of each of the components to be determined must be obtained. In the production of each such spectrum, a known amount of the internal standard is well mixed with the reference substance. A spectrum of the unknown mixture is then obtained, again with a known amount of internal standard well mixed into the sample.

The calculations, though simple, involve several factors. Consider first the Beer's law relations for a reference material Z and the internal standard:

$$A_{Z,R} = a_{Z,R} b_{Z,R} c_{Z,R}$$

$$A_{I,R} = a_{I,R} b_{I,R} c_{I,R}$$

where subscripts Z,R pertain to material Z in the reference spectrum,

194 *Quantitative analysis*

subscripts I, R pertain to the internal standard in the reference spectrum; $c_{Z,R}$ and $c_{I,R}$ are the weights of reference and internal standard, respectively. Now, as

$$b_{Z,R} = b_{I,R},$$

$$\frac{A_{Z,R}}{A_{I,R}} = \frac{a_{Z,R}c_{Z,R}}{a_{I,R}c_{I,R}}. \tag{6-23}$$

Consider the similar relation in the mixture of unknown material and internal standard:

$$\frac{A_{Z,U}}{A_{I,U}} = \frac{a_{Z,U}c_{Z,U}}{a_{I,U}c_{I,U}}, \tag{6-24}$$

where the notation is an obvious extension of that preceding it. Since absorption coefficients are presumably independent of concentration (true over a limited concentration range), $a_{Z,U} = a_{Z,R}$, $a_{I,U} = a_{I,R}$, and $a_{Z,U}/a_{I,U} = a_{Z,R}/a_{I,R}$; when the latter ratio is eliminated between equations 6-23 and 6-24, we have

$$c_{Z,U} = \frac{A_{Z,U}}{A_{Z,R}} \frac{A_{I,R}}{A_{I,U}} \frac{c_{I,U}}{c_{I,R}} c_{Z,R}. \tag{6-25}$$

Finally, $c_{Z,U}$ is the weight of the component itself in the unknown. To determine the weight fraction of the unknown in the mixture (presumably what would be sought), the expression must be divided by the weight of the total unknown mixture used in obtaining its spectrum, c_{TU}. Hence

$$\% \ Z_{\text{in unknown}} = \frac{A_{Z,U}}{A_{Z,R}} \frac{A_{I,R}}{A_{I,U}} \frac{c_{I,U}}{c_{I,R}} \frac{c_{Z,R}}{c_{TU}}. \tag{6-26}$$

A similar equation will exist for each of the other components in the mixture.

Although seemingly appealing, this method has rather limited use. If the material to be analyzed is soluble in any reasonable solvent (see Chapter 5), solution techniques are preferable. These methods would, presumably, be used only for (a) insoluble liquids run as films, (b) copolymer or terpolymer analysis, and (c) analysis in the solid state (mulls only; this technique need not be resorted to in the application of pressed disks, as explained in Chapter 5).

For capillary films, the liquids involved will by definition be polar, hence will almost certainly show strong association effects, so that

Ratio methods of analysis   **195**

absorption coefficients are not independent of concentration.* If this is so, plots of $A_{Z,R}/A_{I,R}$ versus $c_{Z,R}/c_{I,R}$ must be constructed, and to analyze the unknown the ratio $c_{Z,U}/c_{I,U}$ must be read from the curve for the appropriate measured value of $A_{Z,U}/A_{I,U}$. Such a curve may be adapted to any region for which data points have been obtained, provided the concentrations of the other components do not vary greatly, or the ratio $a_{Z,R}/a_{I,R}$ will vary in a way for which no correction can be made. Probably there is no internal standard material generally applicable to liquid films; one must be chosen to suit each application.

The author knows of no case in which internal standards might be incorporated into copolymers to aid in analysis; the problem here is one of finding a suitable material, either liquid or solid, which could be mixed uniformly with a plastic material. Copolymer analyses by simple ratio methods are entirely satisfactory in any event.

The internal standard method is probably the only one by which quantitative analysis may be done in the solid state with mulls (see Chapter 5). No great difficulty is encountered in mixing an internal standard with the solid sample, for a proper grinding operation, either manual or mechanical, promotes intimate mixing. The great difficulties with this method are in the solid state itself, as described at some length in Chapter 5. If the crystalline materials are soft enough to grind easily and tend to stay in a single crystalline form even under the influence of grinding and admixture with other materials, quantitative analysis can perhaps be done to some extent. It has been found that lead thiocyanate [$Pb(SCN)_2$] and hexabromo benzene (C_6Br_6) make useful internal standards, each having but few absorption bands throughout the 2–25 μ region [$Pb(SCN)_2$ has a prominent absorption at 2045 cm^{-1}; C_6Br_6 has absorptions at 1300 cm^{-1} and 1255 cm^{-1}].

VII. The use of integrated intensities

Peak heights, or absorption band maxima, have wide application in quantitative analysis because of the great convenience with which they are measured. However, they have some serious limitations: (a) The peak height (or absorption coefficient, a) is quite sensitive to spectral slit width (see Figure 6-9), and, as a result, deviations from Beer's law are common and analytical standardization data cannot

* Little difficulty in deviations from Beer's law as a result of finite spectrometer slit width is likely to occur, for most bands of polar liquids are quite broad.

be transferred among spectrometers unless $\Delta\omega/\gamma$ is small (< 0.1). (b) The absorption coefficient, a, has little theoretical significance when inherent absorption strength of a particular vibration is considered, for it does not differentiate between narrow and broad absorption bands; obviously a broad band results from greater absorption of infrared energy than a narrow band of equal peak height.

On the other hand, the *integrated intensity* of an absorption band, $\int_{\text{band}} a_\omega \, d\omega$, is a number analogous to absorption coefficient, a, but of much greater theoretical significance, for it measures *total* absorption of energy by a vibration mode. (See Chapter 8.) It can be used for quantitative analysis just as absorption coefficients of peak heights are used, and in certain cases will make possible analytical applications that are impossible with peak heights. Moreover, it offers hope as a form of data that may be transferred among spectrometers so that analytical standardization data obtained with one spectrometer may be used with another. The determination of integrated intensities has certain pitfalls, however, and whether it will become important in quantitative analysis is hard to predict at present. It is a subject on which there is considerable difference of opinion.

A. Brief theory of measurement of integrated intensity

The "true" integrated intensity coefficient of an absorption band is denoted $\mathcal{A}^*$, and is defined

$$\mathcal{A} = \int_{\text{band}} a_\omega \, d\omega, \tag{6-27}$$

where the absorption coefficient, a_ω, is the "theoretical" value which would be obtained only from a spectrometer whose spectral slit width approached zero. The subscript ω indicates that it is a function of frequency; often this function is "Lorentzian" and has the form shown by equation 6-11. When a spectrometer of finite slit width is employed to determine an integrated intensity, we find

$$\mathcal{A} = \int_{\text{band}} a_\omega \, d\omega \geqslant \mathcal{B} = \frac{1}{bc} \int_{\text{band}} \log \frac{1}{T_\omega} \, d\omega. \tag{6-28}$$

The letter $\mathcal{B}$ usually denotes the integral on the right-hand side of the equation. Departure from equality becomes more severe as the ratio of spectrometer spectral slit width to band half-width, $\Delta\omega/\gamma$, becomes larger; conversely, as the ratio approaches zero, $\mathcal{B}$

* The literature often uses A; we have used script for integrated intensity coefficient ($\mathcal{A}$) to avoid confusion with absorbance (A).

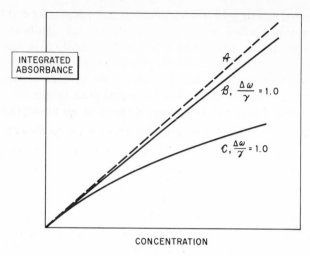

FIGURE 6-14   *A comparison of integrated absorbance forms.*

approaches ᘓ. However, it has been shown (see Reference 6) that the departure of ᘔ from ᘓ for high values of $\Delta\omega/\gamma$ is *much less severe* than the corresponding departure of measured values of absorption coefficient, a, from the ideal value, as shown by Figure 6-9. For example, if $\Delta\omega/\gamma = 1.0$, at absorbance of $\sim$0.3, ᘔ is only $\sim$2% lower than the theoretical value of ᘓ; under similar conditions the experimental value of absorption coefficient, a, is about 25% lower than the theoretical value.

Figure 6-14 compares a plot of $ᘓ \cdot bc$ versus bc with a plot of $ᘔ \cdot bc$ versus bc for $\Delta\omega/\gamma = 1.0$ (a smaller value of $\Delta\omega/\gamma$ would result in closer coincidence of curve ᘔ with line ᘓ, whereas curve ᘔ would depart from ᘓ further for a larger value of $\Delta\omega/\gamma$). These curves are analogous to the curves in Figure 6-9 for peak heights, but there are two important differences: (*a*) For the same value of $\Delta\omega/\gamma$ the integrated intensity approximates the theoretical value much more closely than the peak height approximates its theoretical value. (*b*) At low values of bc, or low absorbance, the integrated intensity coefficient (the slope of the curve) rapidly approaches the theoretical value, whereas absorption coefficient (slope of curves of Figure 6-9) does not approach its theoretical value at low absorbance. Therefore, when a spectrometer of good resolving power ($\Delta\omega \sim 1 \text{ cm}^{-1}$) is employed, the integrated intensities of all but the narrowest bands in solution will have their limiting values at absorbances below $\sim$1.0, which means not only that Beer's law will be closely obeyed but that analyt-

198   *Quantitative analysis*

ical data is transferable with accuracy among spectrometers of good resolving power.

In another method of integrating intensities, often referred to as the "curve-of-growth" method, the actual curve plotted by the spectrometer, $1 - T_\omega$, is integrated:

$$\mathcal{C} = \frac{1}{bc} \int_{\text{band}} (1 - T_\omega) \, d\omega. \tag{6-29}$$

A plot of $\mathcal{C}$ bc versus bc is also shown in Figure 6-14. As can be seen, it is much more curved than the analogous curve for $\mathcal{B}$ and is positively bowed when compared to the curves of Figure 6-9. When such a curve is employed for analytical work, therefore, straight-line approximations cannot be used, but the entire curve must be obtained. Although its slope approaches that of curve $\mathcal{C}$ at small values of bc, the values of bc for which this occurs are too small to be used for practical quantitative analysis. Furthermore, integrated intensities of type $\mathcal{C}$ are not additive, as are those of type $\mathcal{B}$, hence can be applied only to cases in which a band is essentially free of interference, or overlapping, from other bands.

On the other hand, integrated intensities of type $\mathcal{C}$ have certain advantages: (*a*) In order to perform the integral graphically, the band need not be replotted or measured point-by-point, as is necessary when determining $\mathcal{B} \cdot bc$, but can be integrated directly from the spectrometer recording with a planimeter. (*b*) If the band shape is *Lorentzian* (equation 6-11), it can be shown that the integral of equation 6-29 is *independent* of the nature and width of the spectral slit function. (*c*) The curve for $\mathcal{C}$ of Figure 6-14 has a known analytical form (see later) and therefore measurement of the integrated intensity at but one value of bc establishes the entire curve. (*d*) As a result of (*b*) and (*c*), integrated intensity of form $\mathcal{C}$ is, in theory, transferable among different spectrometers even of poor or widely different resolving power.

Although known, the form of the expression of $\mathcal{C} \cdot bc$ as a function of bc is somewhat complex:

$$\mathcal{C} \cdot bc = xe^{-x}[I_0(x) + I_1(x)], \tag{6-30}$$

where $x = \mathcal{C}bc/2\pi\gamma$; $I_0(x)$ and $I_1(x)$ are Bessel functions with all terms positive. The quantity $\mathcal{C}$ is defined in equation 6-27; to determine $\mathcal{C}$ (or $\mathcal{C}/\gamma$) only one value of $\mathcal{C}$ need be obtained at one value of bc; then equation 6-30 is solved for x, hence $\mathcal{C}$. Reference 8 contains tabulations of the function of equation 6-30 for various values of x.

As discussed in Section III, one of the great disadvantages of per-

The use of integrated intensities   **199**

forming quantitative analysis by infrared spectroscopy with peak heights of absorption bands is that data obtained with one spectrometer cannot be used with precision to calibrate an analysis to be performed on another. This operation is possible with integrated intensity data, however, an approach which perhaps deserves more consideration in quantitative analytical applications than it has had in the past.

B. *Application of integrated intensities to quantitative analysis in condensed phases*

Both type ℬ and type ℭ integrated intensities suffer from a serious practical disadvantage. The error produced by a poorly chosen base line against which the integration must be made is embarrassingly large. This is so because a good portion of the area of the band is contained between the wide "wings" of the band and the base line (see Figures 6-4, 6-5, and 6-8), and obviously a small error in the placement of the base line will make a large error in the area of these "wings" and therefore in total integrated absorption. A poorly placed base line which might result in an error of $\sim 2\%$ in measured peak height can easily produce an error of ~ 10–15% in the integrated intensity. Furthermore, the base line must be precise over the entire frequency range of integration, not merely at the absorption maximum, as required for measurement of peak height. Therefore a *fundamental limitation* in the use of integrated intensities for quantitative analysis by infrared spectroscopy is that this method has reasonable accuracy only for cases in which the base line can be determined with precision. (See discussion in Section II-B.) When this is indeed the case, integrated intensities have the following useful applications:

Type ℭ. As previously discussed, this form of integrated intensity is applicable only to isolated Lorentzian-shaped bands. The integral can be determined directly and easily from the recorded spectrum with a planimeter. Although not a linear function of concentration, its function has a known form; it is complex but has been conveniently tabulated (see Reference 8); hence one measurement of a standard reference solution serves to calibrate the analysis, just as in the case of peak heights in which Beer's law is obeyed. Data of this sort are transferable among spectrometers, for it is entirely independent of their resolving power.

These facts—that only one reference spectrum need be obtained and that data are transferable among spectrometers—are the only advantages in the use of integrated intensity of type ℭ in practical quantitative analysis. The determination takes more time than peak-height measurement, and the method is nearly useless in any case in which the absorption band being measured is overlapped by another absorption or the base line cannot be precisely determined.

Type $\mathcal{B}$. This form of integrated intensity is additive and can be used for multicomponent analyses, provided that a precise base line can be established over the entire frequency range of integration. Integrated intensity data of type $\mathcal{B}$ can be applied in much the same manner as peak heights and have the advantage that their deviation from Beer's law is much less severe than that of peak-height data. If a spectrometer of good resolving power is used $(\Delta\omega \sim 1 \text{ cm}^{-1})$, Beer's law will be obeyed accurately for all but the narrowest bands in solution, with the result that one measurement of a standard reference solution serves to calibrate the analysis, and this information is transferable to other spectrometers of comparable resolving power. The great disadvantage of this method is the labor necessary to replot and measure the area of the absorption bands. (Commercial equipment for doing this automatically is under development, however.)

Integrated intensities of type $\mathcal{B}$ can be useful in applications to determine the amount of a given functional group in a mixture of different compounds all containing this group. Suppose, for example, that it is desired to measure the total carbonyl content in a complex mixture of ketones. Although most ketones will have their C=O stretch absorptions in a rather narrow frequency range (see Chapter 12), the various ω_{max} of these bands will not coincide exactly; the carbonyl absorption in the spectrum may therefore be a fairly wide multipeaked structure, which would be nearly impossible to unravel in terms of specific compounds by the method of absorption-band peak heights. However, if all of these materials are saturated aliphatic ketones with no highly polar atoms or groups near the C=O group, it is a reasonable assumption that all of the C=O groups in these molecules will have essentially equal molar absorption strengths, or equal α (as defined by equation 6-27). Therefore determination of

$$\mathcal{B} \cdot bc^* = \int_{\text{C=O bands}} \log \left(1/T\omega\right) d\omega$$ yields a number that is proportional to the total molar carbonyl content of the mixture. The proportionality can be calculated from a single integrated intensity measurement of any one pure aliphatic ketone carbonyl absorption band.

If prism spectrometers are employed for this application in regions

---

* In this type of analysis the concentration must be expressed as molar concentration to have meaning.

in which the prism has low resolving power (as an NaCl prism in the region $\sim$1700 cm^{-1}, where C$=$O absorption occurs), $\Delta\omega/\gamma$ is large enough so that $\mathcal{B} \cdot bc$ versus bc is not a straight line; a curve, as in Figure 6-14, must then be plotted from integration of a C$=$O absorption band of a known pure ketone for several values of bc, just as in the case in which peak heights are employed and Beer's law is not obeyed. (Integrated intensities of type $\mathcal{C}$ cannot be used for this sort of analysis, for they are not additive.)

This method of analysis of a total functional group in a mixture of homologs must be used with some caution. It is not a valid assumption that all members of the homologous series will have equal values of $\mathcal{C}$ for their common functional group if they differ even moderately in structure. In our example of ketones α-chloro-ketones or conjugated ketones, for example, are sure to have different inherent intensities (perhaps as different as a factor of 2) than simple aliphatic ketones, hence could not have been included in this analysis. Similarly, other functional group types must be in similar molecular environments in order to make a determination of their total molar content in a mixture of homologs by the use of integrated intensities a valid procedure.

VIII. The best method of quantitative analysis: an opinion

In view of the spectrometers available today, it is the author's opinion that emphasis should be placed on accuracy and reproducibility of analysis at the expense of transferability of data among spectrometers. It appears that data obtained with prism spectrometers can be transferred only among spectrometers (a) if integrated intensities of type $\mathcal{C}$ are used or (b) if integrated intensities of type $\mathcal{B}$ are used and the spectral slit width is comparable to band half-width. Integrated intensities of type $\mathcal{C}$ have the disadvantage that they are not additive. At reasonable signal-to-noise ratios prism spectrometers are not capable of the narrow spectral slit widths required for transferability of integrated intensities of type $\mathcal{B}$ for the narrowest absorption bands encountered in solution, but perhaps they will serve for wider absorption bands. The transfer of absorption-band peak-height data among prism spectrometers has failed utterly so far. Good grating spectrometers probably will help in this effort, but little work has been done in this direction to date.

The methods that employ peak-height data will probably continue to be the principal routines of quantitative infrared analysis because of the great convenience with which they are measured and their relative insensitivity to lack of precision of base-line determination. Furthermore, as discussed in Section III, strict obediency of data to Beer's law is not necessary for doing precision quantitative analysis.

An important and, it seems, often overlooked point in quantitative analysis is the considerable advantage that results from the use of *wide-slit aperture*. True, agreement with Beer's law and ability to transfer data among spectrometers suffer when $\Delta\omega/\gamma$ is large, and under these conditions no determination of absolute intensities (see Chapter 8) is possible. However, signal-to-noise ratio improves as the *square* of increase of $\Delta\omega$ (see Chapter 3), whereas absorption coefficients decrease *somewhat more slowly than the first power* of increase of $\Delta\omega$ (see Figure 6-9). Surprisingly enough, it appears that if the absorption band to be used for analysis is well isolated from other absorptions, the only practical limit to improvement of analytical sensitivity by widening slit aperture is the width of the detector surface!

It would seem, then, that measurement of absorption-band peak height, using the widest possible slit aperture, is the *best* method of quantitative analysis insofar as convenience and accuracy are concerned. Probably not until better infrared detectors or sources become available, such that good signal-to-noise ratios can be achieved even at very small spectral slit width, will the possibility of transferability of data among spectrometers approach a reality.

Selected references

1. Bauman, R. P., "The Absorption of Infrared Radiation," *Advanced Analytical Chemistry*, Chapter 9, McGraw-Hill, New York, 1958.
2. "Recommended Practices for General Techniques of Infrared Quantitative Analysis," ASTM Proceedings (1959).
3. Robinson, D. Z., "Quantitative Analysis with Infrared Spectrometers," *Anal. Chem.* **23**, 273 (1951).
4. Jones, R. N., and C. Sandorfy, "The Application of Infrared and Raman Spectrometry to the Elucidation of Molecular Structure," *Techniques of Organic Chemistry*, Vol. IX (pp. 261 ff), Interscience, New York, 1956.
5. Lecomte, J., "Spectroscopie dans l'infrarouge," *Handbuch der Physik*, Band XXVI (pp. 849 ff), Springer-Verlag, Berlin (1958).
6. Kostkowski, H. J., and A. M. Bass, "Slit Function Effects in the Direct Measurement of Absorption Line Half-Widths and Intensities," *J. Opt. Soc. Am.* **46**, 1060 (1956).
7. Wilson, E. B., and A. J. Wells, "The Experimental Determination of the Intensities of Infrared Absorption Bands," *J. Chem. Phys.* **14**, 578 (1946).
8. Kaplan, L. D., and D. F. Eggers, "Intensity and Line-Width of the 15-Micron CO_2 Band, Determined by a Curve-of-Growth Method," *J. Chem. Phys.* **25**, 876 (1956).
9. Brugel, W., *An Introduction to Infrared Spectroscopy*, Wiley, New York, 1962.
10. Bauman, R. P., *Absorption Spectroscopy*, Wiley, New York, 1962.

The best method of quantitative analysis: an opinion   **203**

7

Auxiliary devices
and special techniques

By modifying spectrometer operation slightly, or by adding simple auxiliary equipment, certain interesting and powerful extensions of infrared spectroscopic techniques may be made. A good deal of this apparatus is either commercially available or easily constructed. More important than the apparatus for successful application of these techniques, however, is a reasonably thorough understanding of just what the spectrometer is doing or is capable of doing in any given application; this essential background has been discussed at some length in Chapters 3 and 4, and it is urged that these precepts be reviewed carefully before attempting the procedures discussed subsequently.

I. Compensated spectra

The term "compensated spectrum" is often used to describe the situation in which the spectrum of a pertinent material must, for some reason, be obtained in the presence of a large amount of other material whose own absorption overlaps or obscures the absorption bands of the pertinent material (for example, the spectrum of a polar solid obtained in solution in a polar solvent). If an equivalent amount of the interfering material (such as the polar solvent) is placed in the reference beam of a double-beam spectrometer, the resultant spectrum will be that of the pertinent material only, for a double-beam spectrometer measures the *difference* in energy of the two beams, expressing as per cent the ratio of sample-beam energy to the reference-beam energy. Hence no absorption of any material common to both beams will appear in the recorded spectrum. Such a spectrum is commonly referred to as having been *compensated;* this technique can probably best be explained by illustrations of its use.

A. Compensation of a low I_0

Perhaps the simplest case of a compensated spectrum is that in which a low but constant I_0 line is corrected by compensation. A constant low I_0 line results from light losses in the sample beam which are not the result of light absorption by the pertinent molecule (e.g., light loss from scattering, use of a polarizer, vignetting of the beam because of small optical aperture at the sample, or losses resulting from multiple windows of special apparatus). If the I_0 line is roughly constant at about 10% transmission, for example, the entire spectrum is squeezed into the bottom 10% of the chart, with the result that it is hard to interpret. We may expand it to full ordinate scale by *compensating* the spectrum, which is done by placing in the reference beam any device that absorbs or otherwise blocks out 90% of the light at all wavelengths. This is conveniently done with a piece of ordinary wire screen of appropriate mesh; for compensating I_0's at different levels it is convenient to have several screens of different mesh available.

Now, when a screen that will block ~90% of the light is placed in the reference beam, the value of volts-per-unit-attenuator-displacement is reduced to ~$\frac{1}{10}$ its former value; as a result, not enough power is available in the pen servo system to produce a useful spectrum. To correct this situation there are three choices: (*a*) The amplifier gain may be increased by a factor of 10 so that the value of volts-per-unit-attenuator-displacement, hence servo-loop energy, is raised to its normal level, but this results in an increase in noise level by a factor of 10. (*b*) The spectrometer slits may be widened by a factor of $\sqrt{10}$ which will raise servo-loop energy to its normal level with no increase in noise level but will increase spectral slit width by a factor of $\sqrt{10}$. (*c*) The scan time and time constant can be increased by a factor of 100 and the gain increased by a factor of 10, which will produce the necessary servo-loop energy but with no increase in noise or loss of resolution; however, a factor of 100 increase in scan time does not seem practical for most applications.

The second choice—sacrifice of resolution by factor $\sqrt{10}$—seems to be the best decision. In qualitative analytical applications in condensed phases this resolution loss is not highly important; pre-

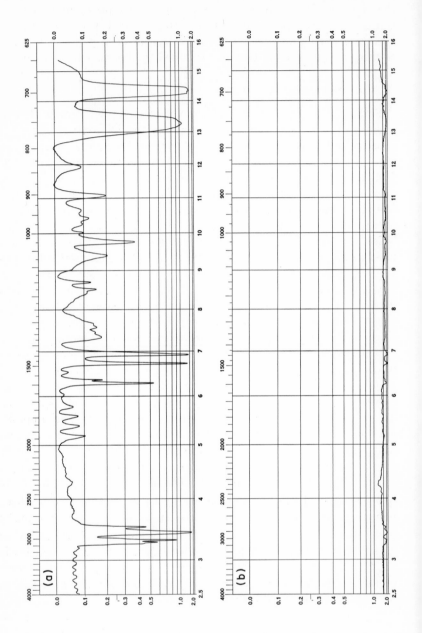

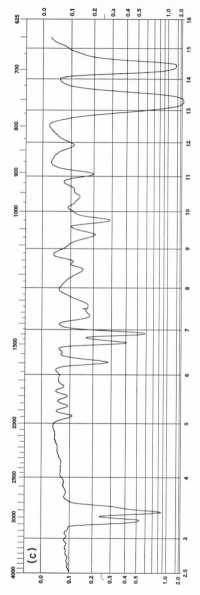

FIGURE 7-1 (a) Spectrum of polystyrene film obtained under standard conditions. (b) Spectrum of polystyrene film obtained with I_0 at ~3% of full-scale energy. (c) Spectrum of polystyrene film with 3% of full-scale energy, compensated by 3% T screen, using wide slits.

sumably in cases in which a low I_0 must be compensated a qualitative analysis or a rough quantitative analysis is what is desired. The spectrum produced can be used with confidence, for its noise level will be no greater than is usually obtained. A spectrum having a very low I_0 is shown in Figure 7-1 before and after compensation.

B. Compensation of solvent absorption

Let us now consider the case in which an I_0 which must be compensated is not at a uniform level of transmission but varies widely as a function of frequency. This is just the case encountered in the compensation of absorption bands, such as those of a polar solvent used to dissolve a polar solid. In Figure 7-2a, for example, the spectrum of methylene chloride obtained undiluted in a 0.2-mm cell is illustrated, whereas Figure 7-2b is a spectrum of a 2% solution of phthalic anhydride in methylene chloride, also in a 0.2-mm cell. Suppose that we wished to compensate the methylene chloride absorptions in the region 600–1600 cm^{-1} so that accurate determinations of frequency or absorbance could be made of the absorption bands of phthalic anhydride, including those that occur at or near absorption bands of the methylene chloride solvent. This is accomplished by placing a cell of appropriate length (see later) filled with methylene chloride in the reference beam of the double-beam spectrometer; the solution of phthalic anhydride in methylene chloride is placed in the sample beam.

The problem of maintaining the value of volts-per-unit-attenuator-displacement at its correct level is now somewhat more complicated, for the level of reference-beam energy will vary rapidly throughout the frequency range 600–1600 cm^{-1}. To obtain useful information at as many frequencies as possible, allowance must be made for the regions of lowest reference-beam energy in which useful information can be expected; no useful information can be expected in regions of total solvent absorption. Reference to Figure 7-2a shows that lowest energy (neglecting complete absorptions) occurs at 895 cm^{-1} and 1420 cm^{-1}, where the transmission is $\sim 3\%$, and therefore the energy available to the detector, hence to the servo loop is $\sim \frac{1}{30}$ the normal value. Therefore, if it is necessary to obtain the spectrum at all points (other than those at which the solvent is totally absorbing), any changes to be made in instrument parameters should be of such magnitude that at these frequencies the low servo-loop energy will be raised to its normal value.

As in the case just discussed, servo-loop energy can be increased in three ways: by raising the amplifier gain by a factor of 30 (with resultant thirtyfold increase of noise level), by increasing slit width by a factor of $\sqrt{30}$ (with a corresponding loss of resolution), or by increasing the time constant by a factor of 900, which allows gain to be increased by a factor of 30 with no increase of noise and no loss of resolution (but requires a factor of 900 slower scan rate). All of these methods will provide normal energy at 895 and 1420 cm^{-1}; as in the foregoing illustration, it is probably best to "pay" for this energy increase in loss of resolution by the factor $\sqrt{30}$ rather than accept a thirtyfold increase in noise or a nine-hundredfold increase in scan time.

However, at frequencies *other* than those at which $\sim$5% or less light is transmitted by the solvent, the energy available to the servo loop will have been increased as high as a factor of 30 over normal as a result of any of the three operations just discussed. This excess energy will cause the servo loop to oscillate in most of the region 600–1500 cm^{-1}. (See Chapter 4, p. 80 ff.) On the other hand, if no change had been made in any of the instrument parameters and the servo-loop energy is at its correct value where there is no solvent absorption, then in the regions of high solvent absorption (895 and 1420 cm^{-1}) the servo loop would have far too little energy, the spectrometer would be sluggish, or "dead," and unable to record solute absorptions properly. Figure 7-2e shows how a compensated spectrum would appear under these conditions. No compromise of instrument parameters, which would keep the spectrometer out of oscillation in regions of no solvent absorption but also keep it "alive" in regions of solvent absorption, seems possible. How, then, is a useful spectrum to be obtained?

A possible but highly tedious method by which a spectrum may be obtained in this case is to widen the slits by a factor of $\sqrt{30}$ and stop the spectrometer scan frequently in regions in which the servo loop energy is changing (these points must be recognized from a blank spectrum of the pure solvent, for they will not be apparent in the *compensated* spectrum), measure the servo-loop energy, or value of volts-per-unit-attenuator-displacement, and adjust the gain control so that the standard operating value is obtained. The scan is then resumed for a short distance and the process is repeated. An alternative method is to use the standard value of gain control setting but to vary the slit width at each stopping of the scan to such value that correct servo energy is maintained. Either procedure will keep the value of volts-per-unit-attenuator-displacement at the correct level even in regions of high energy change, but both are obviously tedious. Furthermore, each scan stop and gain change will

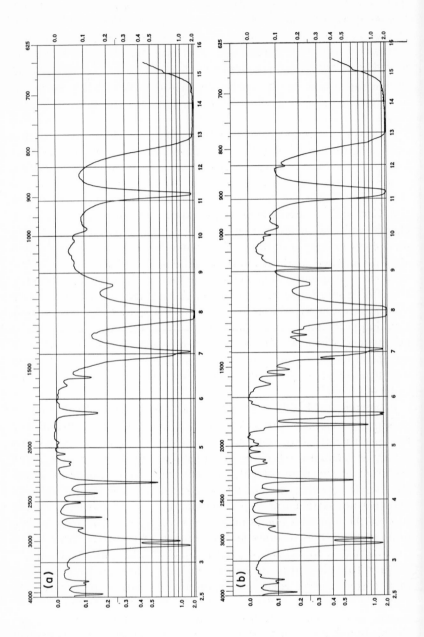

210

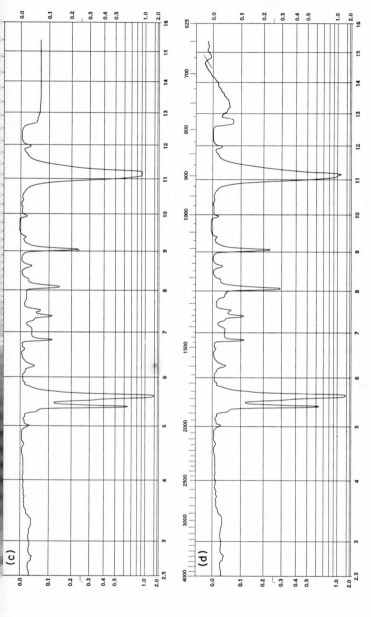

FIGURE 7-2 (a) Methylene chloride solvent in a 0.2-mm cell; standard slits and gain. (b) 2% solution of phthalic anhydride in methylene chloride in a 0.2-mm cell; standard slits and gain. (c) Solution (b) in sample beam, solvent (a) in reference; wide slits, no automatic gain. (d) Same as (c) (wide slits) but using automatic gain. Note differences at 1240 and 900 cm⁻¹, compared to (c). (e) Same as (c) but with standard slits, no automatic gain. (f) Same as (e) (standard slits) but using automatic gain.

211

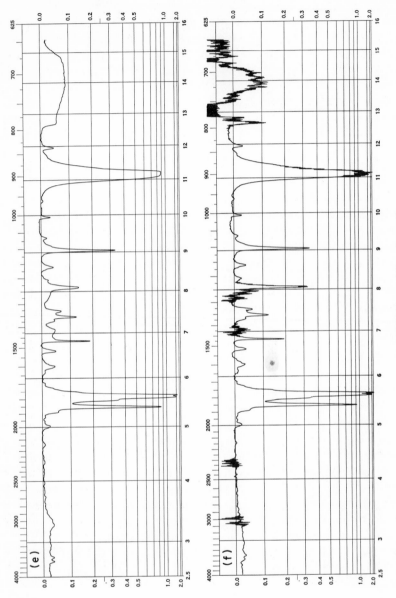

FIGURE 7-2 (Continued)

212

often introduce a discontinuity, or "kick," into the recorded spectrum; each scan stop and slit-width change may produce a transmission discontinuity in any region in which an absorption band of the solute is being recorded. These methods are clearly not satisfactory.

Suppose, however, that a signal proportional at all times to absolute reference-beam energy were available; such a signal could be used to vary continuously the amplifier gain or the slit width in such a way that the correct value of servo-loop energy would be maintained at all times. Now, just such a signal is available from the so-called "automatic servo-energy control" discussed in Section IV-D of Chapter 4. When used to program the amplifier gain, the device is known as "automatic gain control"; when used to program the slit width, it is called "automatic slit control." (See Reference 2.)

Automatic gain control works in the following way: In regions in which reference-beam transmission decreases (solvent absorption) and the signal produced at the detector falls, the automatic gain control increases amplifier gain so that servo energy remains at its normal level; when reference-beam transmission rises, and the signal produced at the detector rises, the gain is automatically reduced by an appropriate amount so that servo-loop energy continues at the correct level. By this means a compensated spectrum is produced with no more difficulty than an ordinary spectrum. Figure 7-2d illustrates this (compare with Figure 7-2c): the correct energy has been obtained at 895 and 1420 cm^{-1} by opening the slits a factor of $\sqrt{30}$, and the automatic gain control provision has been used for reducing gain in the other regions where this extra energy is not required and would otherwise cause the servo system to oscillate.

When the automatic gain control increases amplifier gain, the noise level rises. However, if the slits have been widened to the point at which energy allowance for lowest useful transmission of the solvent has been made, the noise level will be no higher than it is under normal spectrometer operation and will, of course, be much lower than normal in regions of no solvent absorption. On the other hand, if the slits had not been widened and a compensated spectrum were obtained with automatic gain control, there would be no resolution loss, but in each region of low solvent transmission the noise level will be uncomfortably high, for in these regions the automatic gain control is attempting to reach standard servo energy by advancing the amplifier gain far beyond its normal value, which amplifies the noise considerably. A compensated spectrum obtained at normal spectral slit width is shown in Figures 7-2e and 7-2f without and with automatic gain control, respectively.

Compensated spectra   213

Most solvents have frequency regions in which total absorption occurs, and, of course, no "compensated" spectrum of any meaning can be produced in these regions. When the scan proceeds through such a region, the spectrum is likely to appear as shown in Figure 7-2c at 1250–1270 and 675–775 cm^{-1}; if automatic gain control is being used, these regions show peculiar results: high noise level, peculiar drift effects, or the recorder pen being driven against either stop of its range. (See Figures 7-2d and 7-2f.) The recorded spectrum in regions of total solvent absorption is meaningless, and no interpretation should be attempted.

Automatic slit control can also be used in compensation of variable reference-beam transmission and works in a manner similar to automatic gain control. In regions of low reference-beam energy the automatic slit control widens the slits so that servo energy remains at its normal level. In regions of high reference-beam transmission the slit width returns to or near its normal value, so as not to overdrive the servo system. When employing automatic slit control the amplifier gain control is left fixed at its normal setting; hence the noise level will be constant at its normal value. It is not necessary to make a choice concerning energy level or slit width; this is done automatically by the automatic slit control device. During the scan the resolution (spectral slit width) varies as the square root* of reference-beam energy.

Some commercial spectrometers have an automatic gain control device, others, an automatic slit control device; unfortunately, no commercial spectrometer at this writing has both devices, for both are useful.

Automatic gain control causes the spectrum to be produced at variable signal-to-noise ratio and constant spectral slit width. For studying one specific band or for performing quantitative analysis this approach is probably best, for we have seen (Chapter 6) that absorptivity is rather sensitive to spectral slit width and therefore the most reproducible absorptivities presumably will be produced when spectral slit width remains constant. However, if information is required in regions of low reference-beam energy, the spectral slit width must be made quite large to give appropriate energy here, and other regions, in which reference-beam energy might be somewhat higher, will be recorded at lower resolution than energy requirements would otherwise demand; conversely, if the slits are set for higher resolution, the automatic gain control will produce excessive

---

* Recall that energy reaching the detector is proportional to the *square* of the slit width.

noise in regions of low reference-beam energy. (Compare Figures 7-2d and 7-2f.) Neither situation is convenient when the compensated spectrum is being used for qualitative analysis.

Automatic slit control, on the other hand, causes the spectrum to be produced at constant signal-to-noise ratio and variable spectral slit width. For the reasons just discussed, its use is most convenient in qualitative analytical applications, for each band will be recorded at its best possible resolution consistent with the energy requirements imposed by reference-beam transmission; however, we should expect that quantitative analysis done under these conditions would not be so precise.

Before any compensation technique is attempted it is always good practice to have obtained a spectrum of the material that is to be placed in the reference beam. This spectrum is a frequency profile of the energy available to the detector with which the spectrometer will operate, and it would be well to bear it in mind. (Compare Figures 7-2a and 7-2d.)

When compensating a spectrum for solvent absorption, the amount of solvent in both beams must be essentially the same. For example, if a 10% solution in methylene chloride is in the sample beam in a 0.111-mm cell, pure methylene chloride must be in a cell whose length is $0.90 \times 0.111 = 0.100$ mm*; if the solution in the sample beam is 2%, the thickness required would be $0.98 \times 0.111 = 0.109$ mm. Because a great variety of fixed cells is not usually at hand, it is convenient to have available a cell whose length is continuously variable. With such a cell it is a simple matter to compensate solvent absorption quite accurately. Variable-length cells are available from manufacturers of spectrometer equipment.

The solvent compensation technique is a powerful one for performing quantitative analysis on highly polar materials. Consideration of Figure 5-3 shows that by use of these few polar solvents, augmented by compensation techniques, nearly any region from 400–4000 cm^{-1} can be studied qualitatively or used for quantitative analysis. It is the author's opinion that this method should be used for quantitative analysis of polar solids whenever possible, rather than the solid state techniques, as discussed at some length in Chapter 5.

C. Detection and analysis of minor constituents

Compensation techniques can be used in another application to aid in identification or analysis of smaller amounts of materials in the

* This correction assumes that the density of solute and solvent are identical. If they are not, appropriate correction must be made.

presence of larger amounts of known materials. Suppose, for example, that it is necessary to analyze $\frac{1}{2}\%$ of diphenyl oxide in the presence of otherwise pure phenol. The spectra of the pure materials obtained in CCl_4–CS_2 solution are shown by Figures 7-3a and 7-3b. We see that diphenyl oxide has an intense absorption at 1235 cm^{-1}, but if it is present at the level of $\frac{1}{2}\%$ this absorption will not be distinguishable in the presence of a large amount of phenol. However, it is possible to detect and analyze the small impurity if a compensating solution of phenol in CS_2 (at a concentration and cell length equivalent to those in the sample beam) is placed in the reference beam.

The spectrometer parameters are set in accordance with the transmission level at the frequency at which the analysis is to be made: slits are widened by the factor $\sqrt{1/T}$, and the automatic gain control system is made operative. (In Figure 7-3 the transmission at 1235 cm^{-1} is $\sim 6\%$, and the slits should be opened by a factor of $\sqrt{1/0.06} \approx 4$.) If the major constituent has been properly matched, the compensated spectrum will appear as in Figure 7-3c; if ordinate expansion is available, the small absorption can be expanded, as shown by the lower curve.

D. Sensitivity limits

What are the limits to which these techniques can be extended? What is the minimum amount of material detectable under favorable conditions or what is the minimum energy at which reliable measurements may be made by compensating low transmission? For a given spectrometer the ultimate limit in both cases is reached when widening the slits will no longer produce an increase of signal-to-noise ratio for the absorption bands we wish to measure. We shall show why this is so in each case.

The compensation technique provides a basis for the highest sensitivity that can be obtained in the detection and analysis of a small amount of material, for the sensitivity limit is often set by the background in which the small absorption band must be measured, and if compensation of the background can be properly done this limitation will be much less severe. The limitation now consists of the ability to measure a minute absorption band over the noise level.

If reasonable energy is available (i.e., if the background being compensated is not of low transmission, as in the energy-limited case we shall discuss later), sensitivity is gained by expanding the pen motion (ordinate expansion) by a factor as large as possible, until the concurrent Johnson-noise expansion becomes visible in the recorded

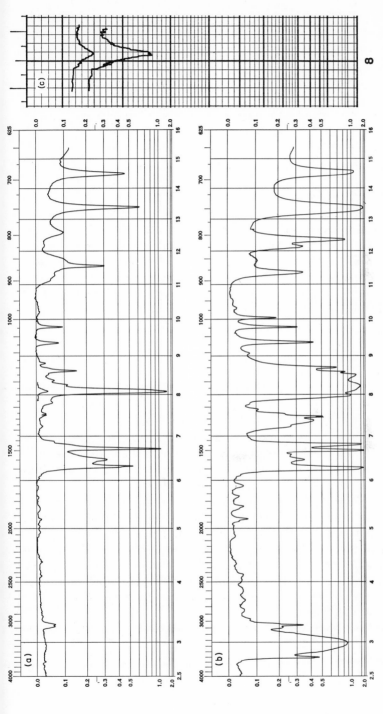

FIGURE 7-3 (a) Spectrum of a 2% solution of diphenyl oxide in a 0.1-mm cell, standard slits and gain; also of a 0.05% solution at 1235 cm⁻¹. (b) Spectrum of a 10% solution of phenol in a 0.1-mm cell, standard slits and gain. (c) A solution of 0.05% diphenyl oxide and 9.95% phenol in sample beam, 10% phenol in reference beam. Slits 4 × N, automatic gain used. Lower curve obtained using 3:1 ordinate expansion.

217

spectrum. At this point no advantage results from further ordinate expansion (because both signal and noise are being increased by the same ratio), unless more energy is available to the detector so that amplifier gain can be reduced, thereby reducing noise.

The only way to increase energy available to the detector is to widen the spectrometer slits, and we now ask how far we can proceed along these lines and still gain sensitivity. As the slits are widened, resolution is lost, departure from Beer's law becomes more serious, and absorptivity (hence actual pen deflection of the absorption band) decreases. Provided it is not necessary to resolve the small absorption band being used for analysis from a neighboring absorption band, resolution loss is not important. Also, presumably, in the detection and analysis of a small quantity of material close adherence to Beer's law is not a major consideration. Finally, as discussed in the concluding remarks of Chapter 6, absorbance always *decreases much less rapidly* than energy *increases* as the slits are widened. Hence, as in the consideration of the precision of quantitative analysis, the limitation for detection and analysis of trace components is reached when increasing the slit aperture results in radiation falling off the detector surface; the gain in signal-to-noise ratio obtained by the wide slits is translated into sensitivity by chart ordinate expansion until the point at which the amplified Johnson noise is detectable in the recorded spectrum.

When using high ordinate expansion ratios, the power requirement of the pen servo system is increased; hence it is helpful to slow the scan rate to ensure that the pen position does not lag the signal. When the scan rate is lowered, the time constant can be increased commensurately, which leads to a small gain in signal-to-noise ratio, but, as we have seen, the increase is not significant unless there is an impractically large increase in scan time.*

The limit to the lowest energy background on which reliable measurements can be made by compensation techniques is also determined by the point at which further increase in slit aperture causes light to fall off the detector surface. If the energy background (I_0) on which an absorption band is to be measured is at, say, only 2% chart transmission, an absorption band can still be reliably measured if the signal-to-noise ratio can be increased by a factor of 50, for

---

* If only one narrow frequency region need be scanned (e.g., if all information sought could be obtained in the range 850–900 cm^{-1}), a large factor of time increase might be practical. Suppose that normal scan time over this region were 30 seconds; it might be practical to increase this by a factor of 100 (i.e., to 50 minutes), hence to gain a potential factor of 10 in energy sensitivity.

now compensation, either with a screen for flat I_0 or a solution for variable I_0, can be used to expand the 2% transmission region to full chart scale, as previously discussed. As long as increase of slit width produces appropriate increase of signal-to-noise ratio, the lower limit of transmission in which bands may be measured can be extended downward. In most cases useful analyses can be performed with as little as 1% of normal energy with careful work.

This low energy limit of the spectrometer can be pushed downward a bit further by increase of scan time and time constant, which allows some increase of gain without producing increased noise. However, as we have seen, the improvement is proportional only to *square root* of scan time, so that only relatively small advantage can be obtained from this approach without employing grossly impractical amounts of time. (See footnote, p. 218.)

E. Difference spectra

A difference spectrum is really a special case of a compensated spectrum, in which the absorption band to be measured is compensated by a nearly equal absorption band in the reference beam. This technique simultaneously provides two important aids to ultimate accuracy in quantitative analysis: (*a*) The problem of I_0 determination (i.e., base-line choice) is nearly perfectly solved. (*b*) The magnitude of unit pen deflection per unit concentration change is materially increased.

Suppose it is necessary to analyze a material which has a suitable absorption band, as in the two spectra in Figure 7-4*a*, as accurately as possible. From the discussion in Chapter 6 it was seen that the limitations on this accuracy result principally from the inability to determine I_0 accurately and the precision limit of measurement of transmission of an absorption band minimum imposed by noise level.

The first of these difficulties is largely overcome by placing in the reference beam of a double-beam spectrometer a solution of the material to be analyzed whose concentration is precisely known and is somewhat smaller than the expected concentration in the sample to be analyzed. When this so-called "difference spectrum" is obtained, the small absorption band recorded by the spectrometer will result from the *difference* between the unknown concentration and the known concentration, as shown in Figure 7-4*b*. Reflection upon the nature of the absorbance-transmission relation shows that the transmission difference resulting from a difference in concentration between sample solution and reference solution has been magnified: a 1% concentra-

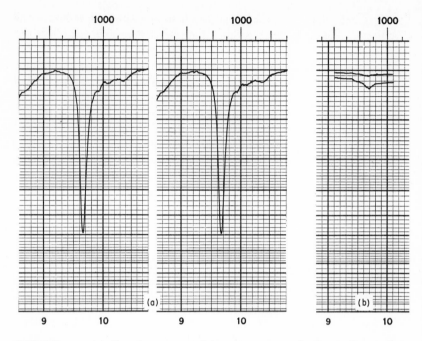

FIGURE 7-4 (a) *Two bands, resulting from two solutions whose solute concentrations differ by 1% of amount present.* (b) *Difference spectra of solutions of* (a), *using wide slits, automatic gain. The lower curve employs 3:1 ordinate expansion.*

tion difference between two samples would have produced at best a 0.34% transmission difference on the spectrometer chart (see Figure 6-6 and compare bands in Figure 7-4a), whereas in the difference spectrum a 1% concentration (hence absorbance) difference is a full 1% transmission difference; with ordinate expansion this can be still larger. (See Figure 7-4b.) Figure 7-5a illustrates a series of difference spectra in which the concentration of the solution in the sample beam has been varied in 1% steps (the dashed spectrum might be that of a difference spectrum of the unknown).

A difference spectrum enables the I_0 to be located more precisely, for the absorption to be measured has been expanded but the background has not. In cases of relatively large background absorption at the analytical frequency, which makes the choice of I_0 difficult for uncompensated spectra, I_0 can be located with good precision by obtaining difference spectra, using a few solutions of closely spaced concentration in the reference beam, as illustrated in Figure 7-5b.

220 *Auxiliary devices and special techniques*

If the spectrum is undercompensated, a positive difference band will result; if it is overcompensated, there will be a negative difference band. A series of these difference spectra allows an accurate and reproducible estimate to be made of the true I_0.

Now, when a difference spectrum is obtained, the servo-loop energy will vary as the reference-beam energy varies; correction must be made so that the servo-loop energy is reasonably constant and at its normal value, as in the other examples of compensated spectra. Such correction can be made by stopping the scan at several points throughout the frequency interval of the analytical absorption band

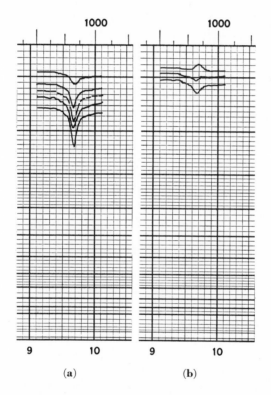

FIGURE 7-5 (a) *A series of calibration difference spectra, in which concentrations in two beams differ in steps of 1% of amount present. Wide slits, automatic gain, 3:1 ordinate expansion employed. Dashed curve represents difference spectrum between an unknown and a known, showing how its concentration may be determined by interpolation.* (b) *Difference spectra of a few solutions of nearly identical concentration. Wide slits, automatic gain, 3:1 ordinate expansion employed.*

Compensated spectra 221

and readjusting the gain control to hold servo-loop energy constant, but this is tedious. Another possible method is to decrease the scan rate by $(1/T)^2$, where T is the minimum transmission of the absorption band in the reference beam. However, this is often impractical because of the time required to make a single determination. The best method, as in the case of compensated spectra, is the use of the automatic gain control, which holds servo-loop energy at the required constant value when reference-beam energy varies.

As we have already mentioned, the second limitation in accuracy of quantitative analysis is the spectrometer noise limitation. If the difference spectra of Figures 7-4b or 7-5 had been obtained under the usual signal-to-noise conditions, no increase in accuracy would have resulted from the factor of ~ 3 increase in transmission sensitivity to concentration, for this is just the factor of gain increase necessary at the analytical frequency (supplied by the automatic gain control). Therefore noise level also increases by the same factor. Hence there is no net increase in signal-to-noise ratio in the use of difference spectra unless other spectrometer parameters are altered.

As developed in Part D of this section, increasing slit width always increases signal-to-noise ratio much faster than inherent absorptivity decreases. *Therefore the ultimate possible accuracy that can be obtained with a given spectrometer in quantitative analysis by infrared methods is reached when the slit aperture is increased to the point at which further increase causes the monochromator exit slit image to become so large that all of it no longer falls on the detector surface.* This will cause rather serious departures from Beer's law, but in the practice of this technique they are not important (see later). Increase of the slit aperture will produce some decrease in observed absorption band intensity, but the rapid gain in signal-to-noise ratio allows a large chart ordinate expansion factor to be used without the appearance of appreciable noise in the recorded spectrum. Of course, a large increase in slit aperture will not be nearly so useful if the analytical absorption band is not resolved from neighboring absorption bands.

In practice, calibrations and determinations are made as follows: A series of precision solutions of the reference material is prepared in small concentration steps (concentrations proportional to 0.96, 0.97, 0.98, 0.99, 1.00, and 1.01). A difference spectrum of each of these solutions is scanned with one of the solutions (the one whose concentration is proportional to 0.97, say, which we call solution S) always in the reference beam. The instrument parameters are set in the same manner to be employed in obtaining the difference spectrum of the unknown mixture. The results will appear as illustrated in

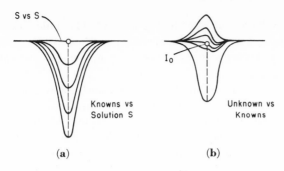

S vs S

I_0

Knowns vs
Solution S

Unknown vs
Knowns

(a)

(b)

FIGURE 7-6 (a) *Difference spectra of a series of solutions of known concentration versus one of the known solutions, S (for calibration).* (b) *Difference spectra of unknown solution versus the series of known solutions (to locate I_0) and versus known solution, S (to make determination).*

Figure 7-6a.* The unknown mixture to be analyzed is then placed in the same cell used in the sample beam, and a series of difference spectra is obtained by placing each of the known solutions in the *reference* beam, using the same cell in the reference beam as before. This series of curves will be similar to those of Figure 7-6b and will serve to locate as precisely as possible the I_0 point. Having determined I_0, the pen deflection in the spectrum of the unknown compensated by solution S is accurately measured† and interpolated between the two appropriate difference spectra of the series, as in Figure 7-6a, to give a high precision analysis. It should be noted that this procedure does not depend on Beer's law but is based on simple interpolation between precisely known steps; for this reason we need not be concerned with Beer's law deviations produced by large increase of slit aperture.

A question on the use of difference spectra which is frequently debated is: What should the value of transmission of the compensating solution be at the analytical frequency to produce the greatest analytical precision? Some maintain that this value should be 36.8% transmission; others have indicated that the value should be lower than this

---

* The curves shown in Figures 7-6a and 7-6b are not actually recorded spectra, as are other spectra in this chapter; they are drawings, much expanded in scale for sake of clarity. Figures 7-6a and 7-6b are analogous to Figures 7-5a and 7-5b.

† When chart ordinate expansion is employed, the absorbance scale of the chart becomes meaningless; hence, under these conditions, absorption peak heights measured for comparison with other absorptions are probably best measured as distance of pen deflection in millimeters.

Compensated spectra 223

figure but have not specified a value. The following argument is offered in support of the first viewpoint.

When obtaining a difference spectrum, the spectrometer should be operated in such a way that the ratio of chart deflection of the difference band to the noise level (i.e., the signal-to-noise ratio) is maximum. When this is done, the chart ordinate can always be expanded in a useful manner to obtain maximum accuracy. Pen deflection of the difference band is equal to $1 - Q$, where Q is the per cent of light transmission by the reference-beam light attenuator of an optical null spectrometer. At the bottom of the difference band, where the servo system is at equilibrium, the light falling on the detector from each beam must be equal:

$$QT_R = T_S,$$

where T_R is the transmission of the compensating solution in the reference beam, T_S is the transmission of the solution in the sample beam.

Hence

$$1 - Q = 1 - \frac{T_S}{T_R}. \tag{7-1}$$

Now, the average noise level in the recorded spectrum is

$$\bar{N} = E_J g Z, \tag{7-2}$$

where E_J is the Johnson-noise voltage at the detector (see equation 4-2), g is the gain control setting (expressed as the fraction of full value), and Z a constant characteristic of the several electronic components between detector and recording pen. Servo loop energy is

$$S = T_R P g Z, \tag{7-3}$$

where P expresses the factors of source power, optical efficiency, slit aperture, and detector efficiency, with which we are not concerned here, and is therefore a constant. As we have repeatedly stressed, servo-loop energy must be kept constant if the spectrometer is to perform correctly; hence S will be held constant in these considerations. When gZ is eliminated between equations 7-2 and 7-3, the result is

$$\bar{N} = E_J \frac{S}{PT_R} = \frac{k}{T_R}, \tag{7-4}$$

where all factors that remain constant in this discussion have been collected together in k.

Finally, the function that must be maximized is the pen deflection per noise, or

$$\frac{1 - Q}{\bar{N}} = \frac{1 - (T_S/T_R)}{k/T_R} = \frac{T_R - T_S}{k}. \tag{7-5}$$

Now, transmission by the reference beam is 10^{-A}, and transmission by the sample beam is $10^{-\alpha A}$, where A is absorbance and α is a number slightly greater than unity of such magnitude that $T_S = 10^{-\alpha A}$. (See discussion preceding equation 6-9.) Therefore

$$\frac{T_R - T_S}{k} = \frac{10^{-A} - 10^{-\alpha A}}{k} = \frac{1 - Q}{\bar{N}}, \tag{7-6}$$

and the situation is clearly analogous to that described in Chapter 6 (see p. 171 ff): Figure 6-6 illustrates how the function of equation 7-6 varies with absorbance or transmission, the maximum occurring near 37% transmission. Therefore greatest possible precision results when the concentration and cell length are such that the transmission in the reference beam is near 37%, although little change from optimum value occurs if the transmission is anywhere in the range of 25 to 50%.

One final point in difference spectroscopy deserves some comment. Absorbance appears to be quite sensitive to temperature, out of all proportion to simple thermal expansion of the solution in the cell. (See Section VII.) In ordinary quantitative analysis this sensitivity is not troublesome if the usual care is exercised; but in difference spectroscopy strict attention must be given to temperature considerations and extra care must be taken to ensure that the temperature of unknown and compensating samples is as nearly the same as possible, for at the sensitivity level obtainable with difference spectra temperature variation is probably the greatest source of error. After being rinsed with solvent, air dried, and refilled with solution, an absorption cell will probably have waves of temperature variation in the salt windows. It is necessary to let these cells stand at room temperature for several minutes before introducing them into the spectrometer, whose sample compartment should be thermostated to room temperature. It is also helpful to rinse, dry, fill, and place in a thermostat or the spectrometer the sample and reference cells at the same time, so that they will have a thermal history as nearly identical as possible.

II. Water solutions

Water is often considered to be the worst solvent conceivable for infrared solution spectroscopy, and indeed in many respects it is.

Examination of spectra of water in thin layers, as shown in Figure 7-7a, shows that the situation is not hopeless, however. Although low, the transmission of water is remarkably constant in the important region of 950–1550 cm^{-1}, and with appropriate compensation techniques spectra may be obtained in this region.

The first problem is a suitable cell. Barium fluoride, BaF$_2$, is essentially insoluble in water and has its low-frequency cutoff (for the thickness of two plates suitable for cell windows) just below that of water (water cuts off at ∼950 cm^{-1}, BaF$_2$ at ∼900 cm^{-1}). Therefore a cell made with BaF$_2$ plates in the usual manner (see Figure 5-8) will serve nicely for use with water solutions. A cell thickness of much over 0.07 mm will be so great that little energy will be transmitted by a layer of water so thick; cells thinner than about 0.025 mm are too difficult to construct; they would require high concentrations of solute and, because the viscosity of water becomes a serious problem in cells of this thickness, would be nearly impossible to rinse or clean properly.

Filling and cleaning of these thin cells is not easy. Usually it is necessary to use a small amount of pressure (from a rubber bulb) to force the water solution into the cell. This should be done with a mild but sudden surge, so that the water solution will flow quickly through the cell. If the cell is filled slowly, small air bubbles are likely to become entrapped, which for some reason are very difficult to coax from the solution between the plates. These cells are probably best cleaned by rinsing with distilled water, followed by acetone, and dried with compressed air.

Presence of sulfate ion in the water solution will ruin the cell, for BaSO$_4$ is much less soluble in water than BaF$_2$, hence a layer of BaSO$_4$, which is opaque near 1100 cm^{-1}, will rapidly be formed on the inside cell faces. This can be prevented by testing some of the unknown solution with BaCl$_2$ reagent (a white precipitate of BaSO$_4$ immediately forms if sulfate ion is present) before introducing it into the cell or by "salting" the solution with BaF$_2$, just as CCl$_4$–CS$_2$ (and other organic solvent) solutions are salted with NaCl to ensure that there will be no attack of NaCl windows.

The absorption of water can be compensated by a simple transmission screen, with techniques similar to those described in Section I-A. A screen of appropriate transmission (depending on the thickness of the water layer in the sample beam) is placed in the reference beam and the slits are widened by the factor $\sqrt{1/T}$. The spectrum of water between 950 and 1550 cm^{-1} now appears as shown in Figure 7-7b. The advantage of this system is its simplicity and the fact that only one BaF$_2$ cell is required.

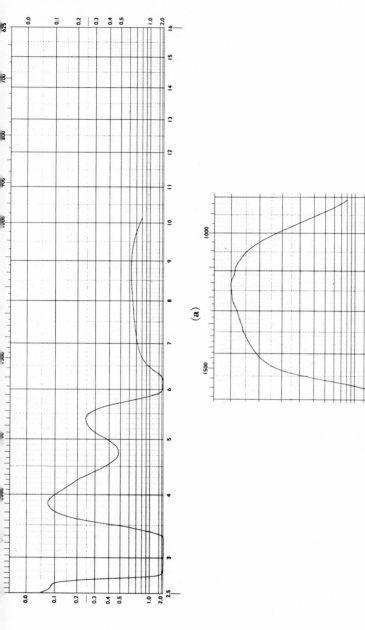

FIGURE 7-7 (a) *Spectrum of water, 0.025-mm cell.* (b) *A portion of the water spectrum with a screen in the reference beam and wide slits employed.*

227

A second BaF$_2$ cell filled with water could be used for compensation. If this is done, automatic gain control (or a much longer scan time) must be employed, for now the reference beam energy will vary widely near 950 and 1550 cm^{-1}.

Little, if any, difficulty is encountered in increasing slit aperture in these applications, for the half-widths of absorption bands in water solution are inherently large because of the highly polar nature of the solvent and resultant severe solvent perturbation of structures being examined. Thus, because the half-width γ is large, a large increase of slit aperture in order to obtain sufficient energy is not serious, for the ratio $\Delta\omega/\gamma$ does not become very large.

The biggest advantage of the ability to obtain spectra of water solutions is, of course, that many systems that are not soluble in other solvents may now be examined in solution in the limited range of 950–1550 cm^{-1}. Some practical analytical applications are the following:

1. Analysis of metal salts of organic acids. Without the water-solution technique, if metal salts of organic acids are to be analyzed quantitatively by infrared spectroscopy, they must first be converted into the acid form, then extracted with organic solvents. These steps are now eliminated, for spectra of the salts can be obtained directly in water solution; Figure 7-8 shows the spectra of the sodium salts of 2-chloropropionic acid and 2,2-dichloropropionic acid in water solution.

2. Direct analysis of the water phase of an organic-water two-layer system. Sometimes a sample which must be analyzed consists of an organic layer and a water layer. The water layer may have in it such water-soluble organic materials as phenol, lower ketones, alcohols, aldehydes, acids, and pyridine. These materials can be determined quantitatively in the water phase directly with an infrared spectrum, without the necessity of successive extraction by an organic solvent and subsequent solvent removal, which otherwise would be necessary before a useful spectrum could be obtained.

3. Biological applications. It seems likely that the examination of biological fluids (such as blood, urine, and albumin) by these techniques of infrared spectroscopy will become a major biological and medical research tool in the near future. Space limitations allow only one brief illustration. Figure 7-9 compares a spectrum of blood serum of a normal human with a spectrum of blood serum taken from a hospital patient suffering from multiple myeloma (tumor of the bone marrow); the spectra show definite differences, which always seem to

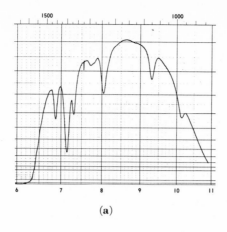

(a)

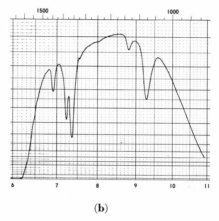

(b)

FIGURE 7-8 (a) *Spectra of 10% water solutions of sodium 2-chloro-propionate and* (b) *sodium 2,2-dichlorochloropropionate, both in a 0.025-mm* BaF₂ *cell. Transmission screen in reference beam, wide slits.*

appear in a comparison of normal blood serum with blood serum from a patient having this disease. Reference 3, the source of this example, gives many other such comparisons and suggests how this technique can be made to serve further.

The use of water solutions to study inorganic ions (such as carbonate, nitrate, and phosphate) does not appear to be satisfactory; many of the absorption bands of these ions, already inherently broad in the solid state (see Chapter 14, Volume II), become much broader in water solution and little information of value results.

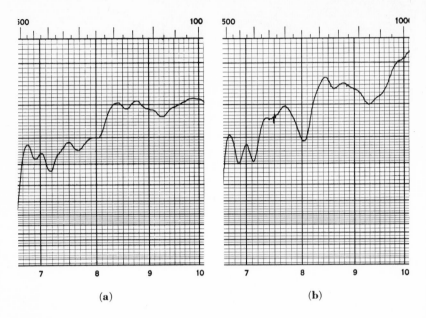

FIGURE 7-9 (a) *Spectrum of normal blood serum.* (b) *Spectrum of blood serum of a patient suffering from multiple myeloma.*

III. Techniques for obtaining spectra of samples of limited size

One of the problems encountered in infrared spectroscopy (or any analytical method, for that matter) is the analysis of a sample of limited size or concentration. The problem of limited concentration is normally·solved by use of longer absorption cells, together with the solvent compensation techniques discussed in Section I. In this section we shall be concerned with problems relating to size limitations of samples which are solved by the application of special optical equipment in the sampling portion of the spectrometer; long-path gas cells and microsampling devices.

A. Long-path gas cells

The problem of low concentration of a component in a vapor-phase mixture is different from the case of solutions: If nearly all of the carrier gas consists of molecules which have no absorption (such as O_2, N_2, monatomic gases, or dry air, which is often the case), the absorption path can be increased manyfold with little or no increase in background absorption. To take full advantage of this situation, the cell optical path must be of the order of several meters in length; hence special optical devices at the sampling point are necessary, for a simple cell whose optical path length is more than about 10 cm will not fit in most spectrometers.

A unique optical arrangement has been devised by which the infrared beam is made to traverse a cell several times, thus simultaneously providing the advantages of compactness, small sample volume, and long path length. The optical arrangement shown in Figure 7-10 is after White. (See Reference 5.) Mirrors A, A', and B are spherical mirrors of identical radius. The midpoint between the centers of mirrors A and A' must lie on the axis of mirror B. The distance between A or A' and B is made to be just the radius of the mirrors. In the arrangement shown each point on the surface of B is an image of the slit, the focus between successive images rendered by A or A'. This optical arrangement also has the property that the number of traversals of the cell can be varied to any multiple of 4 by adjustment of the distance between centers of mirrors A and A':

$$\text{number traversals} = \frac{\text{mirror radius}}{\text{distance between centers of } A \text{ and } A'}. \quad (7\text{-}7)$$

(See Reference 5.)

The advantages of this system are (a) a full aperture, consistent

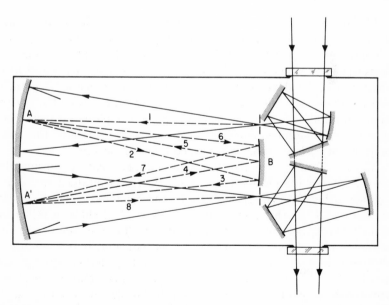

FIGURE 7-10 Schematic optical diagram of a multiple reflection gas cell.

with the aperture of the spectrometer source mirror and collimator can be employed; (b) the path length can be varied by simple adjustment; (c) the focusing adjustments are simple and noncritical; (d) the optical system does not provide cumulative errors nor extraneous images, even if there are minor imperfections in the mirrors.

A cell of this sort has two principal uses. First, it makes it possible to obtain spectra of trace amounts of gases in inert gases (such as small amounts of vapors in air), so that qualitative and semiquantitative analyses may be made of these trace gases. In certain cases identifications and analyses as low as 1 ppm of a vapor in air can be made with a path length of 5 meters, which length can be obtained with this sort of cell without difficulty. Cells having path lengths as large as 40 meters are available commercially.

A second important use of long-path gas cells is that spectra of materials having low vapor pressure may be obtained in the vapor phase. Vapor-phase spectra are often useful in making assignments of vibrational modes. (See Chapter 8.) In this application the entire cell must often be heated to keep the vapor pressure as high as possible and to avoid condensation of the vapor on the mirror surfaces, which can produce peculiar spectra.

B. Microsampling devices

Without special devices and techniques it is difficult to produce infrared spectra of minute amounts of sample; 5–20 mg of material will produce a spectrum satisfactory for use in qualitative analysis, even when spectrometers with large optics are employed; quantitative analysis can be done accurately with 20 mg of material in most cases. These are not normally regarded as large samples, but in many applications nowhere near this much sample is available, and special micromethods must be employed. Fortunately, the great majority of such applications are qualitative in nature.

Many cell designs have the disadvantage that a considerable volume of the sample required to fill them is contained in "dead" volumes other than the space between the windows. The cell shown in Figure 5-8 has this disadvantage. Figure 7-11 shows a cell made in a similar manner but in which essentially all of the liquid contained by the cell is between the windows, hence can contribute to obtaining the spectrum. This cell is filled with a hypodermic syringe and needle whose point has been ground off to a square end; the needle is inserted directly into one of the holes drilled in the salt window and the liquid is discharged. Specially cut Teflon stoppers (see figure) are then

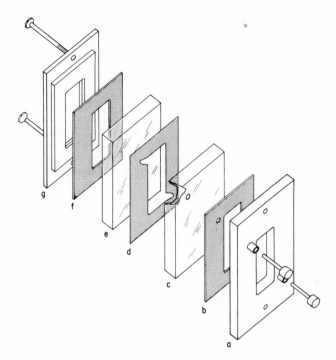

FIGURE 7-11 *An Adaption of the standard cell of Figure 5-8 to semimicro samples. (See p. 113.)*

inserted all the way into the holes drilled in the window; in this manner "dead" space is kept to an absolute minimum.

Because the cell shown in Figure 7-11 was designed for spectrometers of large beam area at the sampling point, its optical area is large ($1\frac{1}{4}$ x 4 cm); a cell of this sort 0.1 mm thick takes ~0.05 ml of liquid to fill it. Obviously this same design can be used to make cells for which the required optical aperture is much smaller and can therefore be made to contain a liquid volume of the order of 0.01 ml (cell 0.1 mm thick, $\frac{1}{2}$ x 2 cm optical area). Cells of this sort still require 1–5 mg of sample (if a 10% solution is used), but they can be employed for accurate quantitative analysis if a microbalance and a microsyringe are available to prepare quantitative solutions.

If samples significantly smaller than ~1 mg are to be identified by infrared spectroscopy, the radiation-beam area must be masked off to a small area (with resulting loss of most of the source energy), or a beam-condensing system that will put a good fraction of the

Samples of limited size   **233**

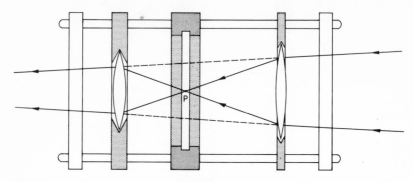

FIGURE 7-12 *A simple beam-condensing system of* KBr *lenses.* P *is a frame in which microcells or other microsample devices may be mounted.*

radiation beam through a small aperture must be employed; the latter approach is clearly best. Probably the simplest commercially available device for its accomplishment consists of two spherical convex KBr or AgCl lenses mounted on a bed so that the whole assembly can be easily positioned into the sampling space of the spectrometer. The optics are sketched in Figure 7-12.* The dashed lines in the figure represent the path of the original beam; in adjusting this microscope, care must be taken to ensure that the light emerging from the second lens will be focused on the monochromator entrance slit and will have the correct solid angle to fill the collimator properly. (See Chapter 3.) Although simple, this lens system has two disadvantages: (*a*) The lenses have chromatic aberration (see Chapter 1); however, if KBr or AgCl lenses are used with a spectrometer having NaCl optics, the frequency region of most serious chromatic aberration is avoided. (*b*) KBr fogs easily in moist air; AgCl becomes darkened in visible light. Mirror-beam-condensing systems do not present these difficulties.

A convenient off-axis elliptical-mirror microscope is commercially available; its optical diagram is shown in Figure 7-13. (See Reference 6.) The ellipse has the property that a large image-reduction ratio may be obtained without spherical aberration; to do this, the light must be at a focus at both foci of each ellipse, hence the requirement

---

* Because the beam from the source mirror is converging, hence comes from a so-called "virtual" object, the focus (where the microsample is placed) will occur *inside* the focal length of the first lens; both object and image of the second lens are real, so that the distance between microsample and second lens is somewhat *greater* than its focal length.

234 *Auxiliary devices and special techniques*

of the plane mirrors before the first ellipse. This system is free
from the major optical aberrations and is rugged, simple, and convenient. An image-reduction ratio of 6:1 is easily obtained.

To achieve significantly higher image-reduction ratios, a compound
mirror system must be employed. One system with high magnifica-
tion is the Schwartzchild microscope whose optical parts are shown in
Figure 7-14. With this device an image-reduction ratio of 8.5 can be
obtained. (See Reference 7.) Because of this high value the system
is often employed between exit slit and detector; were it employed with
light directly from the source, the intense radiation flux produced
at the focus might well overheat the sample seriously. This apparatus
is commercially available.

When using any of these beam-condensing systems, there is inevitably some loss of radiation, so that maximum transmission (with
no chemical sample in place) is likely to be 20 to 60% of the normal
value. This energy loss will be essentially "flat" (independent of
frequency) and can be compensated by the methods described in
Section I-A.

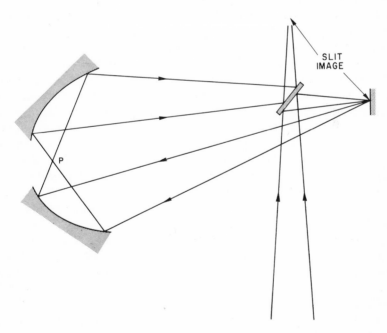

SLIT
IMAGE

P

*FIGURE 7-13.   A 6:1 off-axis ellipsoidal mirror beam condensing system.
Microsample is placed at point* **P.**

Samples of limited size   **235**

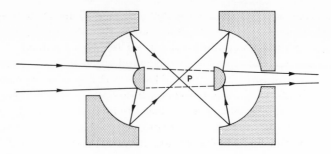

FIGURE 7-14 *The Schwarzchild microscope principle used as a beam condensing system. Microsample is placed at point* **P**.

The great difficulty in obtaining spectra of microsamples does not arise from the optics or cells but comes in the handling and transference of minute samples. This problem is probably best solved by making the proper "gadget" to fit the specific situation and is not discussed further here. We shall confine our discussion to a brief description of certain methods for suspending minute samples in a beam-condensing unit.

If the microsample is a solid, perhaps the most convenient method of handling it is to make a minute pressed disk. This method owes its great convenience to the fact that about 500 times the sample weight of alkali halide is added to the sample and results in a piece of material that can be seen, felt, and handled. The disk is made in much the same manner as a regular size disk but with suitable reduction in the size of the pressing die and the amount of alkali halide and sample used. Pellets as small as ½ mm in diameter, requiring only a microgram of sample, have been successfully made. In these applications it may be best to make the pellet in the shape of a rectangle, which is approximately the shape of the condensed source image. It is reported that the lyophilization technique (see Chapter 5 and Reference 6) is a convenient way to mix the small amounts of KBr and the microsample before pressing.

If the microsample is a nonvolatile liquid (b.p. > 200°C, say), it can be dissolved in a volatile solvent; the solution is then used to wet some previously finely ground KBr powder, the volatile solvent is removed, and a pressed disk is made. This entire operation can be done in the pressing die.

If the microsample is a volatile material (boiling or subliming below ~200°C), its transfer and manipulation into a suitable cell is more difficult. This is unfortunate, for the smaller cuts from vapor-phase chromatography* columns constitute a great need for identification of small samples of this sort. Spectra of volatile samples in the range 0.01–0.1 mg may be obtained in two ways.

One technique is to prepare a 1% solution of the sample in a transparent solvent (only CCl_4, CS_2, $CHCl_3$, CH_2Cl_2, $CHBr_3$, and possibly a few other highly halogenated simple alkanes can serve here) by adding ~100 times its weight of solvent to the sample; the sample is now much more easily manipulated. If the original sample is ~0.1 mg or more, a solution volume of ~10 μl or more is available. The spectrum of this approximately 1% solution must be obtained in a cell of the order of 0.5 mm long (see Chapter 5); hence a volume of 0.01 ml implies that the optical area of the cell should be ~20 mm², or about $2\frac{1}{2}$ x 8 mm. If the original microsample is of the order of ~10 μg or less, the solution volume will be ~1 μl, hence the optical area of a cell 0.5 mm long should be ~2 mm², or about 0.7 x 3 mm. A cell of the type shown in Figure 7-11 might be made in these sizes, but a more convenient cell for microsamples is the so-called "cavity cell." (See Reference 8.) A cavity cell is shown in Figure 7-15 and

* Infrared spectroscopy is compared with and related to several other instrumental methods of analysis in Chapter 15, Volume II.

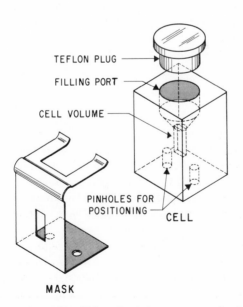

FIGURE 7-15 *A cavity cell for obtaining spectra of microsamples.*

Samples of limited size 237

is made by machining out the appropriate cavity in a small solid block of NaCl. Such machining process does not produce a cell of precision optical path length, but this is not important in qualitative analysis of microsamples. The cell is filled by discharging a microsyringe directly into the actual cell cavity; capillary action holds the liquid in the thin "optical" volume of the cell, thereby minimizing "dead" space. The cell block is masked off so that light falling on its outer surface can only pass through the small cell volume. Cells of this type are commercially available, together with mounting devices for placing them in the beam-condensing systems shown in Figures 7-12 or 7-13. (See Reference 8.)

A second method by which the spectra of small volatile samples can be obtained is in the vapor phase with a multiple-reflection gas cell. This type of cell is built on the same principle as that shown in Figure 7-10, but the optical aperture is scaled down, and the cell is used with an auxiliary beam-condensing system, such as that shown in Figure 7-12. A microgas cell of this type has been described (see Reference 9); if the optics are arranged for 24 passes through the cell body, a path length of 1 meter is obtained. The cell volume is 22 cc, and the over-all transmission of the cell and microscope is ~30% (which can be compensated by the methods described in Section I-A). The cell has provisions for being heated to 250°C so that a less volatile sample will remain in the vapor phase and not condense in some unwanted portion of the cell. With this cell a spectrum suitable for identification should be obtainable with as little as 0.1 mg of sample of materials of high absorptivity.

IV. Attenuated total reflection

An infrared spectrum obtained by reflection of the radiation from the surface of a chemical material (rather than by transmission through it) usually produces a spectrum so poor as to have little value. However, a technique known as *attenuated total reflection*, often abbreviated ATR, has recently been conceived (see Reference 10) whereby reflection spectra of a much more satisfactory quality can be obtained. This technique has some interesting analytical applications.

The intensity of radiation of a given frequency reflected from the surface of a medium with absorption at that frequency is a complex function* of n, the refractive index, θ, the angle of radiation incidence,

---

* The derivation and nature of this function, and its complete implications, are beyond the scope of this treatment. See Reference 10.

and k, the absorption index (the absorption index is related to absorptivity: $a = 4\pi nk/\lambda$). Interpretation of this function shows that when the refractive index of the reflecting material is between 1 and 2 (most organic materials) the intensity of the reflected radiation is low and, worse, quite insensitive to the absorption index unless k is of the order of 0.2; an absorption index of this magnitude results only for the strongest infrared absorption bands. For these reasons an infrared spectrum obtained by direct reflection from the surface of an organic material is essentially useless.

However, if $n \leqslant \sin \theta$, the reflection is *total* when $k = 0$ (i.e., a region of no absorption). Furthermore, the reflection is attenuated when $k \neq 0$, and the degree of attenuation is sensitive to the magnitude of k. Now, n is properly the *ratio* of the refractive index of the reflecting surface to the refractive index of its contiguous phase; if the latter is a vacuum (or air), whose refractive index is unity, then $n > 1$. But, if the phase adjacent to the reflecting surface is a medium of high refractive index, then n will be less than 1, $\sin \theta$ can be made greater than n, and under these conditions it will be possible to produce total reflection, attenuated as a function of k; that is, a useful reflection spectrum can be produced.

Two substances transparent to infrared radiation and having high refractive indices are silver chloride and KRS-5; the refractive index of both substances is $\geqslant 2$ throughout the infrared range. Therefore, if one of these materials is placed over the reflecting surface, the condition that $n < \sin \theta$ can be met. It is desirable to make the optical arrangement such that θ, the angle of radiation incidence, can be varied. This is conveniently done by making the silver chloride or KRS-5 covering the surface in the form of a hemicylinder or a prism, as shown in Figure 7-16. The light must impinge perpendicularly on the silver chloride or KRS-5 surface so that it will not be refracted at its interface with air, thereby leading to loss of definition of angle θ. Commercial devices are available (e.g., see Reference 11) which allow the sample and reflecting hemicylinder or prism to be conveniently mounted and, with the aid of several auxiliary mirrors, makes it possible to vary θ over a useful range.

The reflection intensity is a function of the angle of incidence θ. Also, it is independent of the thickness of the reflecting material. As a result of these properties, certain interesting potential applications are possible.

1. Both the refractive index, n, and the absorption index, k, can be determined for a given wavelength by making two measurements

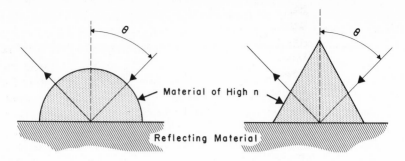

FIGURE 7-16 *Methods of obtaining spectra by attenuated total reflection.*

at widely different θ. Although this may be of little practical importance to analytical and organic chemists, it is useful information for theoretical studies of optical properties of liquids, especially infrared intensities.

2. Useful spectra can be derived from materials which, for some reason, cannot be prepared in sections thin enough to allow their transmission spectra to be obtained. This may prove to be useful in certain difficult sampling problems (e.g., crosslinked polymers and resins or organic coatings on paper, leather, or metal from which they cannot be easily removed). Another possible application is the direct examination of bulk liquids undergoing chemical reaction or in chemical process streams.

3. Variation of θ allows the "attenuation bands" in an attenuated total reflection spectrum to be adjusted to convenient intensity (just as absorption bands in a transmission spectrum can be adjusted to convenient intensity by variation of cell length or concentration). This facility makes it possible in principle to use ATR spectra for quantitative as well as qualitative analysis, provided that reflection intensity is a suitable function of concentration of a component in the reflecting medium. (See Reference 10.) This is presumably so, but has not yet been proven; that is, the existence of a law analogous to Beer's law has not been investigated.

Attenuated total reflection spectra have certain disadvantages.

1. Although simple devices have been designed and are commercially available (see Reference 11) to make obtaining ATR spectra relatively simple, the setup of this equipment takes more time than preparation of a material for the conventional transmission spectra

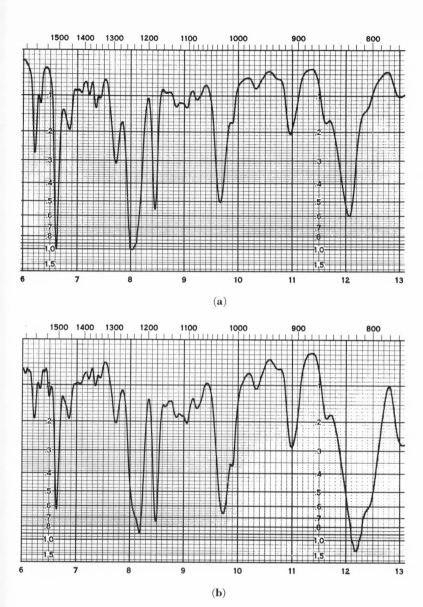

FIGURE 7-17 *A portion of the spectrum of an uncured liquid epoxy resin, obtained by (a) transmission through a capillary film and (b) by attenuated total reflection.*

(solutions, capillary films, mulls, etc.). This might not be so if the auxiliary ATR equipment were left permanently mounted in a spectrometer reserved only for this purpose, for once the optical adjustments are made, introduction of the sample itself is quite simple.

2. The spectra produced by the ATR technique, although similar to conventional spectra, are not completely identical to them. Figure 7-17 compares an ATR spectrum of an uncured liquid epoxy resin with the spectrum obtained by transmission through a capillary film. The difference between transmission and ATR spectra for solids is usually even more pronounced; in fact, unless the contact between the solid reflecting surface and the medium of high refractive index is extremely intimate, the spectrum produced can be so distorted as to be nearly useless. Whether the development of more sophisticated sampling techniques will help in this respect is hard to predict.

V. Spectra of molecules adsorbed on surfaces

An interesting special application of infrared spectroscopy has been its use in the study of the state of molecules which are chemi-sorbed on catalytic surfaces. Presumably, a particular surface catalyzes a chemical reaction because the molecule adsorbed on the surface has somehow been strained or altered by this adsorption process and is in a reactive state. If the infrared spectrum of the molecule can be obtained while it is in the adsorbed state, much can be learned about the nature of the reaction so catalyzed.

Briefly, the technique by which infrared spectra of adsorbed molecules are obtained consists of preparing a thin layer of the catalyst bed supported on a surface that is transparent to infrared radiation, allowing the molecule of interest to be adsorbed on the catalyst surface to a depth of one monolayer, and passing infrared radiation from an infrared source through the bed and into a spectrometer. The experimental techniques, however, are somewhat difficult.

The surface area must be large if there is to be sufficient material adsorbed only one monolayer deep to produce an absorption spectrum. On the other hand, the greater the surface, the larger the number of particles supporting the catalyst, with the result that there will be more Rayleigh scattering and decreased light transmission. It has been reported (see Reference 12) that a good compromise between the catalyst surface area and infrared transmission is obtained if the catalyst bed is made in the following general manner:

A homogeneous slurry of fine silica particles ($\sim$0.02 μ average diameter, produced from a silica "smoke" and commercially available as "Cab-o-sil") is made in a suitable aqueous solution of the catalyst metal [e.g., $Pd(NO_3)_2$]. Silica is chosen as a support because it is available in finely divided form and will produce a catalyst bed of large area; in thin layers it is transparent to ~ 2000 cm^{-1}. The slurry is dried, and the powder is carefully pressed into a thin layer on a CaF$_2$ plate. The catalyst layer on the plate is then heated in vacuum to 200–350°C and reduced with hydrogen gas at this temperature. The resulting metal particles supported on the silica should be no larger than ~ 0.03 μ in diameter, and the metal should constitute about 7–10% by weight of the catalyst bed. After reduction, the catalyst bed is degassed at elevated temperature, cooled to the temperature at which the adsorption study is to be made, and the gas molecules admitted until the appropriate amount has been adsorbed on the catalyst. The spectrum of the adsorbed molecules is then obtained.

The actual optical arrangement needs careful consideration. First, and most important, is the requirement that the CaF$_2$ plate on which the finely powdered catalyst bed rests be horizontal, which requires that the infrared beam be vertical; hence the source optics must be modified considerably. Second, it is convenient to heat the catalyst bed, evacuate it, reduce it with hydrogen, and expose it to the gas to be adsorbed *in situ* in the spectrometer. Finally, the catalyst bed will transmit only a few per cent of the infrared radiation incident on it, for which allowance must be made if a useful spectrum is to be produced.

These difficulties are met by the apparatus shown in Figure 7-18, which is after Eischens and Pliskin (Reference 12). An auxiliary source, a, is focused onto the monochromator entrance slit, d, by the spherical mirror, b, the radiation being passed through the vertical apparatus by plane mirrors, c, c'. The CaF$_2$ windows, e, e', are cemented to the apparatus; the CaF$_2$ window, f, supports the catalyst layer, g. An electrical furnace, i, can heat the catalyst layer to the softening point of the Pyrex (or quartz) apparatus; thermocouple, h, placed in a hole in the window, f, records the temperature. The catalyst layer, after being prepared as described, is placed in the apparatus; here it can be heated, evacuated, reduced with hydrogen at high temperature, degassed, and exposed to various gases, all *in situ;* a spectrum can be obtained at any time during these operations.

A single-beam spectrometer is employed for obtaining the spectra because of the rather extensive modification necessary in the source optics. The low transmission of the apparatus and sample can be expanded to a useful range of the recorder chart by increase of gain, with resultant increase of noise or of slit aperture, with some loss of

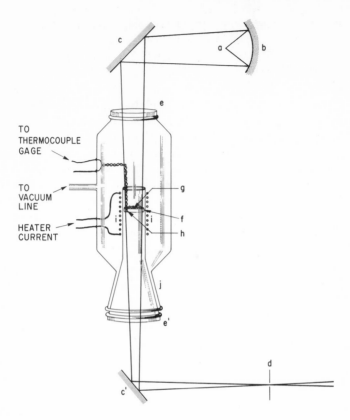

FIGURE 7-18 *Apparatus for obtaining spectra of molecules adsorbed on catalyst surfaces. (After Eischens and Pliskin, Reference 12.)*

resolution. (See Chapter 4.) With this technique spectra may be obtained to a frequency of $\sim$2000 cm^{-1}, beyond which point silica transmits little infrared radiation. Reference 12 describes other methods of catalyst support that allow some extension of these techniques to lower frequencies.

It is reported that spectra of ethylene adsorbed on nickel, for example, show that under certain conditions the C—H stretch vibrations occur at $\sim$3000 cm^{-1}, hence are characteristic of olefinic hydrogen; under certain other conditions the C—H stretch vibrations occur at $\sim$2900 cm^{-1}, typical of alkane hydrocarbons, and therefore show that the two unsaturation valences of the ethylene carbon-carbon double bond are now satisfied by sites on the catalyst surface. (See Reference 12 and Chapter 10, Volume II.)

VI. The construction and use of an infrared polarizer

From the discussion in Chapter 2 of how a particular vibration absorbs radiation, it follows that one of the requirements of radiation absorption is that the vector direction of dipole change for the vibration must be in the same direction as the electric-field component of the quantum of radiation. In most applications of infrared absorption spectroscopy the molecules being studied are randomly oriented, and the electric-field direction of the radiation quanta are also randomly oriented, so that no effects that might result from this factor need be considered.

In certain cases, however, there may be some orientation of the molecules in the material whose spectrum is being obtained. When this is so, and the electric vector of the infrared radiation is also oriented in a known way by a polarizing device, valuable information can be gained about the nature of the vibrations or the orientation of certain groups in the sample. These methods are applicable to solids only when the sample consists of a single crystal or to noncrystalline solids having some degree of orientation (as polymer films and fibers or protein and cellulose fibers).

Studies of this sort are usually done by mounting the sample so that its orientation axes have one specific geometric arrangement with respect to the plane of polarization of the radiation while the spectrum is being obtained; the orientation is then changed by 90° and a second spectrum is obtained. The spectra are then compared. If a certain absorption band is observed to be more intense when obtained at orientation 1, for example, this is strong evidence that in that orientation the majority of the groups giving rise to this absorption band are arranged so that the vector of dipole moment change associated with this vibration makes a smaller angle with (i.e., is more nearly parallel to) the (known) direction of the radiation electric vector than it will when in orientation 2. Similarly, an increase of intensity of some other absorption band in orientation 2 strongly suggests that the vector of dipole moment change associated with the vibration of this other group is approximately perpendicular to the first vector. No change in intensity between orientations 1 and 2 indicates a random distribution for this particular group. In order to make use of these observations, some knowledge of the direction of dipole change associated with the vibration of each pertinent group must be available; this will be better understood after study of the material in later chapters.

A simple efficient polarizer for infrared radiation is based on the

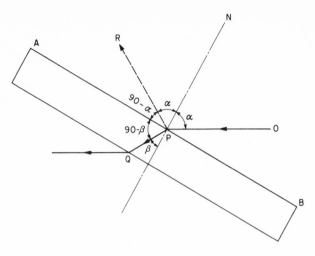

FIGURE 7-19 *Illustration of polarization at the Brewster angle.*

fact that a light ray having its electric vector exactly colinear with direction of propagation has zero intensity; or, to use other words, a light ray, by reflection from a surface, cannot be brought into a direction that is colinear with its electric vector. This situation is illustrated by Figure 7-19. Here **OP** is a light ray striking the surface, AB, of a transparent material of refractive index n and being refracted along **PQ**; PN is the normal to the surface; **PR** is the direction of the reflected ray. Now, for a given refractive index there will exist some value of angle α such that **PR** will be perpendicular to **PQ**; in this situation a ray whose electric vector is *horizontal* (i.e., light that is polarized in the plane of the paper) cannot be reflected along PR, for at point P the electric vector will be perpendicular to **PQ**, hence colinear with **PR**. However, a ray whose electric vector is *vertical* lacks this relation and is reflected along **PR** in the usual manner. If a series of plates of material of convenient refractive index is arranged in the infrared beam at the proper angle, the *horizontal* component will pass through essentially unaffected, whereas the *vertical* component will have been successively diminished to a small value by reflection loss, resulting in horizontally polarized light of good purity.

The correct orientation for the plates is easily derived by reference to Figure 7-19. The condition for no reflection of the horizontally polarized ray is

$$(90° - \beta) + (90° - \alpha) = 90° = \alpha + \beta.$$

Hence $\sin \beta = \cos \alpha$ But, by Snell's law

$$n = \frac{\sin \alpha}{\sin \beta}$$

so that

$$n = \frac{\sin \alpha}{\cos \alpha} = \tan \alpha$$

or

$$\alpha = \text{arc} \tan n. \tag{7-8}$$

This angle, known as the Brewster angle, is 63.5° for silver chloride, which is a convenient material for constructing this type of polarizer for use in the infrared region.

A simple polarizer is illustrated in Figure 7-20. Usually five silver chloride plates are enough to give polarized light of fairly good purity. The sample under study is mounted so that it can be rotated with

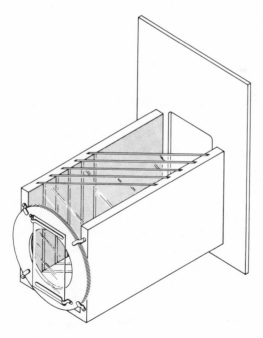

FIGURE 7-20   *A simple polarizer using the Brewster principle.*

The construction and use of an infrared polarizer   247

respect to the polarizer, as shown in the figure. It is not advisable to keep the sample fixed and rotate the polarizer because there are polarization effects in the monochromator of the spectrometer.*

Probably the most extensive application of the use of polarized infrared radiation has been in the study of the orientation of groups in polymers, which has produced a great deal of useful information about polymer structure. Reference 13 discusses some interesting examples, which space and scope limitations will not allow here.

VII. Special cells for obtaining spectra at low and high temperatures

Occasionally it is desirable to obtain spectra at temperatures above or below room temperature; for this purpose, as a rule, special cells must be constructed. The different ways in which they may be built is limited only by the particular application and the imagination of the spectroscopist. We have described only one cell construction for each application, but obviously many variations are possible; several are described in the literature.

A. Precise measurement of solution temperature

If the temperature of the liquid solution in a sealed infrared cell is to be varied only a few degrees above or below room temperature, it can probably best be accomplished by blowing warm or cool air, appropriately thermostated, over the cell. The difficulty here is that the exact temperature of the liquid in the cell is hard to estimate without direct measurement, for it takes a surprisingly long time for a thin liquid film between NaCl or KBr plates to come to thermal equilibrium. Temperature measured near the salt windows, or even in one of the windows, will not necessarily be that of the solution or liquid inside the cell. Standard thermocouples will not fit into a 0.1-mm space between salt plates.

A short length of thin (0.001-in. diameter) nickel wire run through the cell—in one hole in the salt window and out the other—makes an acceptable resistance thermometer. Wire this thin does not impede liquid flow through the cell and blocks only a trivial amount of light radiation. The resistance thermometer is made to be one arm of a Wheatstone bridge circuit; after calibration, temperatures inside the cell accurate to $\pm 0.2°C$ are easily measured.

* Polarization effects in prism monochromators are small and may be ignored; polarization effects in grating monochromators may be serious and should not be ignored.

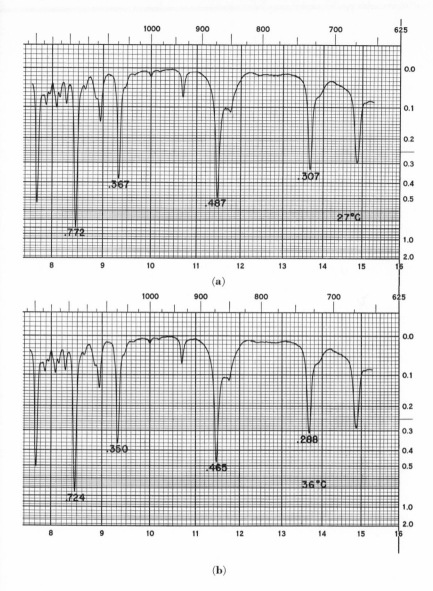

FIGURE 7-21 *Spectrum of a 3% solution of 2,4,5-trichlorophenol in* CS_2; *(a) at 27°C and (b) 36°C.*

A device of this sort is useful in the study of absorption bands in solution as a function of temperature. Both absorption peak height and integrated intensity appear to be sensitive functions of the temperature—much more sensitive than can be accounted for by simple cubical thermal expansion of liquids. An example is shown in Figure 7-21; it can be seen that the absorbances of certain absorption bands have decreased by ∼6%, whereas thermal expansion of the CS_2 solvent over this temperature range would have accounted for only ∼1% of this difference. This should serve as a warning: careful attention must be given to thermostating solutions when quantitative analysis is being done. No really satisfactory explanation of this phenomenon has been advanced. It is a subject that deserves more study.

B. Absorption spectra at low temperatures

Occasionally it is desirable to obtain spectra at temperatures much below room temperature—at solid CO_2 or at liquid-nitrogen temperature, for example. For this a special cell must be constructed, for any salt windows in the apparatus that are exposed to the surrounding atmosphere must be at or near room temperature or moisture from the room will rapidly condense on them and will result in loss of transmission and damage to the plates. This problem can perhaps best be met by placing the cell (or film holder or other sampling device) in an evacuated chamber having salt windows and cooling it from above. Figure 7-22 illustrates a simple form of this device. A simple block for mounting a salt plate is shown, but it can easily be replaced by an absorption cell or other device, provided sufficient thermal contact is made between all of its parts and the cooling reservoir. A gas inlet tube (not shown in the figure) may be placed in the outer wall of the apparatus to allow a gas or gas mixture to be blown at a previously chilled salt plate and condensed in place.

One of the most useful applications of low temperature is to determine whether two closely neighboring absorption bands result from two different vibration modes or whether they result from the same vibration mode in two different rotational isomers of the molecule. If the two (or more) rotational isomers are not identical, presumably one will have slightly greater potential energy than the other; the energy of thermal motion at room temperature will cause both forms to exist. Now, if a molecule showing two absorptions in frequency proximity to each other (as a result of two rotational isomers) is placed in surroundings of low temperature, the low-energy rotation isomer will be favored and the relative intensities of the two absorptions will change rather markedly, the one resulting from the higher energy rotation isomer being reduced in intensity. However, if no fairly marked intensity change is observed, some other explanation for two absorption peaks must be sought. The influence of rotational isomerism on absorption bands is discussed in some detail in the later chapters dealing with vibrations of specific chemical groups.

Any application of low temperatures that depends on quantitative measurements of peak intensities should be carefully considered, for there are serious sources of inaccuracy. As we have already illustrated, the peak intensity of an absorption band may be a sensitive function of temperature; furthermore, it cannot be expected that all absorption bands in the molecule will change at the same rate with temperature. Therefore comparison of absorption-band strengths

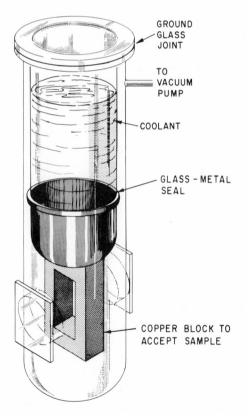

GROUND
GLASS
JOINT

TO
VACUUM
PUMP

COOLANT

GLASS – METAL
SEAL

COPPER BLOCK TO
ACCEPT SAMPLE

FIGURE 7-22 Apparatus for obtaining infrared absorption spectra at low temperature.

Spectra at low and high temperatures 251

among the same or different molecules as the temperature changes over a wide range can have at best only a qualitative significance.

An instrumental source of inaccuracy results from the definition of 0% transmission if an optical-null double-beam spectrometer is used. Suppose the adjustment between attenuator position and pen position is made so that at a frequency at which a material in the sample beam is totally absorbing the chart records zero transmission at room temperature (this, of course, is how the adjustment should be made for normal operating procedure). If the sample were cooled to low temperature, it presumably would still be totally absorbing, but the pen would seek a position *lower* on the chart than the zero defined until it eventually ran into the mechanical stop! Also, low values of transmission, as recorded by the spectrometer, probably would be in error. The reason for this peculiar result is that the optical-null double-beam spectrometer compares a cold material in the sample beam with the reference-beam attenuator which is near room temperature. At a frequency of total absorption by the sample, both it and the reference-beam attenuator may be regarded as black-bodies; but the reference-beam attenuator, being at higher temperature, radiates more energy to the detector than the cold sample. This causes a signal that drives the pen lower on the chart than the transmission level desired, I/I_0. This effect becomes increasingly serious at lower frequencies, for as the frequency decreases blackbody radiation from an object at room temperature becomes an increasingly larger fraction of the radiation, say, from a source at 1500°K. (See Figure 1-2.) The result is that as the frequency decreases 0% transmission becomes more and more poorly defined for a sample at low temperature. This difficulty could be overcome by thermostating the reference-beam attenuator to the same low temperature; however, the technique would probably prove to be experimentally difficult.

C. Absorption spectra at elevated temperatures

Sometimes it is desirable to obtain spectra at elevated temperatures. It has already been noted that when it is necessary to obtain a vapor spectrum of a material of low volatility the long path cells employed are often heated to increase the vapor pressure of the molecules under study. This particular application presents little difficulty, for gas cells at low pressure are easily heated.

On the other hand, the production of spectra of materials in solution at elevated temperature is a more difficult problem. Nearly all solvents having useful infrared transmission are volatile, hence cannot be heated much above their (usually low) atmospheric boiling point without keeping them at elevated pressure; we shall regard the use of pressure equipment as beyond the scope of "simple" extensions of sampling technique. One class of relatively nonvolatile solvents, which have reasonably good infrared transmission, is the higher molecular weight alkane hydrocarbons. If heavier alkane hydrocarbons are used as a solvent, it is not difficult to heat a sealed cell to 200°C by using apparatus similar to that subsequently described.

An interesting application of infrared spectra obtained at elevated temperature in the field of organic chemistry is the study of and evidence for phase transitions between various crystalline forms which occur with temperature change. In this application the samples are usually in the form of mulls, pressed disks, or solid films, hence are easily heated in place in the spectrometer with the simple device shown in Figure 7-23. The upper part of the figure shows a frame similar to that used in mounting films (see Figure 5-17), except that it is arranged so that the screws holding the metal plates together are spring loaded, which allows considerable pressure to be used in clamping NaCl or KBr plates without fracturing them; also, there are long transite standoffs between the pieces supporting the sample and the plate that fits the spectrometer mount to provide some measure of insulation between the hot sample and the spectrometer. A simple metal adapter is easily made to mount pressed disks between the plates. The heater covering is a rectangular copper box, open at the ends, which is wrapped with insulation, resistance wire (to supply heat), more insulation, and finally a layer of aluminum foil to serve as a radiation reflector. This box is made to a size that just slips over the metal plates between which the sample is mounted. With this simple device samples are easily heated to ~200°C. Its use is illustrated with two applications.

Figure 7-24 shows the spectrum of pentachlorophenol at room temperature and at 55°C, at which temperature the material undergoes a change of crystalline form. It can be seen that the spectra show definite differences.

Figure 7-25 shows the spectra of high-density linear polyethylene at room temperature and in the molten form at 135°C. At room temperature linear polyethylene is a mixture of crystalline and amorphous forms; when molten it is amorphous. Note especially the differences at 1900, 1305, and 730 cm^{-1}: (a) The weak 1900-cm^{-1} absorption band allows a simple determination of the crystallinity of polyethylene if a polymer of known crystallinity is available as a standard. (b) The absorption at 1305 cm^{-1} results only from the amorphous form of polyethylene; hence the ratio of its absorbance

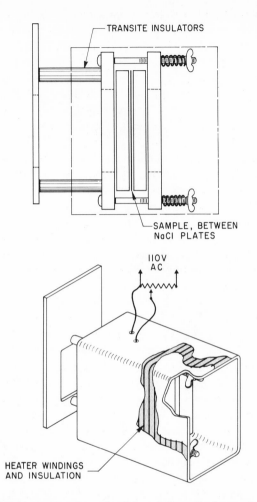

TRANSITE INSULATORS

SAMPLE, BETWEEN
NaCl PLATES

110V
AC

HEATER WINDINGS
AND INSULATION

FIGURE 7-23 *Apparatus for obtaining infrared absorption spectra at elevated temperatures.*

(base-line technique) at room temperature to the absorbance when molten (100% amorphous) gives the per cent of amorphous content at room temperature and therefore the crystallinity by difference. (c) The band at 720–730 cm^{-1} is broad when the material is amorphous, but it is a sharp doublet with peaks at 720 and 730 cm^{-1} when crystalline and thus provides an excellent qualitative determination of crystallinity.

254   Auxiliary devices and special techniques

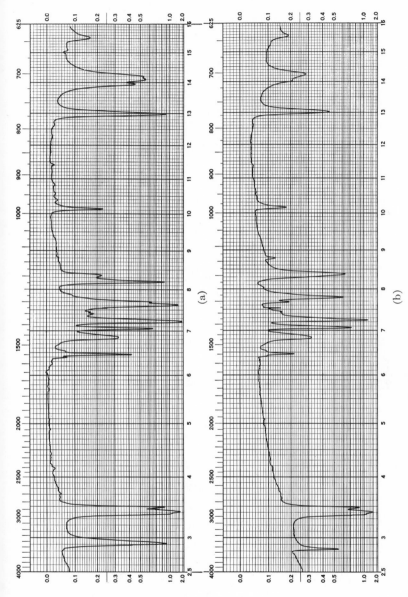

FIGURE 7-24 (a) *A Nujol mull spectrum of pentachlorophenol at room temperature;* (b) *a spectrum of the same preparation at 55°C.*

255

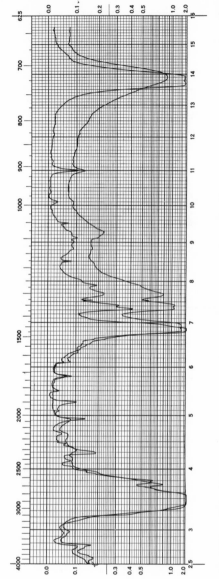

FIGURE 7-25   The spectrum of a film of polyethylene at room temperature and at its crystalline melting point (~135°C).

256

Any polymer, of course, is completely amorphous when molten; a comparison of spectra of a polymer at room temperature and at its melting point quickly provides information about how its crystallinity might be determined by infrared methods.

Selected references

1. Robinson, D. Z., "Quantitative Analysis with Infrared Spectrometers," *Anal. Chem.* **23,** 619 (1952).
2. Herscher, L., H. Ruhl, and N. Wright, "An Improved Optical Null Spectrometer," *J. Opt. Soc. Am.* **48,** 36 (1958).
   K. V. Matthews, H. J. Sloane, and R. E. Sundstrom, "New Concepts for the Improvement of Tracking Accuracy in Double Beam Optical Null Spectrophotometers," presented at the Pittsburgh Symposium on Analytical Chemistry and Applied Spectroscopy, February 1961. (Reprints are available from Beckman Instruments, Inc., Fullerton, Calif.)
3. Stewart, R. D., D. S. Erley, N. E. Skelly, and N. Wright, "Infrared Analysis of Blood Serum, Red Blood Cells, and Other Body Fluids," *J. Lab. Clin. Med.* **54,** 644 (1959).
4. Goulden, J. D. S., "Infrared Spectroscopy of Aqueous Solutions," *Spectrochim. Acta* **14,** 657 (1959).
5. White, J. V., "Long Optical Paths of Large Aperture," *J. Opt. Soc. Am.* **32,** 285 (1942).
6. Mason, W. B., "Infrared Microsampling in Bio-Medical Investigations," presented at the Pittsburgh Conference on Analytical Chemistry and Applied Spectroscopy, March 1958. (Reprints are available from the Perkin-Elmer Corp., Norwalk, Conn.)
7. Coates, V. S., A. Offner, and E. H. Siegler, Jr., "Design and Performance of an Infrared Microscope Attachment," *J. Opt. Soc. Am.* **43,** 984 (1953).
8. "Instruction Manual for Infrared Sampling Accessories," Connecticut Instrument Corp., Wilton, Conn.
9. White, J. U., N. L. Alpert, W. M. Ward, and W. S. Galloway, "Microgas Cell for Infrared Spectroscopy," *Anal. Chem.* **31,** 1267 (1959).
10. Fahrenfort, J., "Attenuated Total Reflection. A New Principle for the Production of Useful Infrared Reflection Spectra of Organic Compounds," *Spectrochim. Acta* **17,** 698 (1961).
11. Wilks, P. A., Jr., "Attenuated Total Reflection—A New Infrared Sampling Technique," CIC Newsletter No. 14, September 1961 (Connecticut Instrument Corp. Wilton, Conn.).
12. Eischens, R. P., and W. A. Pliskin, "The Infrared Spectra of Adsorbed Molecules," *Advan. Catalysis* **10,** 1 (1958).
13. Krimm, S., "Infrared Spectra of High Polymers," *Advan. Polymer Sci.* **2,** 51 (1960).

8

An outline of the theory
of infrared spetcra
of polyatomic molecules

In Chapter 2 we discussed briefly some of the elements of the theory of molecular vibration and interaction with infrared radiation, particularly as they are applicable to diatomic molecules. In this chapter we discuss the theory of polyatomic molecular vibrations and spectra. These subjects are complex, and their rigorous presentation requires far more mathematical detail than we can possibly invoke here; readers desiring a properly complete exposition of this material are referred to other sources. The purpose of this chapter is to present a qualitative description of this theory so that the reader may become familiar with its results and thereby learn to use the concepts of "group frequencies" with a bit more sophistication; the concept of "normal vibration modes" will prove especially helpful in this respect.

I. Theory of polyatomic molecular vibrations

As shown in Chapter 2, nonlinear polyatomic molecules have $3N - 6$ possible independent vibration modes. The relation between these vibration frequencies, the various force constants, and atomic masses and geometry is much more complex than the simple relation of equation 2-13 which pertains to diatomic molecules. In this section we describe what these relations are and some of the useful results that may be obtained from them.

A. The secular equation

Displacement from its equilibrium position of any atom in a polyatomic molecule produces a force tending to return the atom to its equilibrium position. These forces result from the nature of the chemical bonds in the molecule and from possible attractions or repulsions between nonbonded atoms. It is usually assumed that the potential energy of the system may be closely approximated by considering it to be composed only of quadratic terms of the form $f(\varphi)_{m,m'}\varphi_m\varphi_{m'}$, where $f(\varphi)_{m,m'}$ is the second partial derivative of the potential energy of the system with respect to coordinates φ_m and $\varphi_{m'}$, or

$$f(\varphi)_{m,m'} = \frac{\partial^2 V}{\partial\varphi_m\,\partial\varphi_{m'}}. \tag{8-1}$$

The statement that the potential energy can be developed from quadratic terms only implies that the vibrational motion will be harmonic. Although this is not strictly true for molecular vibrations, it is a sufficiently close approximation for most purposes. These second derivatives of potential energy are known as the *force constants*, and, to have complete generality (within the limitation of quadratic terms only), we must include the terms in which $m \neq m'$ as well as those in which $m = m'$.

The potential energy may be defined in any set of coordinates we choose, provided that these coordinates are *complete* in the sense that they must be able to describe any changes in the interatomic distances in the molecule that result from altering the positions of the atoms. Obviously, the $3N$ Cartesian coordinates of the *displacements* of the N atoms from their equilibrium positions will meet this requirement, and because the kinetic energy is conveniently described in Cartesian displacements we begin by developing the potential energy in terms of them. From the well-known principles of mechanics,* potential energy expressed in Cartesian coordinates is

$$2V = \sum_{k}^{3N} \sum_{k'}^{3N} f(x)_{k,k'}(\Delta x_k)(\Delta x_{k'}), \tag{8-2}$$

where Δx_k and $\Delta x_{k'}$ each represent one of the $3N$ Cartesian displacements of the N atoms from their equilibrium positions, and the symbol

* See Reference 1, page 268 ff.

$f(x)_{k,k'}$ has been used to denote the fact that the force constants are second partial derivatives of potential energy with respect to Cartesian displacements:

$$f(x)_{k,k'} = \frac{\partial^2 V}{\partial x_k\, \partial x_{k'}}.$$

In discussing the exact nature of the force constants it is perhaps helpful to use more explicit notation than equation 8-2:

$$
\begin{aligned}
2V = {} & f_{x_1 x_1}(\Delta x_1)^2 + f_{x_1 y_1}(\Delta x_1)(\Delta y_1) + f_{x_1 z_1}(\Delta x_1)(\Delta z_1) + \cdots \\
& \hspace{4cm} + f_{x_1 z_N}(\Delta x_1)(\Delta z_N) \\
& + f_{y_1 x_1}(\Delta y_1)(\Delta x_1) + f_{y_1 y_1}(\Delta y_1)^2 + f_{y_1 z_1}(\Delta y_1)(\Delta z_1) + \cdots \\
& \hspace{4cm} + f_{y_1 z_N}(\Delta y_1)(\Delta z_N) \\
& + f_{z_1 x_1}(\Delta z_1)(\Delta x_1) + f_{z_1 y_1}(\Delta z_1)(\Delta y_1) + f_{z_1 z_1}(\Delta z_1)^2 + \cdots \\
& \hspace{4cm} + f_{z_1 z_N}(\Delta z_1)(\Delta z_N) \\
& \quad\vdots \\
& + f_{z_N x_1}(\Delta z_N)(\Delta x_1) + f_{z_N y_1}(\Delta z_N)(\Delta y_1) + f_{z_N z_1}(\Delta z_N)(\Delta z_1) \\
& \hspace{3cm} + \cdots + f_{z_N z_N}(\Delta z_N)^2 \\
= {} & \sum_{k}^{3N} \sum_{k'}^{3N} f(x)_{k,k'}(\Delta x_k)(\Delta x_{k'}).
\end{aligned}
\tag{8-3}
$$

The potential energy is seen to consist of $(3N)^2$ separate contributions. Because terms such as $f_{x_1 y_2}(\Delta x_1)(\Delta y_2)$ and $f_{y_2 x_1}(\Delta y_2)(\Delta x_1)$ are equal their sum is $2f_{x_1 y_2}(\Delta x_1)(\Delta y_2)$, hence equation 8-3 has $3N + (3N - 1) + (3N - 2) + \cdots + 1 = \frac{1}{2}(3N)(3N + 1)$ different terms or different $f(x)_{k,k'}$. However, it will be convenient to visualize equation 8-3 as a square array of $3N \times 3N$ terms; the $3N \times 3N$ square array of the numbers $f(x)_{k,k'}$ is called the F matrix (in Cartesian coordinates).

The kinetic energy of the system of N atoms in terms of Cartesian displacements is simply expressed:

$$2T = \sum_{l}^{N} m_l[(\Delta \dot{x}_l)^2 + (\Delta \dot{y}_l)^2 + (\Delta \dot{z}_l)^2], \tag{8-4}$$

where m_l is the mass of atom l, $\Delta \dot{x}_l$ is the time derivative, or velocity, of atom l along Cartesian displacement coordinate Δx_l. It is also convenient to show this relation in an expanded notation:

$$2T = \begin{array}{ccccccc} m_1(\Delta\dot{x}_1)^2 + & 0 & + & 0 & + \cdots + & 0 \\ + \quad 0 & + m_1(\Delta\dot{y}_1)^2 + & & 0 & + \cdots + & 0 \\ + \quad 0 & + \quad 0 & + & m_1(\Delta\dot{z}_1)^2 & + \cdots + & 0 \end{array}$$

$$+ \quad 0 \quad + \quad 0 \quad + \quad 0 \quad + \cdots + m_N(\Delta\dot{z}_N)^2.$$

$$(8\text{-}5)$$

This $3N \times 3N$ square array of m_l (along with the zeros) is called the kinetic-energy matrix in Cartesian coordinates.

Now, any system of particles in motion must obey Lagrange's equations;* expressed in Cartesian coordinates these are

$$\frac{\partial V}{\partial x_k} + \frac{d}{dt}\left(\frac{\partial T}{\partial \dot{x}_k}\right) = 0. \tag{8-6}$$

When values of V and T from equations 8-3 and 8-5 are substituted into equation 8-6, and the appropriate differentiations are made, $3N$ equations result:

for $x_k = \Delta x_1$:
$$[f_{x_1 x_1}(\Delta x_1) + m_1(\Delta\ddot{x}_1)] + \quad f_{x_1 y_1}(\Delta y_1) \quad + \cdots + $$
$$f_{x_1 z_N}(\Delta z_N) \quad = 0$$

for $x_k = \Delta y_1$:
$$f_{y_1 x_1}(\Delta x_1) \quad + [f_{y_1 y_1}(\Delta y_1) + m_1(\Delta\ddot{y}_1)] + \cdots + $$
$$f_{y_1 z_N}(\Delta z_N) \quad = 0$$

for $x_k = \Delta z_N$:
$$f_{z_N x_1}(\Delta x_1) \quad + \quad f_{z_N y_1}(\Delta y_1) \quad + \cdots + $$
$$[f_{z_N z_N}(\Delta z_N) + m_N(\Delta\ddot{z}_N)] = 0. \quad (8\text{-}7)$$

Harmonic motion of any given atom along a Cartesian axis has the property that

$$(\Delta\ddot{x}_k) = -\lambda(\Delta x_k), \tag{8-8}$$

where

$$\lambda = 4\pi^2 c^2 \omega^2, \tag{8-9}$$

* See Reference 1, page 268 ff.

Theory of polyatomic molecular vibrations   **261**

and is called the *frequency parameter*. (Compare with equations 2-2 through 2-5.) Hence the condition that all atoms move in phase with the same frequency during a polyatomic molecular vibration is that the equations

$$\left(\frac{1}{m_1}f_{x_1x_1} - \lambda\right)\Delta x_1 + \frac{1}{m_1}f_{x_1y_1}\Delta y_1 + \cdots +$$

$$\frac{1}{m_1}f_{x_1z_N}\Delta z_N = 0$$

$$\frac{1}{m_1}f_{y_1x_1}\Delta x_1 + \left(\frac{1}{m_1}f_{y_1y_1} - \lambda\right)\Delta y_1 + \cdots +$$

$$\frac{1}{m_1}f_{y_1z_N}\Delta z_N = 0$$

$$\cdot$$
$$\cdot$$
$$\cdot$$

$$\frac{1}{m_N}f_{z_Nx_1}\Delta x_1 + \frac{1}{m_N}f_{z_Ny_1}\Delta y_1 + \cdots +$$

$$\left(\frac{1}{m_N}f_{z_Nz_N} - \lambda\right)\Delta z_N = 0 \quad (8\text{-}10)$$

possess nonzero solutions. Equations 8-10 are a series of $3N$ linear homogeneous equations in $3N$ unknowns (the amplitudes of the Cartesian displacements Δx_k) and possess solutions only for certain values of the frequency parameter λ. We have developed these equations in terms of Cartesian coordinates because it is particularly simple to do so. However, we are not interested in solving this problem in its present form, for among the $3N$ possible values of λ that will yield solutions six of them are zero, corresponding to vibrations of zero frequency (i.e., the three translations and rotations of the molecule as a whole). More important, the force constants expressed in Cartesian displacement coordinates presumably will have no generality, being applicable only to a given specific molecule and not transferable among similar molecules, hence of no chemical interest. We must, therefore, define internal coordinates in such a way that they describe the vibrations of the atoms only and are independent of translation or rotation of the molecule as a whole and in such a way that the force constants will conceivably be comparable among similar molecules having similar chemical bonds.

A reasonable approach appears to be the definition of internal displacement coordinates in terms of increments of valence bond lengths and bond angles. The expectation here is that a force constant defined as the second derivative of potential energy with respect to, say, increase of O—H bond length will be the same or nearly so in all molecules having an O—H group. The basis for this is the empirical observation that all molecules containing an O—H group consistently have an absorption near 3600 cm^{-1}; furthermore, there is a wealth of similar experience with other chemical groups, each of which displays essentially constant, characteristic absorption frequencies. (See Chapters 10–14, Volume II.) Another advantage in the use of internal coordinates is that the mathematical complexity of the problem is somewhat reduced, from order $3N$ to order $3N - 6$.

Let us define a set of valence coordinates, v_i, which is sufficient to describe any possible motion of the atoms with respect to one another. By the arguments of Section VI, Chapter 2, this number will be $3N - 6$; hence $3N - 6$ appropriately chosen* valence coordinates will be sufficient to describe the potential energy resulting from atomic displacements from equilibrium in a molecule:

$$
\begin{aligned}
2V = \quad & f_{11}v_1{}^2 + f_{12}v_1v_2 + f_{13}v_1v_3 + \cdots + f_{1,3N-6}v_1v_{3N-6} \\
& + f_{12}v_1v_2 + f_{22}v_2{}^2 + f_{23}v_2v_3 + \cdots + f_{2,3N-6}v_2v_{3N-6} \\
& + f_{13}v_1v_3 + f_{23}v_2v_3 + f_{33}v_3{}^2 + \cdots + f_{3,3N-6}v_3v_{3N-6} \\
& \quad \vdots \\
& + f_{1,3N-6}v_1v_{3N-6} + f_{2,3N-6}v_2v_{3N-6} + f_{3,3N-6}v_3v_{3N-6} \\
& \qquad\qquad\qquad\qquad\qquad + \cdots + f_{3N-6,3N-6}v_{3N-6}{}^2 \\
= \quad & \sum_{i}^{3N-6} \sum_{i'}^{3N-6} f(v)_{i,i'}v_iv_{i'}. \qquad\qquad\qquad (8\text{-}11)
\end{aligned}
$$

As before, since $f(v)_{i,i'} = f(v)_{i',i}$, there are $\frac{1}{2}(3N - 6)(3N - 6 + 1)$ different elements $f(v)_{i,i'}$, where $f(v)_{i,i'} = \partial^2 V/\partial v_i \, \partial v_{i'}$. These elements have been arranged in equation 8-11 in a $(3N - 6) \times (3N - 6)$ square array along with the valence coordinates, and it can be seen that the array is symmetrical about the diagonal, just as in equation 8-3. The $(3N - 6) \times (3N - 6)$ square array of $f(v)_{i,i'}$ values is called the F matrix (in valence coordinates).

Now, this set of $3N - 6$ internal displacement coordinates may be defined in terms of the Cartesian displacement coordinates. A descrip-

---

* We shall not be concerned here with just how these coordinates are chosen except to say that they are changes in valence bond lengths and angles. An excellent discussion of this procedure is given in Reference 2 (see especially p. 54 ff).

tion of one set in terms of another is called a *transformation*, and because the coordinates are linear and the atomic displacements are presumed to be small the transformation will be linear. Hence there exist $3N - 6$ equations of the form

$$v_i = \sum_k^{3N} b_{ik}\, \Delta x_k, \tag{8-12}$$

where $i = 1, 2, 3 \cdots 3N - 6$, each b_{ik} is a measure of the amount of change of valence coordinate v_i per unit change in Cartesian coordinate Δ_k. It can be shown* that when this transformation is properly applied in the development of equation 8-10 there result analogous equations in the valence coordinates v_i and the frequency parameters λ. There are now $3N - 6$ equations, the six "unnecessary" equations and the six zero values of λ having been eliminated by the transformation. In this process the inverse kinetic energy will no longer be simple multipliers of the inverse masses, as in equation 8-10, but its relation to frequency parameters and force constants will be considerably more complex. These equations, called the *secular equation in valence coordinates*, have the form

$$\left[\left(\sum_i^{3N-6} g_{1,i}f_{i,1}\right) - \lambda\right] v_1 + \left(\sum_i g_{1,i}f_{i,2}\right) v_2 + \cdots +$$

$$\left(\sum_i g_{1,i}f_{i,3N-6}\right) v_{3N-6} = 0$$

$$\left(\sum_i g_{2,i}f_{i,1}\right) v_1 + \left[\left(\sum_i g_{2,i}f_{i,2}\right) - \lambda\right] v_2 + \cdots +$$

$$\left(\sum_i g_{2,i}f_{i,3N-6}\right) v_{3N-6} = 0$$

$$\vdots$$

$$\left(\sum_i g_{3N-6,i}f_{i,1}\right) v_1 + \left(\sum_i g_{3N-6,i}f_{i,2}\right) v_2 + \cdots +$$

$$\left[\left(\sum_i g_{3N-6,i}f_{i,3N-6}\right) - \lambda\right] v_{3N-6} = 0. \tag{8-13}$$

The elements $g_{i,i'}$ result from the inverse of the kinetic energy, analogous to $1/m_k$ in equation 8-10; they can be determined† from

---

* See Reference 2, Chapter 4.
† Just how is beyond the scope of this treatment. (See References 2 and 3.)

the masses of the atoms and the coefficients of the equations effecting the transformation from Cartesian to valence coordinates (b_{ik}, equation 8-12). The collection of the $g_{i,i'}$ elements into a $(3N - 6) \times (3N - 6)$ square array (analogous to the $f_{i,i'}$ elements in equation 8-11) is often convenient and is called the G matrix, or inverse kinetic energy matrix, in valance coordinates. With this definition of the G matrix and the definition of the F matrix associated with equation 8-11, equation 8-13 can be abbreviated to the simple-appearing form

$$(GF - \lambda E)\mathbf{v} = 0, \tag{8-14}$$

where G and F are the G and F matrices, and E is the unit matrix. Expansion of matrix equation 8-14 by the rules of matrix multiplication* yields equations 8-13; we mention this notation here because the secular equation is frequently discussed in the literature in the abbreviated form of equation 8-14.

Equations 8-13 are a set of $3N - 6$ homogeneous equations in the magnitudes of the valence coordinates, v_i. They can have nonzero solutions for v_i (i.e., the amplitude of a vibration expressed in valence coordinates) only if the determinant of the system of equations is zero.† If the force constants are known, then expansion of the determinant of equations 8-13 yields a $[3N - 6]$th-order equation in λ which will have $3N - 6$ (real) roots. These $3N - 6$ roots are the possible values of frequency parameter λ for which equation 8-13 can possess solutions and correspond to the $3N - 6$ internal vibrations of the molecule, $\lambda = 4\pi^2 c^2 \omega^2$. If solution of the $[3N - 6]$th-order equation yields one or more sets of identical roots, these frequencies will be *degenerate*. (See Chapter 2, Section VI; also Section II of this chapter.)

If the force constants are not known, which is usually the case, then in general they cannot be determined from the frequencies without simplifying assumptions, for there are $\frac{1}{2}(3N - 6)(3N - 6 + 1)$ different force constants for the completely general quadratic force field, but only $3N - 6$ equations, the former number being the larger if $N \geqslant 3$. Methods of attack on this problem are discussed in Part C of this section.

B. The normal coordinates and their significance

Let us suppose that the force constants (F matrix) are known and that the frequency parameters have been found either from solution of the secular determinant or from the absorption spectrum: then for

* See Reference 1, Chapter 10.
† See Reference 1, p. 299 ff.

each of the $3N - 6$ values of the frequency parameter, λ_j, say, there exists a separate solution for the values of valence coordinates, v_i: this is usually called the jth eigenvector of the secular equation. These numbers describe the amplitudes of the jth vibration (i.e., the magnitude of the motions of each of the atoms in terms of the $3N - 6$ valence coordinates).

A solution of a set of *homogeneous* linear equations does not yield explicit values of each of the $3N - 6$ v_i's, but instead yields the *ratios* of each of the v_i's with respect to the others or, to use other words, determines the v_i's except for a common multiplicative constant or normalizing factor. The normalization condition is essentially the statement that when a given normal vibration is at its position of maximum amplitude its total energy equals the potential energy (compare with equations 2-6 and 2-7); the mathematical formulation is given by equation 8-19.

It is convenient to collect these $3N - 6$ solutions of the secular equation and to arrange them in a square array:

	λ_1	λ_2	λ_j	λ_{3N-6}
v_1	l_{11}	l_{12}	l_{1j}	$l_{1,3N-6}$
v_2	l_{21}	l_{22}	l_{2j}	$l_{2,3N-6}$
v_i	l_{i1}	l_{i2}	l_{ij}	$l_{i,3N-6}$
v_{3N-6}	$l_{3N-6,1}$	$l_{3N-6,2}$	$l_{3N-6,j}$	$l_{3N-6,3N-6}$

$$= L. \quad (8\text{-}15)$$

This L matrix is simply a collection of the normalized eigenvectors (or solutions) of the secular equation.

The elements of the L matrix define the normal coordinates:

$$v_i = \sum_{j}^{3N-6} l_{ij}Q_j, \quad (8\text{-}16)$$

where v_i is the ith internal valence coordinate, the l's are elements of the L matrix defined by equation 8-15, Q_j's are the *normal coordinates*. Physically, each Q_j is a *coordinate* (just as v_i is a coordinate) that describes a certain change in the arrangement of the atoms with respect to one another; the unique significance of Q_j, however, is that it is the *change in the arrangement of the atoms with respect to one another that actually occurs during a normal vibration* of frequency $\omega_j = \sqrt{\lambda_j}/2\pi c$. The curves of Figure 2-6 show how the potential energy of a molecule might vary as a function of a normal coordinate Q_j. One possible *representation* of these normal coordinates is in terms of valence coordinates v_i, as determined by equation 8-16. The meaning of each l_{ij} is

$$l_{ij} = \frac{\partial v_i}{\partial Q_j} \qquad (8\text{-}17)$$

or, in words, l_{ij} is the change of valence coordinate v_i per unit change of normal coordinate Q_j; the jth column of the L matrix is a description of the jth normal mode in terms of valence coordinates.

To provide a visual picture of a normal mode, the normal coordinates can be represented in terms of Cartesian displacement coordinates by a suitable transformation:*

$$x_k = \sum_j^{3N-6} a_{kj}Q_j. \qquad (8\text{-}18)$$

Each element a_{kj} is the change of Cartesian coordinate x_k per unit change of normal coordinate Q_j:

$$a_{kj} = \frac{\partial x_k}{\partial Q_j}.$$

Figures 8-1a, 8-1b, and 8-1c are the Cartesian representations of the normal modes of formaldehyde, methyl chloride, and cis-dibromoethylene, respectively. Under the "picture" of each normal mode is its frequency and an approximate description of the mode in words. These descriptions are essentially those of valence coordinates v_i, which might have been used to set up the secular equation. The valence coordinate chosen to "describe" the mode is the one that contributes the largest amount of potential energy to that particular normal mode. The explicit potential energy distribution of a normal mode (described by contributions from the individual valence coordinates) is given by†

$$\lambda_j = \sum_i^{3N-6} \sum_{i'}^{3N-6} f_{ii'}l_{ij}l_{i'j}. \qquad (8\text{-}19)$$

The potential energy is seen to consist of several terms, each being a

* The determination of the coefficients a_{kj} is beyond the scope of this treatment. (See Reference 4.)
† This equation is the normalization condition for the elements of the L matrix. (See Reference 2, pp. 71 ff.)

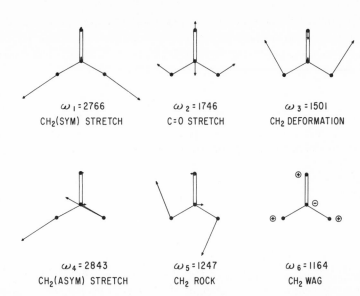

$$\omega_1 = 2766$$
CH₂(SYM) STRETCH

$$\omega_2 = 1746$$
C=O STRETCH

$$\omega_3 = 1501$$
CH₂ DEFORMATION

$$\omega_4 = 2843$$
CH₂(ASYM) STRETCH

$$\omega_5 = 1247$$
CH₂ ROCK

$$\omega_6 = 1164$$
CH₂ WAG

FIGURE 8-1a *The normal modes of formaldehyde,* $H_2C{=}O$. *(Data from unpublished work of Overend and Scherer.)*

product of a force constant and two of the L-matrix elements. Presumably, the larger terms will be those in which $i = i'$, the terms having the diagonal elements of the F matrix (which should be the larger elements of the matrix if the valence coordinates have been wisely, or luckily, chosen). The largest single term in equation 8-19 will result either from a large force constant ($f_{ii} = \partial^2 V/\partial v_i{}^2$) or from the square of a large L-matrix element $[l_{ij}{}^2 = (\partial v_i/\partial Q_j)^2]$; the v_i coordinate whose i is that of i for the largest term in equation 8-19 is chosen as an *approximate* description of the normal mode, hence it is often used to name the mode. As we shall see, the consideration of a valence coordinate as an *approximation* of a normal coordinate is really the basis of the so-called "group frequencies" discussed in Volume II.

The normal coordinates, as depicted by the L matrix, are also useful in considering the intensity of an absorption resulting from a (fundamental) transition to a normal vibration. The integrated intensity coefficient, $\mathcal{Q}$, defined experimentally by equation 6-28, is given by (compare with equation 2-16)

$$\mathcal{Q}_j \propto \left[\int_{\infty} \psi_0(Q_j) P_j \psi_1(Q_j) \, dQ_j \right]^2. \tag{8-20}$$

If the dipole moment operator P_j can be approximated by $\partial\mu/\partial Q_j \cdot Q_j$ and $\partial\mu/\partial Q_j$, the change of dipole moment per unit change of normal coordinate Q_j, can be assumed to be constant over the whole amplitude of the normal vibration in Q_j, the expression becomes

$$\alpha_j \propto \left[\int_\infty \psi_0(Q_j) Q_j \psi_1(Q_j)\, dQ_j \right]^2 \left(\frac{\partial\mu}{\partial Q_j}\right)^2. \qquad (8\text{-}21)$$

Now, if the system is assumed to be a harmonic oscillator, $\psi_0(Q_j)$ and $\psi_1(Q_j)$ are the wave functions of the harmonic oscillator resulting from solution of the Schroedinger equation. (See equation 2-9.) These functions are well known, and the integral of equation 8-21 in terms of

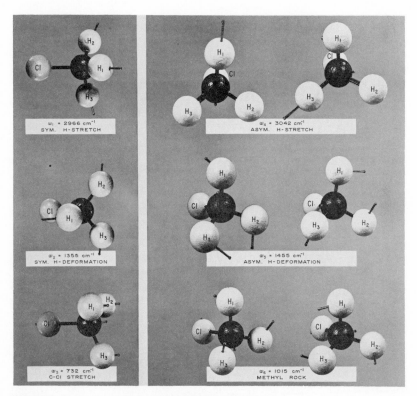

FIGURE 8-1b *Photographs of models illustrating the normal modes of methyl chloride,* CH_3Cl. *Both of each pair of degenerate modes are shown for the degenerate frequencies. (See Section II.) (Data from unpublished work of J. Overend.)*

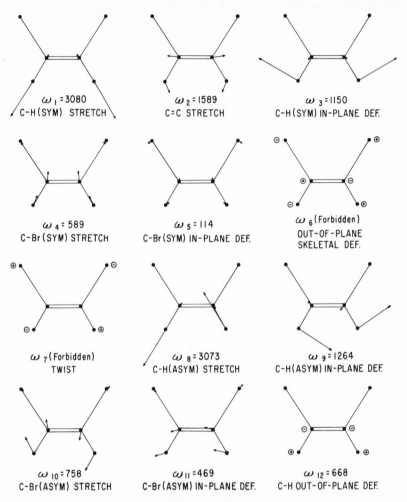

FIGURE 8-1c *The normal modes of cis-dibromo ethylene.* *(Data from J. Scherer and J. Overend, J. Chem. Phys. 33, (1960)).*

these functions has been evaluated.   The final result* is

$$\alpha_j = \frac{N\pi}{3c}\left(\frac{\partial\mu}{\partial Q_j}\right)^2 \tag{8-22}$$

* The proportionality expressed in equation 8-20 is the result of many other factors.   A complete derivation of equation 8-22 is given in Reference 2, pp. 162 ff.

270   *Theory of infrared spectra of polyatomic molecules*

and $\partial\mu/\partial Q_j$ can be determined from intensity measurements except for its sign.

In order to understand the origin of the intensity in terms of the chemical properties of valence bonds, $\partial\mu/\partial Q_j$ is developed in terms of valence coordinates:

$$\frac{\partial\mu}{\partial Q_j} = \sum_i^{3N-6} \frac{\partial\mu}{\partial v_i}\frac{\partial v_i}{\partial Q_i} = \sum_i^{3N-6} \frac{\partial\mu}{\partial v_i} l_{ij}. \tag{8-23}$$

Similar equations existing for every other $\partial\mu/\partial Q_j$ yield $3N - 6$ nonhomogeneous equations in $3N - 6$ unknowns, $\partial\mu/\partial v_i$. The quantity $\partial\mu/\partial v_i$ is, of course, the change in dipole moment with respect to unit change in the valence coordinate, v_i; hence the largest term (or terms) in equation 8-23 contributing to $\partial\mu/\partial Q_j$ gives a "chemical" explanation of the intensity of an infrared absorption band.

It should be noted that the $f_{ii'}l_{ij}l_{i'j}$ (i presumably $= i'$) term of equation 8-19, which is responsible for the largest contribution to the potential energy of a normal vibration j as a result of change of valence coordinate i, does *not necessarily* have the same value of i as the largest term in equation 8-23 (the development of intensity in terms of dipole change resulting from change of valence coordinates). For example, in the case of the 1589-cm^{-1} absorption of *cis*-dibromo-ethylene, the mode is called "C=C stretch" because the force constant $\partial^2 V/\partial v^2_{\text{C=C st}} = f(v)_{\text{C=C st}}$ makes the term $f(v)_{\text{C=C st}} \cdot l^2_{v_{\text{C=C st}}, Q_{1589}}$ the largest in the potential energy development. (See equation 8-19.) However, as can be seen by inspection of the normal mode shown in Figure 8-1c, $\partial\mu/\partial v_{\text{C=C st}} \equiv 0$ because of the symmetry about the center of the molecule. In fact, most of the intensity of this mode ($\partial\mu/\partial Q_{1589}$) probably results from compression of the C—Br bonds as the C=C bond stretches; that is, $\partial\mu/\partial v_{\text{C—Br st}} \cdot l_{v_{\text{C—Br st}}, Q_{1589}}$ is the largest term in equation 8-23.

Just how common this situation is (largest terms in 8-19 and 8-23 resulting from different v_i) is not really known because few molecules have been investigated with sufficient thoroughness to make conclusions. Although the case illustrated here is fairly obvious, lack of appreciation of this point in less obvious situations has no doubt caused some misunderstanding in the application of the characteristic "group frequencies" to chemical interpretations.

C. Determination of force constants

As previously discussed, it is in general not possible to determine the force constants (F matrix) from the experimentally determined fundamental frequencies, because the secular equation yields only $3N - 6$ equations in $\frac{1}{2}(3N - 6)(3N - 6 + 1)$ unknowns. This is unfortunate, for both frequencies and force constants must be known before the L matrix can be found, a visual geometric picture of the normal vibrations obtained, and some understanding of the vibrations gained. Fortunately, means do exist by which force constants may be obtained. The most important methods of approach are (a) use of frequencies from isotopically substituted molecules, (b) use of symmetry operations to factor the secular equation, and (c) simplifying approximations about the nature of the force field.

If one or more atoms in a molecule are substituted by isotopic atoms, presumably the electronic structure of the molecule, hence all force constants, is altered only to negligible degree. However, because the atomic masses differ, the G matrix elements (inverse kinetic energy) and normal vibration frequencies will be different. This will be most pronounced when hydrogen is replaced by deuterium, for in this case the factor of mass change is largest. If a molecule with several isotopic changes is available, enough of the elements of the G matrix will be altered so that several *additional* equations in the $\frac{1}{2}(3N - 6)(3N - 6 + 1)$ force constants will result from the experimental frequencies of this isotopic molecule. If a multiplicity of isotopically substituted molecules is available, then in some cases it is actually possible to have many more independent equations than unknowns, and the force constants may not only be determined but checked independently. Unfortunately, isotopic substitutions other than D for H often do not help much in practice, for only little change is made in the G-matrix elements by replacing, say, mass 16 (of O^{16}) by 18, and this is likely to result in only a small change in the normal coordinates. But substitution of D for H, where applicable, represents a powerful method of obtaining accurate force constants (within the framework of a general quadratic potential function) so that accurate normal coordinates may be obtained.

If the molecule possesses elements of symmetry, both the G and F matrices, hence the secular equation, can be factored into units of smaller order, and each of these units can be treated separately. The smaller the order of the unit, the more closely the number of equations will approach the number of $f_{ii'}$'s to be determined in that unit. For example, the G matrix of formaldehyde can, by suitable symmetry operations,* be transformed to

* These methods are beyond the scope of this treatment. (See Reference 2, Chapter 6, and Reference 5.)

$$\begin{vmatrix} g_{11} & g_{12} & g_{13} & 0 & 0 & 0 \\ g_{12} & g_{22} & g_{23} & 0 & 0 & 0 \\ g_{13} & g_{23} & g_{33} & 0 & 0 & 0 \\ 0 & 0 & 0 & g_{44} & g_{45} & 0 \\ 0 & 0 & 0 & g_{45} & g_{55} & 0 \\ 0 & 0 & 0 & 0 & 0 & g_{66} \end{vmatrix},$$

and the F matrix can also be similarly transformed. The resulting secular determinant (equation 8-13) will now consist of one block of order 3, containing six f's, three λ's, hence three equations in f, one block of order 2 containing three f's and two λ's, and one block of order one containing one f and one λ; each of these blocks can be treated as a separate problem. By this factoring operation we have reduced a problem of determining $\frac{1}{2}(3N - 6)(3N - 6 + 1) = 21$ f's from six equations to three separate problems: determination of six f's from three equations, determination of three f's from two equations, and determination of one f from one equation. If we can now obtain frequencies from enough molecules with atoms of different isotopes, the problem can be solved completely. Use of isotopically substituted molecules, coupled with symmetry factoring, represents the only route to obtaining nonapproximate force constants for larger molecules. Some of the applications of symmetry considerations to the problems of infrared spectroscopy are described in Section II of this chapter.

It is possible to describe the force field of a molecule by making certain approximations to the general quadratic force field. These approximations usually consist of letting certain values of $f_{ii'}$, which might be predicted to be small, be zero. The success of any such approximation is reflected in how accurately the calculated frequencies coincide with the observed frequencies.

One method, called the "central force" approximation, defines all internal coordinates as distances between atoms (both bonded and nonbonded) and associates with each internuclear distance $d_{n,n'}$ a force constant $f_{n,n'}$; a system of N atoms will have $\frac{1}{2}N(N - 1)$ such force constants. For nonlinear molecules containing three or four atoms, $\frac{1}{2}N(N - 1) = 3N - 6$, so that "central force" constants may be uniquely determined from the observed frequencies and approximate normal coordinates obtained. However, this approximation has proven unsatisfactory in application to all but the simplest molecules.

A more reasonable force field from a chemical point of view is the "valence force field" approximation, in which the force constants are defined in terms of the valence internal coordinates (changes in both valence bond distances and angles), as in equation 8-11, but all values of $f_{ii'}$ in which $i \neq i'$ are set equal to zero; that is, terms such as $f_{ii'}v_iv_{i'}$ are assumed to make such a small contribution to the potential energy that they can be neglected without serious error. This results in the existence of only $3N - 6$ different force constants, f_{ii}, which can always be determined from the $3N - 6$ equations that result from expansion of the secular determinant. Also, the F matrix is now the simple diagonal matrix,

$$
\begin{vmatrix}
f_{11} & 0 & 0 & \cdots & 0 \\
0 & f_{22} & 0 & \cdots & 0 \\
0 & 0 & f_{33} & \cdots & 0 \\
\cdot & & & & \\
\cdot & & & & \\
\cdot & & & & \\
0 & 0 & 0 & \cdots & f_{3N-6,3N-6}
\end{vmatrix},
$$

which makes expansion and solution of the secular equation considerably simpler than in the general case. Although mathematically simple, the approximation that $f_{ii'} = 0$, $i \neq i'$, is not accurate enough to be useful in most cases, for it makes no provision for changes in force constant associated with one internal coordinate (v_i) which may occur as the result of a change of another internal coordinate $(v_{i'})$; the general force field makes an indirect provision for this condition by the terms $f_{ii'}v_iv_{i'}$.

Even the completely general force field of equation 8-11 (consisting of elements of form f_{ii} and $f_{ii'}$) has certain disadvantages. A diagonal force constant, f_{ii}, has some chemical significance in the sense that it describes potential energy change as a result of a change in the electronic structure of a valence bond that occurs when it is stretched or bent, hence should be much the same for a similar valence bond in another molecule; that is, the diagonal elements of the F matrix should be transferable among similar molecules. On the other hand, the off-diagonal force constants, $f_{ii'}$, do not appear to have much chemical significance, for they describe potential energy change as the result of the *simultaneous change of two different electronic structures* that occur when two different valence coordinates change; a different $f_{ii'}$ exists for each pair of valence coordinates, and if these two valence coordinates do not bear the same relation to each other in some different molecule then elements $f_{ii'}$ cannot be transferable between these molecules.

An approximate force field has been conceived which has the advantages that (a) it is usually simpler than the general force field of equation 8-11 and (b) all of its elements are related to strictly chemical forces that should be transferable among similar molecules without introducing large error. Known as the Urey-Bradley force field, it consists of the diagonal elements of equation 8-11 (f_{ii}), neglects the off-diagonal elements ($f_{ii'}$), but adds instead the central forces between nonbonded atoms. It is essentially a combination of the "central force" and "valence force" approximations we have already discussed. As a further simplification, forces between nonbonded atoms widely separated in the molecule are neglected and only forces between closely adjacent nonbonded atoms are considered, an obviously appropriate assumption.

These forces between nonbonded atoms should be analogous to the well-known Van der Waals forces. If judicious choice of coordinates is made, the number of independent Urey-Bradley force constants is something less than $\frac{1}{2}(3N - 6)(3N - 6 + 1)$, thereby reducing the difficulty of the problem. In actual calculations the Urey-Bradley force field is incorporated into the secular equation by making the transformation

$$f'(v)_{ii'} = \sum_N z_{ii'n}\Phi_n,$$

where Φ_n's are the Urey-Bradley force constants, and the $z_{ii'n}$'s are the coefficients that transform the Urey-Bradley force constants into $f'(v)$, the best approximation to the general quadratic $f(v)$ possible, consistent with the Urey-Bradley force constants chosen.* This method has shown the greatest promise for determining force constants of chemical significance that conceivably could be transferred between similar molecules. At the present writing, the wider availability of sophisticated high-speed digital computers has led to a tremendous rebirth of interest in the field of force-constant calculations, and we may look forward to knowing the normal coordinates of a considerably larger number of basic molecules than have been studied in the past. This knowledge should certainly increase our understanding of infrared spectroscopy.

II. Symmetry considerations

When a molecule possesses elements of symmetry, it is at once possible to simplify greatly the description of the vibrations by dividing

* The elements $z_{ii'n}$ depend only on the geometry of the molecule; however, the expression of potential energy in terms of Urey-Bradley force constants and the determination of the elements $z_{ii'n}$ are complex and beyond the scope of this treatment. (See Reference 6.)

them into symmetry species. This is useful for several reasons. (*a*) The secular equation can be factored into much smaller units, which individually are much easier to solve. (*b*) It is possible to assign each normal mode to a symmetry type; often this assignment can be determined experimentally quite simply from certain properties of the fundamental transition to that mode. (See Section III.) Assignment of normal modes to symmetry classes is useful, for this sometimes allows us to make *approximate* descriptions of the normal mode corresponding to each observed fundamental without the necessity of solving the secular equation. (See examples following.) (*c*) Often, fundamentals of a certain symmetry type are forbidden; these *selection rules* are deduced easily from symmetry considerations. (*d*) The symmetry selection rules for overtone and combination bands are also easily deduced from formal symmetry considerations.

All of these applications of symmetry considerations can be conveniently performed by application of the branch of mathematics known as group theory. Although the derivation of its theorems requires some mathematical skill, application of its results does not demand a thorough understanding of the derivations. We are concerned here with the simplest applications.

In this description only the barest outline of group theory is presented. However, this material is felt to be sufficient for practical treatment of the great majority of molecules of concern to the organic or analytical chemist.

A. An outline of the results of group theory

Perhaps the simplest way in which to explain the concept of symmetry operations is to illustrate immediately with an example. Consider the ethylene oxide molecule. Obviously it has certain elements

of symmetry. We can describe this symmetry formally by defining certain geometrical operations, called *covering operations*, which have the property that after the operation has been completed the molecule is in a position completely equivalent to the original position: each atomic site is occupied by the same or a similar atom as it was before the operation was performed. The greater the symmetry of a molecule, the larger the number of possible covering operations, as just defined. The covering operations for ethylene oxide are the following:

1. The identity operation, usually denoted E. This operation is simply the statement that if the molecule has not been moved it is unchanged. It is analogous to unity in other multiplicative structures.

2. The twofold (i.e., 180°) rotation about the axis through the oxygen atom that bisects the C $\diagup$ O $\diagdown$ C angle. A 180° rotation is denoted C_2. This operation clearly results in a configuration identical to the original one.

3. Reflection at the plane perpendicular to the C——C plane and bisecting the C $\diagup$ O $\diagdown$ C angle. This operation also results in a configuration identical to the original. Reflection at a plane of symmetry containing the principal rotation axis (in this case the rotation axis just defined) is denoted σ_v.

4. Reflection at the C——C plane. This again results in a configuration identical to the original. This plane also contains the principal axis, but it is denoted σ_v' to distinguish it from σ_v.

These four operations form a closed *group;* that is, the result produced by the successive application of any two of the covering operations is equivalent to the result produced by the single application of some other covering operation in this group. These relations are often described as a multiplicative structure, multiplication of two operations being defined as the successive application of the two covering operations. From this multiplication table it is obvious that the operation E is analogous to unity in number multiplicative structures.

	E	C_2	σ_v	σ_v'
E	E	C_2	σ_v	σ_v'
C_2	C_2	E	σ_v'	σ_v
σ_v	σ_v	σ_v'	E	C_2
σ_v'	σ_v'	σ_v	C_2	E

A group describing the symmetry of a geometric object is called a *point group;* the point group describing the symmetry of ethylene oxide is denoted C_{2v}. Each of the covering operations E, C_2, σ_v, and $\sigma_v{}'$ constitutes a *class*. In point group C_{2v} each class consists of only one operation, but this is not always true for other point groups. The table is a *class* multiplication table.

Let us illustrate with another point group, C_{3v}; this group describes the possible covering operations of a molecule with the symmetry of methyl chloride, CH_3Cl. The covering operations are the following:

1. Identity operation, E.
2. Rotation about the C—Cl axis by 120° either clockwise or counterclockwise. These are two distinct covering operations, but because of their similarity they are placed in a single class, denoted $2C_3$. (The rotation C_2 is a class containing only one operation because rotation of 180° either clockwise or counterclockwise yields identical results.)
3. Reflection at a plane containing the principal axis (C—Cl bond) and one of the hydrogen atoms. There are three such planes, hence this class has three operations, $3\sigma_v$.

These operations also form a group, in this case consisting of six operations or elements (the sum of the numbers of operations in each class). The number of elements in a group is denoted N_G.

Figure 8-2 schematically illustrates the point groups that are most common in describing the symmetry of organic chemical molecules. (There are several other point groups, but they do not correspond to common molecular geometries of organic compounds.) Each is illustrated by a molecule of appropriate symmetry. Under each schematic representation is the symbol customarily used to denote the group. The various classes of operation and the symbol representing them on the schematic diagram are the following:

E, *identity:* the figure itself, unchanged (no specific symbol on the diagram).

C_n, *proper rotation:* rotation about the principal, or z, axis by $2\pi/n$ (a solid small ellipse indicates a twofold rotation, a solid small triangle indicates a threefold rotation, etc.; these rotations are about the z axis, the axis perpendicular to the plane of the paper).

$C_2{}'$, *dihedral rotation:* rotation about a twofold axis in the xy plane (two opposed solid ellipses on the edge of the figure connected by a solid or dashed line).

I, *inversion:* reflection of all points through the center of the group (no specific symbol on the diagram).

σ_h, *horizontal reflection:* reflection at the xy plane, which is the plane

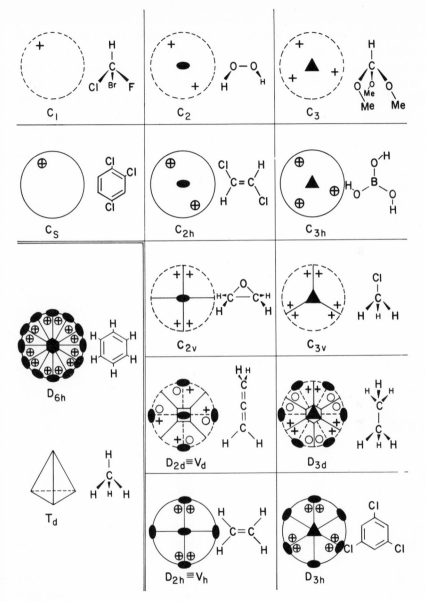

FIGURE 8-2 *Schematic illustrations of the point groups which represent common organic molecular symmetry types. (See text for explanation of symbolism.)*

perpendicular to the z, or principal symmetry, axis and is also the plane of the paper (when the element is present the circle bounding the diagram is solid; if not present it is dashed).

σ_v, *vertical reflection:* reflection at a plane containing the z axis (intersection of this plane and the xy plane is a solid line on the diagram).

S_n, *improper rotation:* a rotation about the z axis of $2\pi/n$, followed by reflection at the xy plane, whether or not it is a symmetry plane (an open square or hexagon at the center of the diagram).

It will be convenient in what follows to regard all operations as either *proper* rotations or *improper* rotations: E and C_n are *proper* rotations (E is a proper rotation of $0°$); S_n, σ, and I are *improper* rotations ($I \equiv S_2$; all reflections are improper rotations of $0°$).

Group theory states that any point group has several different methods of representation. One form of representation is a set of matrices, one of which corresponds to each class of covering operation. There may be many different sets of matrices, or *representations*, that will represent the group; however, it will be found that many of them can be simplified, or reduced in order, and still have all the necessary properties of a representation. If a representation *cannot* be reduced in order, it is termed *irreducible;* it so happens that the number of different irreducible sets, or representations, always equals the number of classes of the point group. All other possible matrix representations of the point group can be reduced to one of these irreducible sets.

Group theory further shows that the simplest property of the matrices constituting a representation that still preserves the class function is the *trace** of the matrices. The set of traces of the matrices forming an irreducible representation is called its *character* and is usually given the symbol $\chi_l(R)$: χ indicates the collection over all the classes of operations R; l is the index of the representation, for there are as many different representations as there are classes. As we shall see later, the various $\chi_l(R)$ are sufficient to describe the symmetry properties of all geometrical objects pertaining to that group. It is convenient to list all characters, $\chi_l(R)$, of the various irreducible representations in a table, known as the *character table* of the point group. Because there are as many irreducible representations as classes, the character table is a square array of numbers. The character tables of the point groups of Figure 8-2 are given by Tables 8-1, *a* through *n*.

The character tables are often arranged so that the most symmetric representations are at the top, the least symmetric at the bottom. The unique *totally symmetric* representation (all matrix traces $= +1$) is

---

* The trace of a matrix is the sum of its diagonal elements.

Table 8-1

Character Tables of the Point Groups of Figure 8-2

C_1	E	
A	1	$\begin{cases} \mathbf{x,\ y,\ z} \\ R_x,\ R_y,\ R_z \\ x^2,\ y^2,\ z^2,\ xy,\ yz,\ xz \end{cases}$

(a)

C_2	E	C_2	
A	1	1	$\begin{cases} \mathbf{z} \\ R_z \\ x^2,\ y^2,\ z^2,\ xy \end{cases}$
B	1	-1	$\begin{cases} \mathbf{x,\ y} \\ R_x,\ R_y \\ yz,\ xz \end{cases}$

(b)

C_3	E	C_3	$\bar{C}_3$	
A	1	1	1	$\begin{cases} \mathbf{z} \\ R_z \\ z^2,\ (x^2+y^2) \end{cases}$
E	$\begin{cases} 1 \\ 1 \end{cases}$	$\begin{matrix} e^{2\pi i/3} \\ e^{-2\pi i/3} \end{matrix}$	$\left.\begin{matrix} e^{-2\pi i/3} \\ e^{2\pi i/3} \end{matrix}\right\}$	$\begin{cases} \mathbf{x,\ y} \\ R_x,\ R_y \\ (x^2-y^2),\ 2xy,\ xz,\ yz \end{cases}$

(c)

C_s	E	σ_h	
A'	1	1	$\begin{cases} \mathbf{x,\ y} \\ R_z \\ x^2,\ y^2,\ z^2,\ xy \end{cases}$
A''	1	-1	$\begin{cases} \mathbf{z} \\ R_x,\ R_y \\ xz,\ yz \end{cases}$

(d)

C_{2h}	E	C_2	I	σ_h	
A_g	1	1	1	1	$\begin{cases} R_z \\ x^2,\ y^2,\ z^2,\ xy \end{cases}$
A_u	1	1	-1	-1	$\mathbf{z}$
B_g	1	-1	1	-1	$\begin{cases} R_x,\ R_y \\ xz,\ yz \end{cases}$
B_u	1	-1	-1	1	$\mathbf{x,\ y}$

(e)

C_{3h}	E	C_3	$\bar{C}_3$	σ_h	S_3	$\bar{S}_3$	
A'	1	1	1	1	1	1	$\begin{cases} R_z \\ z^2,\ (x^2+y^2) \end{cases}$
A''	1	1	1	-1	-1	-1	$\mathbf{z}$
E'	$\begin{cases} 1 \\ 1 \end{cases}$	$\begin{matrix} e^{2\pi i/3} \\ e^{-2\pi i/3} \end{matrix}$	$\begin{matrix} e^{-2\pi i/3} \\ e^{2\pi i/3} \end{matrix}$	$\begin{matrix} 1 \\ 1 \end{matrix}$	$\begin{matrix} e^{2\pi i/3} \\ e^{-2\pi i/3} \end{matrix}$	$\left.\begin{matrix} e^{-2\pi i/3} \\ e^{2\pi i/3} \end{matrix}\right\}$	$\begin{cases} \mathbf{x,\ y} \\ (x^2-y^2),\ 2xy \end{cases}$
E''	$\begin{cases} 1 \\ 1 \end{cases}$	$\begin{matrix} e^{2\pi i/3} \\ e^{-2\pi i/3} \end{matrix}$	$\begin{matrix} e^{-2\pi i/3} \\ e^{2\pi i/3} \end{matrix}$	$\begin{matrix} -1 \\ -1 \end{matrix}$	$\begin{matrix} e^{-2\pi i/3} \\ e^{2\pi i/3} \end{matrix}$	$\left.\begin{matrix} e^{2\pi i/3} \\ e^{-2\pi i/3} \end{matrix}\right\}$	$\begin{cases} R_x,\ R_y \\ xz,\ yz \end{cases}$

(f)

Table 8-1 (*Continued*)

C_{2v}	E	C_2	σ_v	$\sigma_v{}'$	
A_1	1	1	1	1	$\begin{cases} \mathbf{z} \\ x^2,\, y^2,\, z^2 \end{cases}$
A_2	1	1	-1	-1	$\begin{cases} R_z \\ xy \end{cases}$
B_1	1	-1	1	-1	$\begin{cases} \mathbf{x} \\ R_y \\ xz \end{cases}$
B_2	1	-1	-1	1	$\begin{cases} \mathbf{y} \\ R_x \\ yz \end{cases}$

(g)

C_{3v}	E	$2C_3$	$3\sigma_v$	
A_1	1	1	1	$\begin{cases} \mathbf{z} \\ z^2,\, (x^2 + y^2) \end{cases}$
A_2	1	1	-1	R_z
E	2	-1	0	$\begin{cases} \mathbf{x},\, \mathbf{y} \\ R_x,\, R_y \\ (x^2 - y^2),\, 2xy,\, xz,\, yz \end{cases}$

(h)

$D_{2h} \equiv V_h$	E	C_2	$C_2{}'$	$C_2{}''$	I	σ_h	σ_v	$\sigma_v{}'$	
A_g	1	1	1	1	1	1	1	1	$x^2,\, y^2,\, z^2$
A_u	1	1	1	1	-1	-1	-1	-1	
B_{1g}	1	1	-1	-1	1	1	-1	-1	$\begin{cases} R_z \\ xy \end{cases}$
B_{1u}	1	1	-1	-1	-1	-1	1	1	$\mathbf{z}$
B_{2g}	1	-1	1	-1	1	-1	1	-1	$\begin{cases} R_y \\ xz \end{cases}$
B_{2u}	1	-1	1	-1	-1	1	-1	1	$\mathbf{y}$
B_{3g}	1	-1	-1	1	1	-1	-1	1	$\begin{cases} R_x \\ yz \end{cases}$
B_{3u}	1	-1	-1	1	-1	1	1	-1	$\mathbf{x}$

(i)

$D_{2d} \equiv V_d$	E	C_2	$2S_4$	$2C_2{}'$	$2\sigma_d$	
A_1	1	1	1	1	1	$z^2,\, (x^2 + y^2)$
A_2	1	1	1	-1	-1	R_z
B_1	1	-1	-1	1	-1	$(x^2 - y^2)$
B_2	1	-1	-1	-1	1	$\begin{cases} \mathbf{z} \\ xy \end{cases}$
E	2	-2	0	0	0	$\begin{cases} \mathbf{x},\, \mathbf{y} \\ R_x,\, R_y \\ xz,\, yz \end{cases}$

(j)

Table 8-1 (*Continued*)

D_{3d}	E	I	$2C_3$	$2S_6$	$3C_2'$	$3\sigma_d$	
A_{1g}	1	1	1	1	1	1	z^2, $(x^2 + y^2)$
A_{1u}	1	-1	1	-1	1	-1	
A_{2g}	1	1	1	1	-1	-1	R_z
A_{2u}	1	-1	1	-1	-1	1	$\mathbf{z}$
E_g	2	2	-1	-1	0	0	$\begin{cases} R_x, R_y \\ (x^2 - y^2), 2xy, xz, yz \end{cases}$
E_u	2	-2	-1	1	0	0	$\mathbf{x}, \mathbf{y}$

(*k*)

D_{3h}	E	σ_h	$2C_3$	$2S_3$	$3C_2'$	$3\sigma_v$	
A_1'	1	1	1	1	1	1	z^2, $(x^2 + y^2)$
A_1''	1	-1	1	-1	1	-1	
A_2'	1	1	1	1	-1	-1	R_z
A_2''	1	-1	1	-1	-1	1	$\mathbf{z}$
E'	2	2	-1	-1	0	0	$\begin{cases} \mathbf{x}, \mathbf{y} \\ (x^2 - y^2), 2xy \end{cases}$
E''	2	-2	-1	1	0	0	$\begin{cases} R_x, R_y \\ xz, yz \end{cases}$

(*l*)

D_{6h}	E	C_2	$2C_3$	$2C_6$	$3C_2'$	$3C_2''$	I	σ_h	$2S_6$	$2S_3$	$3\sigma_v$	$3\sigma_v'$	
A_{1g}	1	1	1	1	1	1	1	1	1	1	1	1	z^2, $(x^2 + y^2)$
A_{1u}	1	1	1	1	1	1	-1	-1	-1	-1	-1	-1	
A_{2g}	1	1	1	1	-1	-1	1	1	1	1	-1	-1	R_z
A_{2u}	1	1	1	1	-1	-1	-1	-1	-1	-1	1	1	$\mathbf{z}$
B_{1g}	1	-1	1	-1	1	-1	1	-1	1	-1	1	-1	
B_{1u}	1	-1	1	-1	1	-1	-1	1	-1	1	-1	1	
B_{2g}	1	-1	1	-1	-1	1	1	-1	1	-1	-1	1	
B_{2u}	1	-1	1	-1	-1	1	-1	1	-1	1	1	-1	
E_{1g}	2	-2	-1	1	0	0	2	-2	-1	1	0	0	$\begin{cases} R_x, R_y \\ xz, yz \end{cases}$
E_{1u}	2	-2	-1	1	0	0	-2	2	1	-1	0	0	$\mathbf{x}, \mathbf{y}$
E_{2g}	2	2	-1	-1	0	0	2	2	-1	-1	0	0	$(x^2 - y^2)$, $2xy$
E_{2u}	2	2	-1	-1	0	0	-2	-2	1	1	0	0	

(*m*)

T_d	E	$8C_3$	$3C_2$	$6\sigma_d$	$6S_4$	
A_1	1	1	1	1	1	$(x^2 + y^2 + z^2)$
A_2	1	1	1	-1	-1	
E	2	-1	2	0	0	$(2z^2 - x^2 - y^2)$, $\sqrt{3}\,(x^2 - y^2)$
F_1	3	0	-1	1	-1	$\begin{cases} \mathbf{x}, \mathbf{y}, \mathbf{z} \\ xy, yz, xz \end{cases}$
F_2	3	0	-1	-1	1	R_x, R_y, R_z

(*n*)

always the first row of the table. There is a standard symbolism for the various representations of the point groups, $\chi_l(R)$:

The symbol A is used for the representations symmetric to rotation about the principal axis. The totally symmetric representation will always have symbol A.

The symbol B is used for representations antisymmetric to rotation about the principal axis.

The symbols E and F are used respectively for twofold and threefold degenerate representations,* which are necessary to describe similar but not identical geometrical objects with the same representation, hence transform in the same way under the class operations; an example is the x and y axes in the C_{3v} point group. As can be seen from the character tables, any planar group having the class C_n ($n > 3$) has at least one doubly degenerate representation, E.

If a point group has inversion symmetry (I), the subscript g or u is added to the representation symbol to indicate whether the representation is symmetric or antisymmetric, respectively, to inversion. If a point group has the class σ_h, but not I, the notation $'$ or $''$ indicates symmetry or antisymmetry, respectively, of the representation to reflection at the xy plane.

The element of the representation for class E (identity) indicates the degeneracy of the representation: A and B representations always have $+1$ for the identity operation and are nondegenerate; E representations have $+2$ and are doubly degenerate,† and F representations have $+3$ and are triply degenerate.

One great value of the character table results from the ease with which it can be used to determine to what representations the various geometric objects belong. Once their representations are known, they may be manipulated by the rules of group theory (see later) to determine important functional relations between the corresponding geometric objects. A few illustrations will show how these representations are determined.

Consider the point group V_h. Suppose we wished to know the character of a vector in the x direction: $\chi_x(R)$. In applying the covering operations of the group, it is seen that the vector $\mathbf{x}$ is unchanged by,

* E also is commonly the class symbol of the identity operation, as discussed above. This is an unfortunate overlapping of symbolism.

† For those representations having some imaginary numbers, the degeneracy of the E representation is expressed by the fact that one representation is the complex conjugate of the other. The sum of the representations is real and yields 2 for the character of the identity class. For those representations not having two explicit representations for the degenerate cases and 2 for the character of the identity operation (example: D_{3h}) the degeneracy is implied.

or is *symmetric to*, these operations:

identity, E
rotation about the x axis, C_2''
reflection at the xy plane, σ_h
reflection at the xz plane, σ_v.

It can also be seen that vector **x** changes sign by, or is *antisymmetric to*, these operations:

rotation about the z axis, C_2
rotation about the y axis, C_2'
inversion, I
reflection at the yz plane, σ_v'.

Now, these transformation coefficients ($+1$ for *symmetric to*, -1 for *antisymmetric to*) have exactly the same values as the characters of representation B_{3u}; hence we say that vector **x** belongs to representation B_{3u}: $\chi_\mathbf{x}(R) = \chi_{B_{3u}}(R)$. In a similar manner rotation about the z axis, R_z, is

Symmetric to	Antisymmetric to
E	C_2'
C_2	C_2''
I	σ_v
σ_h	σ_v'

hence R_z belongs to representation B_{1g}: $\chi_{R_z}(R) = \chi_{B_{1g}}(R)$.

In point groups with degenerate representations the situation is a bit more complex. In point group C_{3h} it is obvious by analogy from the foregoing examples that **z** belongs to representation A''. However, when we consider what happens to the vector **x** under the covering operations, we note that it is symmetric to E and σ_h; but under the rotation operations it is neither symmetric nor antisymmetric, but instead, the result of the rotation operations is a *linear combination of vectors* **x** *and* **y**. This result is obtained with either of the representations of the E' type, and, furthermore, vector **y** also transforms in a similar manner; hence the concept of *degeneracy* of the representation.

In point group D_{3h}, in which the degeneracy is implied rather than expressed, the vectors **x** and **y** obviously do not belong to any of the A-type representations, do not change sign under operations E and σ_h, and form linear combinations of one another under the other operations. Both E' and E'' representations are irreducible but may be thought of as sums of (ficticious) explicit representations, such as those of point group C_{3h}; $+2$ for σ_h of representation E' implies that each of the two "components" has "+1" for that element of the representation, whereas -2 for σ_h of representation E'' implies "-1" for σ_h of its two "components." Therefore in point group D_{3h} vectors $\mathbf{x}$ and $\mathbf{y}$ properly belong to representation E' because they do not change sign under operation σ_h.

In the right-hand column of each of the character tables the important geometrical objects are listed in the row of the representation to which each belongs. These include the vectors $\mathbf{x}$, $\mathbf{y}$, and $\mathbf{z}$; rotation about the x, y, and z axes: R_x, R_y, R_z. The other objects are the symmetrical tensors of rank 2 whose meaning we shall not be concerned with here except to state that they denote the representations of the polarizability tensors, important for the selection rules of Raman spectroscopy. (See Chapter 15, Volume II.)

Finally, the representations also form a multiplicative structure: multiplication of any two representations of a point group results in another representation of the group (or the *sum* of various other representations of the group if both representations being multiplied are degenerate). In multiplication of two representations $\chi_i(R) \times \chi_j(R) = \chi_k(R)$ is defined as the character resulting from multiplication of the elements of the two representations class by class. For example, in point group D_{3h}, $\chi_{A_2''}(R) \times \chi_{E'}(R)$ is

	E	σ_h	$2C_3$	$2S_3$	$3C_2'$	$3\sigma_v$	
A_2''	1	-1	1	-1	-1	1	$= \chi_{A_2''}(R)$
E'	2	2	-1	-1	0	0	$= \chi_{E'}(R)$
E''	2	-2	-1	1	0	0	$= \chi_{A_2''}(R) \times \chi_{E'}(R)$

The resulting character is seen to be E''; hence

$$\chi_{A_2''}(R) \times \chi_{E'}(R) = \chi_{E''}(R).$$

The product of any two irreducible representations of a point group, provided that both are not degenerate, is itself an irreducible representation of the group whose identity is immediately obvious from inspection of the character table.

If two *degenerate* representations are multiplied, the result is *not* the character of an irreducible representation but the *sum* of several irreducible representations. Without specifying the mathematical details of their derivation, we have the rules

$$E_1 \times E_1 = E_2 \times E_2 = A_1 + A_2 + E_2$$
$$E_1 \times E_2 = B_1 + B_2 + E_1.$$

(8-24)

These simple rules cover all of the groups of Figure 8-2 if modified by the additional specifications:

1. When applied to groups having no representations with numerical subscripts, these are dropped.

2.
$$g \times g = u \times u = g$$
$$g \times u = u$$

3.
$$' \times ' = '' \times '' = '$$
(8-25)
$$' \times '' = ''.$$

Simple inspection of the character tables, or applications of the foregoing rules, now allows us to find the product of any two representations. The product of more than two representations is found by successive application of these methods. The results will be necessary in the following applications.

B. Applications of group theory to characterization of infrared spectral transitions

Classification of normal modes. If a molecule has elements of symmetry such that it corresponds to one of the point groups (see examples of Figure 8-2), its normal coordinates may be regarded as geometrical objects whose symmetry can be described by the appropriate representations and each normal mode is said to belong to that representation. The normal modes of *cis*-dibromoethylene (C_{2v} symmetry), which are illustrated in Figure 8-1c, belong to the representations

A_1: Q_1 ($\omega_1 = 3080$ cm^{-1}) B_1: Q_8 ($\omega_8 = 3073$ cm^{-1})
  Q_2 ($\omega_2 = 1589$ cm^{-1}) Q_9 ($\omega_9 = 1264$ cm^{-1})
  Q_3 ($\omega_3 = 1150$ cm^{-1}) Q_{10} ($\omega_{10} = 758$ cm^{-1})
  Q_4 ($\omega_4 = 587$ cm^{-1}) Q_{11} ($\omega_{11} = 469$ cm^{-1})
  Q_5 ($\omega_5 = 114$ cm^{-1}) B_2: Q_{12} ($\omega_{12} = 668$ cm^{-1})
A_2: Q_6 (forbidden)
  Q_7 (forbidden)

as can readily be seen by study of the character table of point group C_{2v}.* It is common practice to number the modes in the order shown:

* For example, the atomic displacement vectors in modes ω_8–ω_{11} are unchanged by operations E (identity) and σ_v (reflection in the molecular plane) but change sign under operations C_2 (180° rotation about the axis in the molecular plane which is the perpendicular bisector of the C=C bond) and σ_v' (reflection in the symmetry plane which is the perpendicular bisector of the C=C bond); obviously representation B_1 of C_{2v} describes this behavior.

ω_1 is by definition the highest frequency mode of the totally symmetric representation, the index of the modes running in descending frequency order through each of the representation types, in their order in the character table.

The normal modes of methyl chloride shown by Figure 8-1b contain doubly degenerate modes; recognition of the representations to which they belong is, therefore, a bit more difficult. The symmetry of the three nondegenerate modes is clear:

$$A_1: \quad Q_1 \ (\omega_1 = 2966 \text{ cm}^{-1})$$
$$Q_2 \ (\omega_2 = 1355 \text{ cm}^{-1})$$
$$Q_3 \ (\omega_3 = \ 732 \text{ cm}^{-1}).$$

However, it is seen that any of the other modes $(Q_4–Q_9)$ are not simply either symmetric or antisymmetric under the C_3 operation, but instead the C_3 operation on Q_4 or Q_5 results in a *linear combination of* Q_4 *and* Q_5. Hence Q_4 and Q_5 constitute a *degenerate pair* of vibrations: they are modes that have identical frequency and will have identically shaped potential curves (potential energy as a function of normal coordinate, as shown in Figure 2-6). Similarly, Q_6 and Q_7 form a degenerate pair, as do Q_8 and Q_9; the two members of each pair have identical frequency. Each of these pairs gives rise to one fundamental, as described in Chapter 2. These three fundamentals belong to the E representation:

$$E: \quad \left. \begin{matrix} Q_4 \\ Q_5 \end{matrix} \right\} \quad (\omega_4 = 3042 \text{ cm}^{-1})$$

$$\left. \begin{matrix} Q_6 \\ Q_7 \end{matrix} \right\} \quad (\omega_5 = 1455 \text{ cm}^{-1})$$

$$\left. \begin{matrix} Q_8 \\ Q_9 \end{matrix} \right\} \quad (\omega_6 = 1015 \text{ cm}^{-1}).$$

Prediction of the number of modes belonging to each representation. The results of group theory may be used to calculate the distribution of the $3N - 6$ normal modes of a molecule among the representations of the point group to which it belongs, even though the normal coordinates are not known. This is done in the following manner:

First, we need a quantity $\Xi(R)$:

$$\Xi(R) = \begin{cases} (u_R - 2)(1 + 2 \cos \varphi) & \text{[proper rotations]} \\ (u_R)(-1 + 2 \cos \varphi) & \text{[improper rotations]} \end{cases} \qquad (8\text{-}26)$$

where φ is the angle of rotation (which will be 0 for identity or reflection operations), and u_R is the number of atomic nuclei not moved under covering operation R. When $\Xi(R)$ has been determined, the number of normal modes belonging to each representation i is given by

$$N_i = \frac{1}{N_G} \sum n\, \Xi(R)\chi_i(R), \qquad (8\text{-}27)$$

where N_i is the number of normal modes belonging to representation i, $\chi_i(R)$ is the character of the representation, and n is the number of elements in the class of the operation, the sum being taken over all classes.

To illustrate this application, we calculate the symmetry distribution of the normal modes of 1,3,5-trichlorobenzene, which belongs to point group D_{3h}. First $\Xi(R)$ is found from equation 8-26:

	E	σ_h	$2C_3$	$2S_3$	$3C_2$	$3\sigma_v$
$\Xi(R)$	30	12	0	0	-2	4

Reference to the character table for D_{3h} now supplies the numbers that are used in equation 8-27:

$$N_{A_1'} = \tfrac{1}{12}[1(30)(1) + 1(12)(1) + 2(0)(1) + 2(0)(1) + 3(-2)(1) + 3(4)(1)] = 4$$

$$N_{A_1''} = \tfrac{1}{12}[1(30)(1) + 1(12)(-1) + 2(0)(1) + 2(0)(-1) + 3(-2)(1) + 3(4)(-1)] = 0$$

$$N_{A_2'} = \tfrac{1}{12}[1(30)(1) + 1(12)(1) + 2(0)(1) + 2(0)(1) + 3(-2)(-1) + 3(4)(-1)] = 3$$

$$N_{A_2''} = \tfrac{1}{12}[1(30)(1) + 1(12)(-1) + 2(0)(1) + 2(0)(-1) + 3(-2)(-1) + 3(4)(1)] = 3$$

$$N_{E'} = \tfrac{1}{12}[1(30)(2) + 1(12)(2) + 2(0)(-1) + 2(0)(-1) + 3(-2)(0) + 3(4)(0)] = 7$$

$$N_{E''} = \tfrac{1}{12}[1(30)(2) + 1(12)(-2) + 2(0)(-1) + 2(0)(1) + 3(-2)(0) + 3(4)(0)] = 3.$$

Remembering that each mode belonging to a doubly degenerate representation must be counted twice, we see that the total number of modes is equal to $3N - 6$, as, of course, it should be

$$4_{A_1'} + 0_{A_1''} + 3_{A_2'} + 3_{A_2''} + 2 \times 7_{E'} + 2 \times 3_{E''} = 30 = 3N - 6.$$

This division of the normal modes is useful, for it allows us to make reasonable guesses regarding the approximate nature of the normal modes without solving the secular equation (8-13). The more highly symmetrical the molecule, the more accurate these estimations can be made. For vibrations belonging to degenerate representations this is not a simple matter; however, guesses about the form of the normal vibration modes belonging to nondegenerate representations can be made from consideration of the character table, and some experience with the empirical "group frequencies." (How this empirical knowledge of characteristic frequencies helps in this respect will become clearer after study of Chapters 10–14, Volume II.) As an example, we shall write down approximate normal modes of the A_2'- and A_2''-type vibrations for 1,3,5-trichlorobenzene.

A_2' type (three vibrations). As is determined from inspection of $\chi_{A_2'}(R)$ in the character table of D_{3h}, the vibrations are planar (symmetric to σ_h) and geometrically similar to a rotation about the z axis; that is, a group consisting of similar atoms must move as a rotation about the z axis with respect to a group consisting of another set of similar atoms. The three hydrogen atoms are such a group, and experience with characteristic group vibrations (see Volume II) has shown that because hydrogen is so light, compared to the other atoms, modes exist in which most of the displacement of the coordinates results from hydrogen motion. Hence one of the A_2' modes must be approximately

The chlorine atoms might be expected to have a similar mode. Chlorine is so heavy compared to carbon and hydrogen, however, that most of the motion is in these lighter atoms, the chlorine atoms moving only to small extent:

The only other mode possible with symmetry characteristics of representation A_2' must be one which has essentially carbon-carbon displacements. A little reflection with reference to the character table

suggests the mode

each hydrogen atom "riding along" with its carbon atom. Although these descriptions of the normal coordinates are not exact, they are at least qualitatively accurate approximations to the true normal coordinates, and the true normal coordinates will always be simple linear combinations of these approximate coordinates.

A_2'' type (three vibrations). Here the vibrations are out-of-plane (asymmetric to σ_h) and are geometrically similar to translation along the z axis. Arguments similar to those for the in-plane modes suggest

Again, although these descriptions of the normal coordinates are not exact, they are probably good qualitative approximations.

With this system of finding approximate descriptions of the normal modes of highly symmetrical molecules, surprisingly good predictions of their vibration frequencies can be made by the empirical methods in Chapters 10–14, Volume II.

Selection rules. As discussed in Chapter 2, in order for an infrared radiation-induced transition to occur between two states, there must be a dipole moment change during this transition; that is, the integral $\int_\infty \psi_n P \psi_m \, d\tau$ must be nonzero. (See equations 2-16 and 8-20.) The results of group theory allow us to tell immediately whether the integral is zero, without the necessity of evaluating it: the integral is nonzero if the integrand belongs to the totally symmetric representation of the point group pertinent to the molecule. The representation to which the integrand belongs is found by taking the product of the representation of the initial state, the dipole moment operator, and

Symmetry considerations **291**

the final state:

$$\chi_{\text{integrand}}(R) = \chi_{\psi_n}(R) \times \chi_P(R) \times \chi_{\psi_m}(R). \qquad (8\text{-}28)$$

For fundamental transitions (between ground state and a first excited state of one of the normal modes) the selection rules are quite simple; they are formulated from these facts:

1. The vibrational ground state always belongs to the totally symmetric representation.

2. The dipole moment operators belong to the same representations as the vectors x, y, and z (see character tables, p. 281 ff.).

3. As can be seen by study of the character tables, and the rules of multiplication of representations on pp. 286 and 287, the product of two representations is (or contains*) the totally symmetric representation only when they are identical. Therefore the integrand of equation 8-20 is totally symmetric only when the representation of the excited state is the same as that of one of the translation vectors x, y, or z.

The selection rule for fundamentals is thus: Only those fundamentals are allowed for which the normal mode belongs to the same representation as one of the translation vectors, as determined from the character tables. The physical meaning of this statement is that only those transitions in which the vibration produces a change of dipole moment are allowed to occur. (Compare with discussion of diatomic molecules, p. 18, Chapter 2.) In our example of 1,3,5-trichlorobenzene, only normal modes belonging to A_2'' and E' can be excited by absorption of infrared radiation; transitions to excited states of normal vibrations of the other species (A_1', A_1'', A_2', and E'') are infrared *forbidden* (i.e., do not occur in the infrared absorption spectrum of the molecule).

As discussed in Chapter 2, molecular vibrations are not strictly harmonic, hence overtones, combination tones, and difference tones are observed, but usually with low intensity; the greater the anharmonicity, the greater their intensity. But overtone, combination, and difference bands are subject to the symmetry selection rules and will have zero or very little intensity unless allowed by them. The symmetry selection rules for these transitions are also the result of the general rule that the integrand of the transition moment integral must be totally symmetric if the integral is to be nonzero.

A difference tone is allowed if the product of the representations of the initial state, final state, and at least one translation vector is (or

* That is, it is the sum of this and other representations. (See p. 286.)

contains) the totally symmetric representation. The rule differs from that for fundamentals in that the initial state is not the ground state, hence does not necessarily belong to the totally symmetric representation.

A combination tone results from the simultaneous excitation of a molecule in the ground state to the first excited state of two different normal modes. The representation of this upper state is the product of the representations of the two normal modes. If it is (or contains) one of the representations of the translation vectors, the integrand is totally symmetric, and the combination band is allowed. Study of the character tables and the rules for multiplication of representations shows that combination tones involving modes whose fundamentals are symmetry forbidden can in many cases become symmetry allowed. Such combination bands are often observed; when one of the modes in the combination band has an allowed fundamental, so that its frequency is known, the frequency of the other mode is then easily calculated. This is an important method by which frequencies of modes having forbidden fundamentals can be determined.

A first (or higher) overtone absorption results from the excitation of a molecule to the second (or higher) excited state of a normal mode. If the mode is *nondegenerate*, the representation of the second excited state is the product of the representation of the mode with itself, and this will always be the totally symmetric representation (see rules of multiplication of representations, pp. 286 and 287). Overtones of any *nondegenerate* fundamentals are forbidden in any molecule for which none of the translation vectors belongs to the totally symmetric representation. For a *degenerate* mode the representations of the higher excited states are not simply the product of the representation with itself;[*] if the representation of the higher excited state can be found,[†] however, the selection rules can easily be deduced as for any other transition we have considered. It is interesting to note that as a result of the symmetry selection rules no first overtones are observed for any molecule with a center of inversion symmetry (operation I): the representation of any second excited state is always g and all translation vectors are always u; $g \times u = u$. Hence the integrand of the transition moment integral is not totally symmetric.

Symmetry reduction. It often happens that a fundamental transition to a particular mode is forbidden in a highly symmetric molecule

* The reason is beyond the scope of this treatment. (See Reference 2, p. 152 ff.)
† Reference 3, p. 127, gives a table of the representations of excited degenerate states.

but is allowed in certain of the derivatives of the molecule in which some of the elements of symmetry are no longer present. The symmetry of the derivative molecules and the representation to which the mode belongs in the symmetric parent molecule determine in which of the derivative molecules the fundamental is allowed. The prediction of modes active in the derivative molecules is a simple matter with the use of the tables of symmetry reduction (Tables 8-2a,b,c), which show how the representations reduce to simpler ones embracing fewer covering operations as the elements of symmetry are removed. The tables, as presented here, are grossly abbreviated but complete enough for the majority of applications to organic molecules.*

Table 8-2a shows how the symmetry of D_{6h} molecules (benzene and homo-hexa-substituted benzenes) reduce as derivatives are made; Table 8-2b gives similar information for derivatives of molecules of symmetry $D_{2h} \equiv V_h$ (ethylene and naphthalene are examples); and Table 8-2c applies to parent molecules of C_{2v} symmetry (e.g., ethylene oxide, phthalic anhydride, formaldehyde). Because in certain cases the choice of symmetry reduction is not unique, the manner of symmetry reduction is indicated above the symmetry notation of each lower symmetry group. For example, D_{6h} can be reduced to C_{2v} by having the dihedral rotation axis through a carbon atom (C_2') become the C_2 axis in the derivative molecule (benzene → chlorobenzene) or by having the dihedral rotation axis through the midpoint of a C—C bond (C_2'') become the C_2 axis in the derivative molecule (benzene → o-dichlorobenzene). The manner of symmetry reduction must be carefully considered in determining the selection rules of analogous modes between parent molecules and molecules of reduced symmetry.

The symmetry reduction tables are used in the following way: Suppose it is known that a particular mode to which the fundamental transition is forbidden in a symmetrical molecule (say, benzene) is reasonably similar to a mode in a less symmetrical molecule (say, p-dichlorobenzene). The representation to which this mode belongs in benzene is located in the column under D_{6h} of Table 8-2a, and the representation to which it reduces in p-dichlorobenzene is found in the same row under column D_{2h}. If this representation corresponds to a translation vector in point group D_{2h} (see Table 8-1i), the mode is allowed in p-dichlorobenzene. If the symmetry reduction is to another point group (D_{3h} for 1,3,5-trichlorobenzene or C_s for 1,2,4-trichlorobenzene, for example) the representation for the mode in these molecules is found in the column headed by the appropriate point group notation. Table 8-2a may be used for symmetry reduction of any of

* Complete tables can be found in Reference 2, p. 333 ff.

Table 8-2
Tables of Symmetry Reduction

D_{6h}	$C_2' \rightarrow C_2'$ D_{3h}	$C_2'' \rightarrow C_2'$ D_{3h}	C_{3h}	C_3	$\sigma_h \rightarrow \sigma_{xy}$ $\sigma_v \rightarrow \sigma_{yz}$ D_{2h}	$C_2' \rightarrow C_2$ C_{2v}	$C_2'' \rightarrow C_2$ C_{2v}	$C_2 \rightarrow C_2$ C_{2h}	$\sigma_h \rightarrow \sigma$ C_s
A_{1g}	A_1'	A_1'	A'	A	A_g	A_1	A_1	A_g	A'
A_{1u}	A_1''	A_1''	A''	A	A_u	A_2	A_2	A_u	A''
A_{2g}	A_2'	A_2'	A'	A	B_{1g}	B_1	B_1	A_g	A'
A_{2u}	A_2''	A_2''	A''	A	B_{1u}	B_2	B_2	A_u	A''
B_{1g}	A_1''	A_2''	A''	A	B_{2g}	A_2	B_2	B_g	A''
B_{1u}	A_1'	A_2'	A'	A	B_{2u}	A_1	B_1	B_u	A'
B_{2g}	A_2''	A_1''	A''	A	B_{3g}	B_2	A_2	B_g	A''
B_{2u}	A_2'	A_1'	A'	A	B_{3u}	B_1	A_1	B_u	A'
E_{1g}	E''	E''	E''	E	$B_{2g}+B_{3g}$	A_2+B_2	A_2+B_2	$2B_g$	$2A''$
E_{1u}	E'	E'	E'	E	$B_{2u}+B_{3u}$	A_1+B_1	A_1+B_1	$2B_u$	$2A'$
E_{2g}	E'	E'	E'	E	A_g+B_{1g}	A_1+B_1	A_1+B_1	$2A_g$	$2A^1$
E_{2u}	E''	E''	E''	E	A_u+B_{1u}	A_2+B_2	A_2+B_2	$2A_u$	$2A''$

(a)

D_{2h}	$C_{2(y)} \rightarrow C_2$ C_{2v}	$C_{2(x)} \rightarrow C_2$ C_{2v}	$C_{2(z)} \rightarrow C_2$ C_{2h}	$\sigma_h \rightarrow \sigma$ C_s
A_g	A_1	A_1	A_g	A'
A_u	A_2	A_2	A_u	A''
B_{1g}	B_2	B_1	A_g	A'
B_{1u}	B_1	B_2	A_u	A''
B_{2g}	A_2	B_2	B_g	A''
B_{2u}	A_1	B_1	B_u	A'
B_{3g}	B_1	A_2	B_g	A''
B_{3u}	B_2	A_1	B_u	A'

(b)

C_{2v}	C_2	$\sigma \rightarrow \sigma$ C_s	$\sigma' \rightarrow \sigma$ C_s
A_1	A	A'	A'
A_2	A	A''	A''
B_1	B	A'	A''
B_2	B	A''	A'

(c)

Symmetry considerations **295**

the triclinic (C_3 and higher) groups. For molecules whose parent symmetry is D_{2h} or C_{2v}, Tables 8-2b and 8-2c, respectively, must be used. This application of group theory can be illustrated by a practical example: There is a normal mode in benzene that can be illustrated approximately

and is denoted ω_{20}.* Reference to the character table for D_{6h} shows that the mode is degenerate, since it is neither symmetric nor antisymmetric to several of the rotation axes. It does not change sign under operation C_2 but does change sign under both σ_h (reflection at the plane of the ring) and I (inversion). Hence it belongs to representation E_{2u}, for which the fundamental transition is forbidden. Reference to Table 8-2a now allows us to predict for which of the simple substituted benzenes† the degeneracy of an analogous mode will be split (to two nondegenerate modes) and which of these is infrared active.

In 1,3,5-trisubstituted benzenes (D_{3h}) the representation reduces to E'', which is doubly degenerate and still forbidden. (See Table 8-1l.)

In p-disubstituted and 1,2,4,5-tetrasubstituted benzenes (D_{2h}) the representation reduces to $A_u + B_{1u}$, showing that the degeneracy has been split into two modes: A_u is forbidden but B_{1u} is allowed.

In monosubstituted, 1,2- and 1,3-disubstituted, 1,2,3-trisubstituted, 1,2,3,4- and 1,2,3,5-tetrasubstituted, and pentasubstituted benzenes (all C_{2v} symmetry‡) representation E_{2u} reduces to $A_2 + B_2$, again showing that the degeneracy has been split into two modes: A_2 is forbidden, but B_2 is allowed.

Finally, in 1,2,4-trisubstituted benzenes (C_s symmetry) E_{2u} reduces

* See Reference 3, p. 118.
† Strictly speaking, this discussion pertains only to substituted benzenes in which all substituents are identical. Actually, as long as the substituents are not grossly dissimilar, a p-disubstituted benzene behaves as if the molecule had essentially D_{2h} symmetry; the other substituted benzenes behave in analogous fashion. This point is amplified in later chapters in Volume 2, which discuss some of the characteristic modes of aromatic molecules in detail.
‡ The symmetry reduction for 1,2-disubstituted benzenes is different from the others of symmetry C_{2v}, but the results in this case are the same.

to $A'' + A''$, showing that the degeneracy has been split into two modes, but both of representation A'' and both allowed.

It is interesting to note that these transitions have been characterized for several alkylbenzenes:[*] all D_{2h} and C_{2v} types show a strong absorption near 475 cm^{-1}; benzene and 1,3,5-trialkylbenzenes show no such strong absorption in this region, whereas 1,2,4-trialkylbenzenes show *two* strong absorptions.

III. Rotation-vibration bands

In Chapter 5 we briefly noted that molecules in the vapor phase are free to rotate, hence to undergo transitions between (quantized) rotation states as well as vibrational transitions. The result is that a transition between the ground state and a first excited state of a normal mode is accompanied by a manifold of rotational transitions, which leads to a complex rotation-vibration band; a few of these bands were illustrated in Figures 5-11, 5-12, and 5-13. Although, as discussed in Chapter 5, vapor-phase spectra are not often useful for practical qualitative and quantitative analysis, they can be applied in assigning a particular fundamental to its proper symmetry representation; for linear molecules, planar molecules, and molecules with a high degree of symmetry this is particularly true. As we saw in the preceding section, the identity of the representation to which a mode belongs, together with the empirical data of the "group frequencies," can be used to deduce a great deal about the nature of the mode. This section shows how the appearance of a rotation-vibration band can be used to determine its symmetry representation.

The theory of rotation-vibration spectra is complex, and the following discussion can be regarded only as a qualitative outline. We shall confine our discussion to the appearance of rotation-vibration bands for molecules of high symmetry, but these are just the molecules for which we would use rotation-vibration information to assign representations of normal modes.

A. Diatomic molecules

Although diatomic molecules do not constitute a useful portion of organic chemistry, the theory of rotation-vibration bands of diatomic molecules is simple, and we shall begin by discussing this type. Just as vibrational energy is *quantized* into discrete levels (see equation 2-10),

* See Reference 10.

so also is rotational energy. These levels are given by the relation

$$E_{\text{rotation}} = \frac{h^2}{8\pi^2 I} (J)(J + 1), \qquad J = 0, 1, 2, 3, \cdots, \qquad (8\text{-}29)$$

where h is Plank's constant, $I = \sum_{i}^{N} m_i r_i^2$ is the moment of inertia of the (diatomic) molecule about its center of mass,* and $J =$ the *total angular momentum quantum number* and may have only the values of zero and positive integers. The energy in terms of wave numbers (cm^{-1}) is

$$\frac{E_{\text{rotation}}}{hc} = \omega_{\text{rotation}} = \frac{h}{8\pi^2 c I} (J)(J + 1) = B(J)(J + 1). \quad (8\text{-}30)$$

It is usually assumed in considering the energy states (both vibrational and rotational) of molecules that the energy is accurately separable into a term depending only on rotational energy and another term depending only on vibrational energy:

$$E_{\text{rotation-vibration}} = E_{\text{rotation}} + E_{\text{vibration}}. \quad (8\text{-}31)$$

Although not strictly true (e.g., vibration of the molecule alters the moment of inertia and causes rotation-vibration interactions), this is a reasonably good approximation which is often employed.

Now, transitions between rotational levels can occur as the result of absorption of quanta of radiation of the appropriate frequency, as determined by equation 8-30. In order to produce pure rotational transitions, the frequencies required are low and occur in the so-called "microwave" region of the spectrum (see Figure 1-1). Transitions between rotational states can also occur simultaneously with transitions between vibrational states as a result of radiation absorption provided that (a) the energy of the quantum absorbed is the *algebraic sum* of the energy difference between vibrational states and the energy difference between rotational states and (b) the direction of dipole moment change during the vibration *is not colinear with the axis about which rotation occurs*. (The second condition is important; it is the basis for the use of rotation-vibration bands to determine the direction of dipole-moment change for a normal mode, hence its symmetry representation.)

* Diatomic molecules have two equal moments of inertia about two mutually perpendicular axes which are perpendicular to the molecular axis. The moment of inertia about the molecular axis is, for the purpose of this discussion, zero.

We shall be concerned here only with fundamental transitions ($n = 0 \rightarrow n = 1$). Condition (a) and equations 8-30 and 31 show that the frequency of an individual rotation-vibration absorption maximum is

$$\omega = \Delta \left(\frac{E_{\text{rotation-vibration}}}{hc} \right) = \left(\frac{E'_{\text{vibration}}}{hc} - \frac{E_{\text{vibration}}}{hc} \right)$$
$$+ \left(\frac{E'_{\text{rotation}}}{hc} - \frac{E_{\text{rotation}}}{hc} \right)$$
$$= \omega_0 + B'J'(J' + 1) - BJ(J + 1). \tag{8-32}$$

where the prime designates the first excited vibrational state of the mode being excited (B' is not exactly equal to B because the moment of inertia may change slightly on excitation of vibration), and ω_0 is the frequency that would be observed if no rotation occurred, that is, the frequency of vibration alone.

Just as radiation-induced transitions between energy levels of a quantum-mechanical oscillator are subject to selection rules, so are transitions between energy levels of a quantum-mechanical rotator. For diatomic molecules the selection rule is

$$\Delta J = \pm 1. \tag{8-33}$$

When $\Delta J = +1$, then $J' = J + 1$, and from equation 8-32

$$\omega = \omega_0 + (B' - B)(J^2 + J) + 2B'(J + 1). \tag{8-34a}$$

An analogous equation results when $\Delta J = -1$:

$$\omega = \omega_0 + (B' - B)(J^2 + J) - 2B'J. \tag{8-34b}$$

If the moment of inertia in ground and first excited vibrational states may be regarded as essentially identical, then $B' \approx B$, and

$$\omega = \omega_0 \begin{cases} +2B(J + 1) & \Delta J = +1 \ (R \text{ branch}) \\ -2BJ & \Delta J = -1 \ (P \text{ branch}). \end{cases} \tag{8-35}$$

Transitions of this sort for $J = 0$ through $J = 5$ are illustrated schematically by Figure 8-3. It can be seen that transitions of one group (called the "R branch") have frequencies successively higher than ω_0, and equally spaced, whereas transitions of the other group (called the "P branch") have frequencies lower than ω_0; no transition corresponding to ω_0 is possible in this case. The rotation-vibration spectrum of HCl is illustrated in Figure 5-13. This spectrum is quite typical of the rotation spectrum of any diatomic molecule; the

Rotation-vibration bands **299**

spacing between the individual rotation lines depends on the magnitude of B, the rotational constant, which in turn depends on the moment of inertia of the molecule. (See equation 8-30.) In the case of HCl the individual lines are well resolved, for I_{HCl} is small, hence B is large. A much heavier molecule, such as ICl, would have a much smaller value for B, and the individual lines would not be resolved by the spectrometers used for practical chemical analysis (see Chapter 4); in this case only a *band contour* would result, as sketched in Figure 8-4. If a spectrometer of low resolving power is employed, molecules of intermediate moment of inertia, such as CO, would have a band contour similar to that of Figure 8-4.

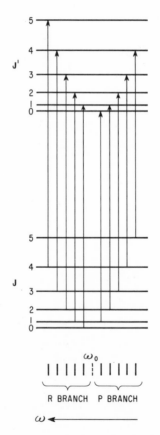

FIGURE 8.3   Energy levels and allowed transitions in the rotation-vibration band of a diatomic molecule.   (After Herzberg, Reference 3.)

300   *Theory of infrared spectra of polyatomic molecules*

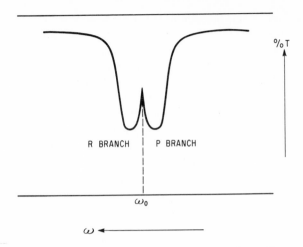

R BRANCH | P BRANCH

ω_0

$\omega \longleftarrow$

FIGURE 8-4   The rotation-vibration band contour for a diatomic molecule.   (Compare with Figure 5-13.)

B. Linear molecules

The rotation-vibration bands of linear molecules are somewhat similar to those of diatomic molecules, for linear molecules also have two equal moments of inertia about axes perpendicular to the molecular axes and to one another.   However, an important difference results from the fact that linear molecules have two distinct types of vibrations.

1. For all infrared-active stretching vibrations the dipole-moment change occurs along the direction of the molecular axis.   A dipole moment change in this direction can lead to excitation of rotation, just as in the case of diatomic molecules.

2. For all infrared-active bending vibrations the dipole-moment change occurs in a direction perpendicular to the molecular axis.   A dipole-moment change in this direction can still excite rotation about the *other* rotation axis (perpendicular to both the molecular axis and the direction of dipole-moment change); however, the selection rules for rotational transitions are different in this case, as discussed later. Perpendicular vibrations are, of course, not possible in a diatomic molecule.*

The rotational energy levels of a linear molecule are the same as

* It is, however, possible for a diatomic molecule containing an unpaired electron (such as NO) to have the *appearance* of a perpendicular band.   See Reference 3, p. 44.

Rotation-vibration bands   **301**

those of a diatomic molecule and the frequency of a specific rotation peak in a rotation-vibration band is given by equation 8-32.

When the dipole-moment change is along the molecular axis (stretching vibration), the rotational selection rule is $\Delta J = \pm 1$. As a result, equations 8-34a and 8-34b describe the frequency of each rotation peak in the R and P branches, respectively, and the transitions are as illustrated by Figure 8-3, just as in diatomic molecules. This type of band is called a *parallel band*. If the moment of inertia is large (B is small) or the spectrometer resolving power is not high, a band envelope as sketched in Figure 8-4 will be observed for the transition.

When the dipole-moment change is perpendicular to the molecular axis (bending vibration), the rotational selection rule is $\Delta J = 0, \pm 1$. As a result, P and R branches arise, just as in a parallel band; however, because ΔJ is allowed to be zero, a transition is also allowed to occur from each J level to the corresponding J' level in the excited state ($J = 1 \rightarrow J' = 1$, $J = 2 \rightarrow J' = 2$, etc.). The equation for these $\Delta J = 0$ transitions is simply

$$\omega = \omega_0 + (B' - B)(J^2 + J), \qquad (8\text{-}36)$$

which means that, if $B' \approx B$, there will be many individual transitions of identical or nearly identical frequency, and this frequency is essentially that of vibration alone, ω_0. The coincidence of these many

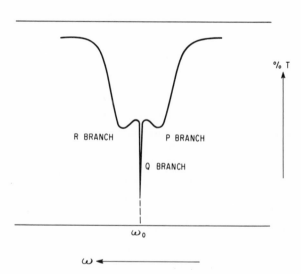

R BRANCH   P BRANCH

Q BRANCH

%T

ω_0

$\omega \longleftarrow$

FIGURE 8-5   The rotation-vibration band contour of a perpendicular band of a linear molecule. (Compare with Figure 5-11.)

302   *Theory of infrared spectra of polyatomic molecules*

transitions results in a sharp, intense absorption maximum at ω_0, which is called the "Q branch." The combination of the usual broad P and R branches with the sharp, central Q branch is called a *perpendicular band*. Figure 5-11 illustrates a perpendicular band for a linear molecule obtained on two spectrometers of different resolving power. If the moment of inertia of a linear molecule is large (B is small) or the spectrometer resolving power is not high, a band envelope as sketched in Figure 8-5 will be observed for the transition.

C. *"Symmetric top" molecules*

Nonlinear molecules will have three moments of inertia defined about three mutually perpendicular axes (rather than the two equal moment-of-inertia axes of linear molecules), and as a result the rotational energy levels are more complex. The simplest case for non-linear molecules is the so-called "symmetric top," which is any molecule having a threefold or greater symmetry axis (i.e., all molecules belonging to point groups having the element C_3—see Tables 8-1). I_A is defined as the moment of inertia about the symmetry axis. The other two moment-of-inertia axes are perpendicular to the symmetry axis and mutually perpendicular; the moments of inertia about these axes are identical as a result of the threefold (or greater) symmetry and are defined I_B. We define, in a manner analogous to equation 8-30,

$$B = \frac{h}{8\pi^2 c I_B}; \qquad A = \frac{h}{8\pi^2 c I_A}.$$

The quantized energy of rotation for a symmetric top is given by

$$\frac{E_{\text{rotation}}}{hc} = BJ(J + 1) + (A - B)K^2. \tag{8-37}$$

In this case J is called the *total angular momentum quantum number* and can have the values $J = 0, 1, 2, 3 \cdots$; K is the *quantum number of angular momentum about the symmetry axis* and can have the values $K = 0, 1, 2, 3, \cdots$. Because angular momentum about the symmetry axis cannot be greater than total angular momentum, $J \geqslant K$ (i.e., states where $K = 4$, say, can exist only when J is 4 or more).

It is convenient to differentiate between two different types of symmetric top: prolate and oblate. A *prolate* symmetric top is one which is essentially rod-shaped, so that the moments of inertia about the axes *perpendicular* to the symmetry axis are larger than the moment of inertia about the symmetry axis, $I_B > I_A$; as a consequence, $A > B$.

An *oblate* symmetric top is essentially disk-shaped, so that $I_A > I_B$, hence $B > A$. Equation 8-37 shows that for a given J the energy of the state *increases* with increasing K for a prolate top but *decreases* with increasing K for an oblate top.

If the fundamental vibrational transition is to a mode whose dipole-moment change is along the symmetry (I_A) axis (modes which belong to A-type representations), it is not possible for rotation about the symmetry axis to be excited; hence $\Delta K = 0$. When $\Delta K = 0$, the J selection rules are

$$\Delta J = \pm 1 \qquad \text{for } K = 0$$
$$\Delta J = 0, \pm 1 \qquad \text{for } K \neq 0.$$

Equations analogous to 8-34a and 8-34b can be derived by analogous means:

for $K = 0$: $\quad \omega = \omega_0 + $
$$\begin{cases} (B' - B)(J^2 + J) + 2B'(J + 1) & \Delta J = +1 \text{ (R branch)} \\ (B' - B)(J^2 + J) - 2B'J & \Delta J = -1 \text{ (P branch)}, \end{cases}$$
$$(8\text{-}38)$$

for $K \neq 0$: $\quad \omega = \omega_0 + [(A' - B') - (A - B)]K^2 + $
$$\begin{cases} (B' - B)(J^2 + J) + 2B'(J + 1) & \Delta J = +1 \text{ (R branch)} \\ (B' - B)(J^2 + J) & \Delta J = 0 \text{ (Q branch)} \\ (B' - B)(J^2 + J) - 2B'J & \Delta J = -1 \text{ (P branch)}. \end{cases}$$
$$(8\text{-}39)$$

The energy levels are illustrated by Figure 8-6; the diagram is analogous to Figure 8-3, but consists of many columns, each corresponding to a different value of K. The transitions for a given K are called a sub-band. Equation 8-38 shows that the $K = K' = 0$ sub-band consists of P- and R-branch collections of lines, similar to those illustrated in Figure 8-3. Equation 8-39 shows that the $K = K' \neq 0$ sub-bands also give a P- and R-branch collection of lines, and in addition yield a Q branch $(\Delta J = 0)$; the collection of these lines for a single nonzero K would give a band contour similar to that of Figure 8-5. If $A' \approx A$ and $B' \approx B$, the several collections of lines will have nearly the same frequency for each of the several K values; they will be essentially superimposable and will produce a band contour similar to that of Figure 8-5. This is a *parallel band*. Parallel bands of symmetric tops have similar appearance, whether for prolate or oblate molecules. The spacings between the individual lines (if they can be resolved) and the width of the over-all band contour depend on the magnitude of B.

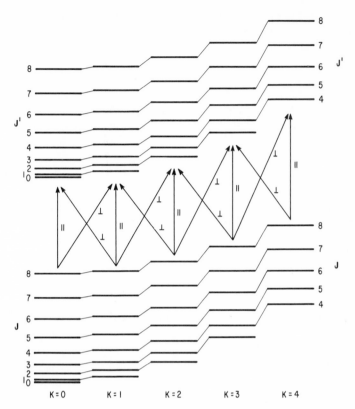

FIGURE 8-6 *The energy levels in a rotation-vibration band of a symmetric top molecule. (After Herzberg, Reference 3.) The case illustrated is for a prolate top; oblate tops have decreasing energy with increasing K. (See equation 8-37.)*

If the fundamental vibrational transition is to a mode whose dipole-moment change is perpendicular to the symmetry axis (modes which belong to E-type representations), rotation about the symmetry axis can be excited. For angular momentum change about the symmetry axis the selection rule is $\Delta K = \pm 1$; when $\Delta K = \pm 1$, the selection rule for total angular momentum change is $\Delta J = 0, \pm 1$. The equations for the individual lines then become (with $A' \approx A$, $B' \approx B$, and neglecting coriolis interaction*)

* Coriolis interactions can have pronounced effects on band contours, particularly on perpendicular bands of prolate tops. A discussion of this effect is beyond the scope of this treatment, however. See Reference 3, Chapter 4.

for $\Delta K = +1$: $\quad \omega = \omega_0 +$

$$
\begin{cases}
(A - B)(2K + 1) + 2B(J + 1) & \Delta J = +1 \ (R \text{ branch}) \\
(A - B)(2K + 1) & \Delta J = 0 \ (Q \text{ branch}) \\
(A - B)(2K + 1) - 2BJ & \Delta J = -1 \ (P \text{ branch}),
\end{cases}
$$

$$(8\text{-}40)$$

for $\Delta K = -1$: $\quad \omega = \omega_0 +$

$$
\begin{cases}
-(A - B)(2K - 1) + 2B(J + 1) & \Delta J = +1 \ (R \text{ branch}) \\
-(A - B)(2K - 1) & \Delta J = 0 \ (Q \text{ branch}) \\
-(A - B)(2K - 1) - 2BJ & \Delta J = -1 \ (P \text{ branch}).
\end{cases}
$$

$$(8\text{-}41)$$

The transitions possible are illustrated schematically by Figure 8-6. Equations 8-40 and 8-41 show that each collection of transitions between adjacent K levels (a sub-band) produces P, Q, and R branches; however, each different sub-band has a different energy separation, this difference resulting from the term $(A - B)(2K \pm 1)$ in the equations. For this reason the band contours of perpendicular bands of symmetric tops vary widely as the relative magnitudes of A and B vary.

Prolate (rod-shaped) symmetric tops have $I_A \ll I_B$, and $A \gg B$; hence the term $(A - B)(2K \pm 1)$ in equations 8-40 and 8-41 is large. The separation of individual lines in a sub-band depends on the magnitude of B; the separation between Q branches of sub-bands depends on $(A - B)$, which for the case of prolate tops may be much larger than B. As a result, the appearance of a band contour for a perpendicular band of a prolate top is complex and will consist of more or less continuous absorption on which is superimposed the various intense Q branches of the individual sub-bands: the larger $(A - B)$, the larger the separation between the sharp Q branches. Figure 8-7 is a vapor spectrum of methyl chloride, a typical prolate top. The bands at $3042 \text{ cm}^{-1} = \omega_4$, $1455 = \omega_5$, and $1015 = \omega_6$ are perpendicular bands.*

Oblate (disk-shaped) symmetric tops can have I_A at most only twice as large as I_B ($I_A = 2I_B$ for planar molecules), or $A \geq \frac{1}{2}B$. Therefore $|A - B|$, which determines the spacing between individual sub-bands, can be no larger† than $\frac{1}{2}B$ so that the spacing between

---

* The calculation of these band centers from each of these band contours is a complex process and beyond the scope of this treatment. (See Reference 3, Chapter 4.)
† In certain cases *Coriolis coupling* can increase the effective value of $|A - B|$; however, it can never be larger than B, thus giving a Q-branch spacing of at most $2B$, which is no greater than the spacing between adjacent lines in a P- or R-branch sub-band. (See Reference 3, Chapter 4.)

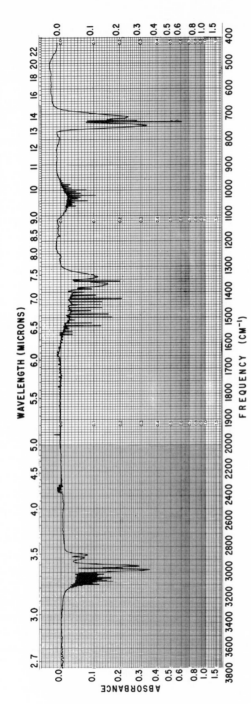

FIGURE 8-7 The vapor spectrum of methyl chloride. $\omega_1 = 2966\ cm^{-1}$ (symmetric C-H stretch), $\omega_2 = 1355\ cm^{-1}$ (symmetric C-H deformation), and $\omega_3 = 732\ cm^{-1}$ (C-Cl stretch) have their dipole moment change along the principal symmetry axis, hence are parallel bands. (A-representation of point group C_{3v}). $\omega_4 = 3042\ cm^{-1}$ (asymmetric C-H stretch), $\omega_5 = 1455\ cm^{-1}$ (asymmetric C-H deformation), and $\omega_6 = 1015\ cm^{-1}$ (methyl rock) have their dipole moment change perpendicular to the principal symmetry axis, hence are perpendicular bands (E-representation of point group C_{3v}). The normal coordinates of these vibrations are shown in Figure 8-1b. The band at $2879\ cm^{-1}$ is the first overtone of ω_5.

307

Q branches is no greater than B, or half the spacing between adjacent lines in a P or R branch ($2B$). The result is that a perpendicular band for oblate tops will have somewhat the same appearance as a parallel band (Figure 8-5), but the collection of Q branches will not be so sharp and intense as the Q branch for parallel bands.

D. "Asymmetric top" molecules

As might be expected, the energy-level pattern for an asymmetric-top molecule will be considerably more complicated than that of a symmetric top. We shall be concerned here only with planar molecules, or molecules that are *nearly* planar (as ethylene oxide, acetyl chloride, or toluene), for in the case of planar molecules it is still possible to determine the direction of dipole-moment change from the nature of the rotation-vibration band in certain cases.

An asymmetric top is one in which the three moments of inertia about the (mutually perpendicular) axes are all different: $I_C > I_B > I_A$. Convention defines I_C as the moment of inertia about the axis for which it is largest, I_A as the moment of inertia about the axis for which it is smallest; I_B is the moment of inertia about the axis perpendicular to these perpendicular axes and about which the moment of inertia is intermediate between I_C and I_A. As a result,

$$A = \frac{h}{8\pi^2 c I_A} > B = \frac{h}{8\pi^2 c I_B} > C = \frac{h}{8\pi^2 c I_C}. \qquad (8\text{-}42)$$

The energy levels for an asymmetric top are given by

$$\frac{E_{\text{rotation}}}{hc} = \tfrac{1}{2}(A + C)J(J + 1) + \tfrac{1}{2}(A - C)E_\tau, \qquad (8\text{-}43)$$

where E_τ is itself a complex function* of A, B, C, and J. As before, J is the quantum number of *total angular momentum* and can have the values $J = 0, 1, 2, 3, \cdots$. The energy-level diagram, hence the appearance of the rotation-vibration band contour, depend strongly on the relative values of A, B, and C.

It is convenient in the following discussion of vibration-rotation bands of asymmetric top molecules to consider them in reference to certain limiting cases. (This discussion is strictly applicable only to planar molecules, for which $I_C = I_B + I_A$.) If the molecule has $I_A \approx I_B \approx \tfrac{1}{2}I_C$, so that $A \approx B \approx 2C$, it is essentially an oblate top

* See Reference 3, p. 44 ff.

(example: pentafluorobenzene, H⟨F F / F F⟩F).   At the other extreme, if

$I_A \ll I_B \approx I_C$, so that $A \gg B \approx C$, it is essentially a prolate top

(example: formaldehyde, $\text{H}{\diagdown}\atop{\diagup}\text{H}$ $C{=}O$).

If a planar asymmetric top molecule has C_{2v} or $D_{2h} \equiv V_h$ symmetry, the axes of the moments of inertia are identical to the direction of dipole-moment change during the various normal vibrations.
This makes it possible to determine the symmetry representation of
each fundamental, for the form of the rotation-vibration band contour
depends strongly on whether the dipole moment change is along the
axis of smallest, intermediate, or largest moment of inertia.

1. When the dipole-moment change is along the axis of *least* moment
of inertia (I_A), the band is known as type A.   In the limiting case
of a prolate top $(A \gg B \approx C)$ the band contour is that of a *parallel
band* of a symmetric (prolate) top: a sharp Q branch and rather broad
P and R branches, as shown by Figure 8-5.   In the other limiting case
of the oblate top $(A \approx B \approx 2C)$ the band contour will be that of a
perpendicular band of a symmetric (oblate) top, similar to a parallel
band of a prolate top, but the Q branch will be somewhat less sharp
and intense.   For intermediate cases $[0 < (B/A) < 1]$ a type-A band
will have a contour showing a fairly sharp Q branch, as in Figure 8-8.

2. When the dipole-moment change is along the axis of *intermediate*
moment of inertia (I_B), the band is known as type B.   In the limiting
case of a prolate top $(A \gg B \approx C)$ the band contour will be that of a
perpendicular band of a symmetric (prolate) top: several widely spaced
intense Q branches superimposed on a broad near-continuum (as the
perpendicular bands in Figure 8-7).   In the limiting case of an oblate
top $(A \approx B \approx 2C)$ the band will be like a *perpendicular band* of a
symmetric (oblate) top and will be indistinguishable from a type-A
band.   However, for cases intermediate between the two, as the molecule leaves the oblate case $(B/A \approx 1)$ and approaches the prolate case
$(B/A \ll 1)$ the Q branch splits into two strong maxima, leaving a low-
intensity minimum between the two.   This splitting increases as B/A
decreases until for values of B/A near 0 the band is like the perpendicular bands in Figure 8-7.   For values of $B/A \sim 0.2$ (representative

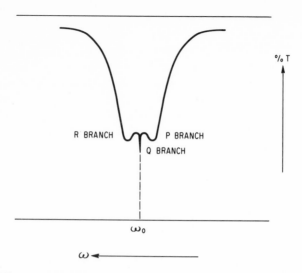

FIGURE 8-8 A typical "type-A" rotation-vibration band contour.

of many molecules of C_{2v} and D_{2h} symmetry) the type-B band contour is similar to that shown in Figure 8-9.

3. When the dipole-moment change is along the axis of *largest* moment of inertia (I_C), the band is known as type C.   In the limiting case of the prolate top ($A \gg B \approx C$) a type-C band will be like a perpendicular band of a symmetrical (prolate) top; it will have a con-

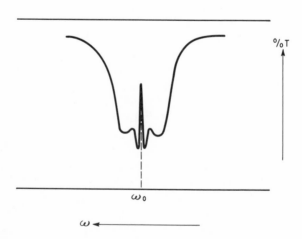

FIGURE 8-9   A typical "type-B" rotation-vibration band contour.

310   Theory of infrared spectra of polyatomic molecules

tour similar to that shown for the perpendicular bands of Figure 8-7 and will be indistinguishable from a type-B band for prolate tops. In the limiting case of the oblate top ($A \approx B \approx 2C$) the band contour is now that of a parallel band of a symmetric (oblate) top: there will be a strong, sharp Q branch, similar to the contour shown in Figure 8-5. In the intermediate cases, as the molecule leaves the prolate case ($B/A \ll 1$) and approaches the oblate case ($B/A \approx 1$), the Q branches at the band center rapidly rise in intensity while all the Q branches shrink together into a strong, sharp maximum; these intermediate cases will therefore have a contour more nearly like that shown in Figure 8-5.

For many molecules of C_{2v} or D_{2h} symmetry little difficulty is encountered in determining the bands that are type-B, but type-A and type-C bands are often hard to distinguish, since they are similar in general form. However, there is some tendency for the Q branch to be sharper and stronger in type-C bands. (Compare Figures 8-8 and 8-5.) The general form of the band contours of the various band types has been calculated* for several relative values of A, B, and C, and reference to these "standard" band contours can often be helpful in determining the band type.

If the molecule is planar (or nearly so), but does not have C_{2v} or D_{2h} symmetry, then the dipole-moment change of the in-plane modes will not be along the moment of inertia axes. As a result, the rotation-vibration band contours are neither type A nor type B, but are hybrids of the two, and are not very useful for assigning the vibration types. However, vibrations whose dipole-moment change is perpendicular to the plane of the molecule still have an appearance quite similar to type-C bands of the more symmetrical molecules: a sharp, intense Q branch is observed, similar to that shown in Figure 8-5.

It must be emphasized that the band contours illustrated here for asymmetric-top molecules can serve only as a rough guide to the appearance of band contours in actual cases. Dissimilarity of the moments of inertia in excited and ground states, and particularly Coriolis interactions, can in some cases distort the band contour so severely that deductions of direction of dipole-moment change cannot be made from low-resolution spectra. With the aid of vapor spectra obtained at very high resolution and the theory of these perturbations, it again becomes possible to determine the direction of dipole-moment change in some cases. These methods, however, are beyond the scope of our discussion here. (See Reference 3.)

* See Reference 11.

Selected references

1. Margenau, H., and G. M. Murphy, *The Mathematics of Physics and Chemistry*, Van Nostrand, Princeton, New Jersey, 1943.
2. Wilson, E. B., Jr., J. C. Decius, and P. C. Cross, *Molecular Vibrations*, McGraw-Hill, New York, 1955.
3. Herzberg, G., *Infrared and Raman Spectra*, Van Nostrand, Princeton, New Jersey, 1945.
4. Crawford, B. L., and W. H. Fletcher, *The Determination of Normal Coordinates*, *J. Chem. Phys.* **19**, 141, 1951.
5. Meister, A. G., and F. F. Cleveland, "Application of Group Theory to the Calculation of Vibrational Frequencies of Polyatomic Molecules," *Am. J. Phys.* **14**, 13 (1946).
6. Overend, J., and J. Scherer, "Transferability of Urey-Bradley Force Constants," *J. Chem. Phys.* **32**, 1289 (1960).
7. Coulson, C. A., "Some Theoretical Considerations about Vibrational Band Intensities," *Spectrochim. Acta* **14**, 161 (1959).
8. Meister, A. G., F. F. Cleveland, and M. J. Murray, "Interpretation of the Spectra of Polyatomic Molecules by Use of Group Theory," *Am. J. Phys.* **11**, 239 (1943).
9. Duncan, A. B. F., "Theory of Infrared and Raman Spectra," *Techniques of Organic Chemistry*, Vol. IX (p. 187 ff) Interscience, New York, 1956.
10. Bentley, F. F., and E. F. Wolfarth, "Analytical Applications of Far Infrared Spectra—II. Spectra-Structure Correlations for Aliphatic and Aromatic Hydrocarbons in the Cesium Bromide Region," *Spectrochim. Acta* **15**, 165 (1959).
11. Badger, R. M., and L. R. Zumwalt, "The Band Envelopes of Unsymmetrical Rotator Molecules," *J. Chem. Phys.* **6**, 711 (1938).

Index

Aberration, chromatic, 11, 234
spherical, 32
Absorbance, 158 ff.
additivity in multicomponent analysis, 181 ff, 201 f.
baseline, 165 ff.
Beer's law, 156 ff., 174 ff., 223
cell-in-cell-out, 161 ff.
definition, 159
integrated, 196 ff.
relation to concentration, 159, 164, 180, 184 ff., 189 ff., 222 f.
relation to transmission, 159, 171 f., 222 f.
Absorption band, see Band
Absorption cells, see Cells
Absorption coefficient, 157 f.
Absorption spectrum, 20, 28
Absorption (transition between states), 18 ff.
Absorptivity, 157 f.
Accuracy in quantitative analysis, 170 ff., 187 f., 218, 220 ff.
Acetone (solvent), 99 ff., 131, 133, 134, 144
Acetonitrile (solvent), 99 ff.
Adsorbed molecules, spectra of, 242 ff.

AgCl, see Silver chloride
Amplification and amplifiers, 59 ff., 75 f., 78 ff.
Amplitude of vibration, 11, 17, 266 ff.
Angular dispersion, 39, 46 f., 50 f.
Angular momentum quantum number, 298 ff.
Anharmonicity, 22 ff., 25 f.
constant, 23
negative, 23 f.
Anharmonic oscillator, 23
Aperture stop, 49
Asymmetric rotor, 308 ff.
Atmospheric absorptions, 65, 69, 80, 85
Attenuated total reflection, 238 ff.
"A type" band contour, 309 f.
Automatic gain control, 90, 210 ff.
Automatic slit control, 90, 214 ff.
Automatic speed suppression, 89
Auxiliary apparatus, 204 ff.

BaF₂, see Barium fluoride
Band contour, Lorentzian, 177 ff., 197 ff.
Band contour, rotation-vibration bands, 122 ff., 299 ff.
asymmetric rotor, 308 ff.

Band contour, rotation-vibration
bands, diatomic molecule, 297 ff.
linear molecule, 301 ff.
relation to dipole-moment change,
298
symmetric rotor, 303 ff.
Band pass of amplifiers, 62, 78 f.
Barium fluoride windows, 10
preparation, 112
water solutions, 226
Baselines, 165 ff., 200, 222 f.
compared to "cell-in-cell-out," 165
Beam condensers, 233 ff.
lens, 233 f.
off-axis ellipse, 234 f.
Schwartzchild microscope, 235 f.
Beer-Lambert law:
application, 159, 164, 180, 184 ff.,
189 ff., 222 f.
derivation, 156 ff.
failure of, 174 ff., 203, 218, 222 f.
Biological applications, 228 f.
Blackbody radiation, 7 ff., 53
slit program for, 52 ff.
sources of, 29 ff.
Blaze angle, 43
Bolometer detector, 57 f.
Boltzmann distribution, 21
Brewster's angle, 246 f.
Brightness, 7, 32, 51
"B type" band contour, 309 f.

Calcium fluoride prism, 10, 41
Calcium fluoride windows, 10
preparation, 112
Calibration of frequency (wavelength),
86, 124
Calibration in quantitative analysis, 86,
161 ff., 181, 184, 186, 192 f., 194 f.,
200 ff., 222 ff.
Cam, slit, 53
wavelength, 38
Capillary films, 130 ff.
Carbon disulfide (solvent), 94 ff., 99,
105 f., 250
Carbon tetrachloride (solvent), 94 ff.,
105
Cartesian coordinates, force constants
in, 259 ff.
representation of normal modes, 267 ff.

"CCl$_4$-CS$_2$" technique, 94 ff.
"Cell-in-cell-out" method, 161 ff.
compared to baselines, 165 ff.
Cell length, Beer's law, 157 ff., 163 f.
measurement, 117 ff.
quantitative analysis, 163 f.
relation to solvents and concentration, 94 ff.
Cells (liquid), compensated spectra, 215
construction and repair, 113 ff.
maintenance and use, 116 f.
windows for, 10 f., 107 ff.
Cells (special purpose), high temperature, 253
low temperature, 250 f.
micro, 233, 237
temperature measuring, 248 f.
variable length, 215
water solutions, 226
Cells (vapor), 127 ff.
high pressure, 129 f.
long path length, 230 ff., 238
Central force approximation, 273
Cesium bromide and iodide prisms, 10,
41
Cesium bromide and iodide windows,
10 f.
preparation, 112
Character (group theory), 280 ff.
of covering operations, 280 ff.
of geometric objects, 284 ff.
tables for point groups, 281 ff.
Chloroform (solvent), 100
Chopper (light), 59 ff., 63, 66 f., 70 f., 90
ac signal, 60
automatic servo programming, 90
optical-null spectrometer, 66 f.
ratio-recording spectrometer, 70 f.
scattered light, 60
speed of chopping, 63
Christiansen effect, 137 ff.
Chromatic aberration, 11, 234
Classical harmonic oscillator, see Harmonic oscillator
Cleaving salt crystals, 107 f.
Cloth lap (polishing), 108 f.
Collimator, 32 ff., 46, 49 ff.
Combination band, 25 f., 293
Compensated spectra, 204 ff.
difference spectra, 219 ff.

Compensated spectra, low I_0, 205 ff.
optimum transmission, 224 f.
solvent compensation, 105 ff., 208 ff.
Concentration, Beer's law relation,
157 ff., 163 f.
difference spectra, 222 ff.
quantitative analysis, 163 f.
relation to cell length and solvent,
94 ff., 215
solubility, 96, 97 ff.
Coordinates of molecular vibration,
259 ff.
Cartesian, 259 ff.
normal, 265 ff.
valence, 262 ff.
Copolymers, 134, 191 ff., 193 f.
Covering operations (group theory),
276 ff.
Crystalline solids, Christiansen effect,
137 ff.
infrared transmitting, see Windows
polymorphism, 139 ff., 152
preparation of samples, 135 ff.
mull technique, 141 ff.
pressed disk technique, 148 ff.
quantitative analysis, 141, 145, 152,
194 ff.
transmission by particles, 135 ff.
CsBr and CsI, see Cesium bromide and
iodide
"C type" band contours, 310 f.
Cutoff (optical materials), prisms, 40 f.
windows, 10

Damping, 81
"Dead" spectrum, 79 f., 105 ff., 205,
208 ff.
"Dead" spot, 85
"Dead" zero, 81 f.
Degeneracy, 26 ff., 284 f., 288, 296 f.
representations, 284 ff.
vibrations, 26 ff., 288, 296 f.
Degrees of freedom, 24, 262 f.
Detector, 36 f., 56 ff., 61 ff., 76, 78 f., 203
construction and types, 56 ff.
heat capacity and chopping speed, 63
minimum detectable power, 51, 62
mirror, 36 f.
noise, 62, 76, 78 f.
optics, 36 f.

Detector, slit image limitation, 203, 218,
222
theory, 61 ff.
Diatomic molecule, 17 ff., 297 ff.
o-Dichloro benzene (solvent), 134
Difference spectra, 219 ff.
Diffraction grating, see Grating
Diffraction limitation in monochromator, 47
Diffraction order, 42 ff.
elimination of overlap, 43 ff.
Dimethoxypropane (drying agent), 147
Dimethyl formamide (solvent), 134
Dioxane (solvent), 99, 102
Dipole-moment change in vibration,
condition for absorption, 18 ff.
direction and band contours, 298 ff.
intensity, 268 ff.
polarized light, 245
symmetry selection rules, 291 ff.
Dispersion, 39 f., 46 ff., 50 f.
grating, 47, 50 f.
prism, 39 ff., 47, 50 f.
relation to resolving power, 47 ff.
Double-beam spectrometer, 66 ff., 75 ff.,
165 ff., 204 ff.
compared to single-beam, 69 f., 88
compensated spectra, 105 ff., 204 ff.
limitations and uses, 69 f., 71 f., 75 ff.
operation and testing, 82 ff.
optical-null, 66 ff., 75 ff., 88
principle, 66 ff.
quantitative analysis, 165 ff., 219 ff.
ratio-recording, 70 ff., 82
special devices, 88 ff.
Double monochromators, 72 ff.
Drift, amplifiers, 60
servo system, 81, 85
spectrometer, 73

Electric vector of radiation, 2 ff., 245 ff.
Electromagnetic radiation, see Radiation
Electromagnetic spectrum, 6 f.
Ellipsoidal mirrors, 36 f., 234 f.
beam condenser, 234 f.
detector, 36 f.
Energy, detector, 12
kinetic energy, 13 f., 260 ff.
limited spectrometer, 51, 62

Energy, monochromator, 49 ff.
  per spectral slit width, 50 f.
  potential energy, 13 f., 259 ff.
  radiation, see Radiation
  relation to frequency, 4, 13, 16, 18 ff.,
    261 ff.
  rotation, see Rotation
  servo, 76 f., 79 ff., 85, 205, 208 ff.
  units, 5
  vibration, see Vibration
Entrance and exit slits, see Slit
Errors in quantitative analysis, 170 ff.,
  174 ff., 187 ff.
Excited states, see Rotation; Vibration
Extinction coefficient, 157 f.

Films, capillary, 130 ff.
  polymer, 132 ff.
Filter, electrical, 61, 78 f.
  order eliminating, 44
  scattered light, 55
Flatness (of windows), 111
Fluorolube (mulling agent), 145 f.
F matrix, 260, 263 ff., 271 ff.
f number, 49
Focal length, collimator, 33, 46 ff.
  effect on monochromator, 46 ff.
  ellipsoidal mirror, 37
  paraboloid, 33
  source mirror, 32
  spherical mirror, 32
Force constant, 12 ff., 16 f., 259 ff., 271 ff.
  central force approximation, 273
  determination, 271 ff.
  general quadratic (valence), 263 ff.
  matrix, 263, 271
  secular equation, 259 ff.
  Urey-Bradley, 274 f.
  valence approximation, 273 f.
Fore-prism, 44 f.
Frequency, 3 ff., 16 ff.
  absorption (function of), 20
  calibration of spectrometer, 86, 124
  Lorentzian band (function of), 177
  parameter, 261
  radiation, 3 ff.
  resolution of, 46 ff., 51 f., 78, 177
  scan, 37 f.
  vibration, 13 f., 261, 265

Fringes (optical), cell assembly, 114 f.
  cell measurement, 118 ff.
  window flatness, 111
Fundamental, 22, 24 ff.
  absorption band, 20
  number of, 24 ff.

Gain (amplifier), 60, 64 f., 76 ff., 79 ff.,
  83 ff., 90, 163, 205, 208 ff.
  automatic, 90, 213 ff.
  noise, 76 ff., 83 f., 205, 208 ff., 224 f.
  servo energy, 76 f., 79 ff., 84 f., 90,
    205, 208 ff.
Gas, see Vapor
Gaussian slit function, 177 ff.
Glass prisms, 41
Glass windows, 10
Globar, 30
G matrix, 264 f., 272 f.
Golay detector, 58 f.
Graphical methods (quantitative analysis), 181, 185 ff., 193
Grating, 37, 41 ff., 47, 51
  blaze angle, 43
  condition for diffraction, 42
  constant, 42, 47
  efficiency, 43
  monochromator, 37, 47, 51
  order, 41, 43 ff.
  order eliminator, 43 ff.
  resolving power, 47
Grinding (windows), 108
Ground state (harmonic oscillator),
  15 ff., 22
Group theory, 275 ff.
  characterization of normal modes,
    287 ff.
  normal mode distribution, 288 ff.
  selection rules, 291 ff.
  symmetry reduction, 293 ff.

Halocarbon (mulling agent), 145 f.
Harmonic oscillator, 12 ff., 15 ff., 20,
  261 ff.
  classical, 12 ff.
  energy levels, 15 ff.
  quantum-mechanical, 14 ff.
  selection rule, 20 f.
Heat capacity (of detectors), 63
Hexane (solvent), 99 f.

High-pressure vapor cells, 129
High-temperature cells, 252 ff.
Hooke's law, 12 f.
"Hot" bands, 21 f., 26
Hunting of servo system, 76, 80

"I_0" (100% transmission), 65, 68 ff., 84, 85, 157 f., 162 f., 200, 223
 compensation of, 205 f.
 double-beam spectrometers, 68 ff., 84, 85, 167 ff.
 quantitative analysis, 157 ff., 162 f., 167 ff., 200, 223
 single-beam spectrometers, 65 f., 162 ff.
Index of refraction, see Refractive index
Infrared radiation (see also Radiation), 1 ff., 6
 polarized, 245 ff.
Intensity, baseline, 165 ff.
 Beer's law, 156 ff., 179 f., 197 ff.
 calibration, 86, 163 f., 184, 197 ff.
 "cell-in-cell-out," 161 ff.
 integrated intensity, 196 ff.
 measurement, 197 ff.
 quantitative analysis, 200 ff.
 "peak height," 160 f., 202 f.
 quantitative analysis, see Quantitative analysis
 theoretical significance, 21, 268 ff.
 transference of data, 180 f., 196 f., 202
Interference fringes, see Fringes
Intermolecular effects in quantitative analysis, 174 ff.
Internal standards, 145, 194 ff.

Johnson noise, see Noise

KBr, see Potassium bromide
KBr disk, see Pressed disk
Kinetic energy, 13 f., 260 f., 264 f.
KRS-5, 10

Lens, chromatic aberration, 11, 234
 microscope, 233 f.
LiF, see Lithium fluoride
Light, see Radiation
Light attenuator, 66 ff., 79 ff., 252
Light by-pass, 82
Linear molecules, 24 f., 301 f.

Liquid, cells, 94 ff., 97, 113 ff.
 films, 130 ff.
 solution, see Solution
Lithium fluoride prisms, 41
Littrow mirror, 34, 37 f.
L matrix, 266
Long-path cells (vapor), 230 ff., 238
Lorentzian bands, 177 ff.
 integrated intensity, 199
 quantitative analysis, 167, 177 ff.
Low I_0 (compensation), 205 ff.
Low-temperature cells, 250 ff.

Mass (relation to frequency), 13, 17 f., 260 f., 264 f.
Methylene chloride (solvent), 99, 101, 106, 208 ff.
Microcells, 233, 237 ff.
Microsamples, 232 ff.
Microscopes, see Beam condensers
Microwave radiation, 1, 6
Minimum detectable power, 51, 62
Minimum deviation (prisms), 34
Mirrors, 11
 collimator, 32 f.
 detector, 36 f.
 ellipsoid, 36 f.
 off-axis ellipsoid, 234 f.
 off-axis paraboloid, 33
 source, 32
 spherical, 32
Molecular vibrations (see also Vibrations), 17 ff., 24 ff., 258 ff.
 diatomic molecules, 17 f.
 polyatomic molecules, 24 ff., 258 ff.
Moment of inertia (effect on band contours), 298 ff.
Monochromator (see also specific parts, as Collimator), 29 ff., 72 ff.
 block diagram, 30
 construction, 29 ff.
 double, 72 ff.
 equations, 46 f., 49 ff.
 grating, 41 ff., 47
 performance, 46 ff.
 prism, 39 ff., 47
 quality, 46 ff.
Mulls, 141 ff.
 application to solid samples, 141 ff.
 compared to pressed disks, 151 ff.

Mulls, Fluorolube, 145 f.
  Nujol, 141, 145 f.
  preparation, 142 ff.
  theory, 135 ff.
Multicomponent analysis, 181 ff.
  graphical methods, 185 f.
  limitations, 187 f.
  linear equations, 184 f.

NaCl, *see* Sodium Chloride
Negative anharmonicity, 23
Nernst glower, 31
Nitromethane (solvent), 99, 103
Noise, 61 ff., 76 ff., 83 ff., 170 ff., 203,
  205 ff., 208 ff., 224 f.
  compensated spectra, 205 ff., 208 ff.,
    224
  detector, 61 ff., 76, 78
  effect on spectrum, 76 ff., 83 ff., 205 ff.,
    208 ff.
  Johnson noise, 62, 76, 78
  limitations, 51, 62, 76 ff., 83 f.
  quantitative analysis, 170 ff., 203,
    224 f.
  relation to:
    gain, 76 ff., 83 f.
    slit width, 77 ff., 83 ff.
    time constant, 78 f., 83 f.
    voltage, 61 f., 76, 78
Normal coordinates, 25, 265 ff.
  Cartesian representation, 267 ff.
  definition, 266
  determination, 266 ff.
  intensity, 268 ff.
  L matrix, 266
  potential energy as function of, 25,
    267
Normal vibration, 262 ff., 268 ff.
  definition, 262, 265
  frequency, 261 f., 265
  potential energy, 25, 259 ff.
  representation (group theory), 287 ff.
  symmetry species and band contours,
    301 ff.
Nujol mull, *see* Mulls

Oblate symmetric top, 304 ff.
Off-axis ellipse (beam condenser), 234 f.
Off-axis paraboloid, 33

Operation of spectrometer, 82 ff.,
  161 ff., 165 ff., 205 ff.
Optical density, *see* Absorbance
Optical-null double-beam spectrometer,
  66 ff., 75 ff., 88, 165 ff., 173, 204 ff.
Optics, *see* specific subjects, as Mono-
  chromator, Prism
Optimum transmission (quantitative
  analysis), 171 f., 224 f.
Order of diffraction, 43 ff.
Ordinate expansion, 88, 163, 216, 218,
  220 ff.
Overshoot, 80 f., 85
Overtones, 22 ff., 293

Paraboloid, 33
"Parallel" band, 302, 304
P branch, 299 ff.
"Peak height," 160 f., 202 f., 219 ff.
"Perpendicular" band, 302 f., 305 f.
Photoconductive detector, 56
Photometry, 63 ff., 81 f., 86, 88, 161 ff.,
  165 ff., 219 ff., 251 f.
  double-beam, 66 ff., 81 f., 165 ff.,
    204 ff.
  optical-null, 66 ff., 81 f., 165 ff., 204 ff.
  ratio-recording, 70 ff.
  single-beam, 64 ff., 161 ff.
Pitch lap (polishing), 109 ff.
Planck's constant, 4
Planck's law of blackbody radiation,
  7 ff., 52 ff.
Plastics and resins (sample prepara-
  tion), 132 ff.
Pneumatic detector, 58 f.
Point groups, 277 ff.
  character tables, 281 ff.
Polarized infrared radiation, 245 ff.
Polishing windows, 108 ff.
Polyatomic molecules, number of funda-
  mentals, 24
  theory of spectra, 258 ff.
Polymers, 132 ff.
Polymorphism, 139 ff., 152 f.
Potassium bromide prisms, 10, 41
Potassium bromide windows, 10
  preparation, 112
Potential energy (*see also* Force con-
  stant), 13 f., 23, 25, 259 ff.
  distribution, 267

Potential energy (*see also* Force constant), function of normal coordinate, 25, 266 f.
relation to frequency, 13 f., 16, 261 ff.
Precision in quantitative analysis, 170 ff., 187 ff., 202 f., 219 ff.
Pressed disk, 148 ff.
application to solid samples, 148 ff.
compared to mulls, 151 ff.
preparation, 148 ff.
theory, 135 ff.
Pressure, effect on band shapes, 126 f.
high pressure cells, 128 ff.
Prism, 10 f., 34, 39 ff., 44 ff., 50 ff., 63 ff., 72 ff.
cutoff, 40 f.
fore-prism, 44, 72 f.
materials, 10, 40 ff.
minimum deviation, 34
monochromator, 34, 39 ff., 63 ff.
refraction by, 39 ff.
refractive index, 39 ff.
resolving power, 39, 50 ff.
Prolate symmetric tops, 303 ff.
Propylene dibromide (spectrometer testing), 86 f.

Q branch, 302 f., 304, 306 ff., 308 ff.
Quality of monochromator, 46 ff.
Quantitative analysis, 155 ff., 219 ff.
accuracy and precision, 170 ff., 187 ff., 202 f., 219 ff.
baseline, 165 ff., 222 f.
best method, 173 f., 202 f., 222 ff.
calibration, 163 f., 184, 197 ff., 222 f.
"cell-in-cell-out," 161 ff.
difference spectra, 219 ff.
elementary, 161 ff.
errors, 170 ff., 174 ff., 187 ff.
graphical methods, 181, 185 ff., 193
integrated absorbance, 196 ff.
multicomponent, 181 ff.
noise limitation, 62, 170 ff., 203, 224 f.
"peak-height," 160 ff., 202
ratio methods, 191 ff.
reference standards, 163 f., 222 f.
slit width, 163, 203, 205 ff., 208 ff., 219 ff.
solid state, 141, 145, 152 f., 196
total functional group, 201 f.

Quantitative analysis, without reference standards, 188 ff.
Quantum (of light), 3 f., 19 f.
Quantum-mechanical harmonic oscillator, 15 ff.
Quantum theory, 14 ff.
Quartz, 10, 41

Radiation, blackbody, 7 ff., 53
electric vector, 2, 18 f., 245 ff.
electromagnetic, 1 ff., 6 f.
energy of, 3 f.
frequency, 3
infrared, 1 ff.
interaction with matter, 6, 18 ff.
microwave, 1, 6
polarized, 245 ff.
power, 49 ff., 61
quantization, 3 f.
scattered, 54 f., 73, 135 ff., 159 f., 162 f.
ultraviolet, 6
velocity, 3
visible, 6
wavelength, 2 f.
Ratio methods (quantitative analysis), 191 ff.
Ratio-recording double-beam spectrometer, 70 ff.
Rayleigh scattering (by crystalline particles), 136 f.
R branch, 299 ff.
Rectifier (ac signal demodulator), 61, 75
Reduced mass, 17 f.
Reduction of symmetry, 293 ff.
Reference beam, compensated spectra, 105 ff, 204 ff.
double-beam spectrometer, 66 ff., 204 ff.
Reference-beam attenuator, 66 ff., 79 ff., 252
Reference spectrum, 161 ff., 181, 184, 222 f.
Reflection (*see also* Mirrors), 11
crystalline particles, 136
gratings, 41 ff.
polarization (Brewster angle), 245 f.
Refraction (*see also* Prism), 39 ff.
crystalline particles, 135 f.

Refractive index, ATR, 238 ff.
   Christiansen effect, 137 ff.
   crystalline particles, 135 ff.
   function of wavelength, 39 ff., 138
   prisms, 39 ff.
   sodium chloride, 40
Representation (group theory), 280 ff.
Resins, 132 ff.
Resolution, 46 ff., 49 ff., 77 ff., 83 f.,
   122 ff., 177 ff., 197 ff.
   effect on band shapes, 48, 177 ff.
   energy limited, 51
   factors affecting, 46 ff., 77 ff., 83 f.
   monochromator, 46 ff.
   slit width, 46 ff., 77 ff., 83 f.
Resolving power, 46 ff.
   grating, 47
   prism, 39, 47
Rocksalt, see Sodium chloride
Rotation, effect on vibrational spectra,
   297 ff.
   energy levels, 298 ff.
   quantization, 298 ff.
   selection rules, 299, 302, 304 ff.
Rotation-vibration bands, 297 ff.

Sample beam (double-beam spectrometer), 66 ff., 204 ff.
Sample preparation, 92 ff., 204 ff.
   crystalline solids, 135 ff.
   liquids, 130 ff.
   microsamples, 233 ff.
   plastics and resins, 132 ff.
   solutions, 92 ff.
   vapors, 122 ff.
Scale expansion, 88, 216, 218, 220 f.
Scan (of spectrum), 37 f., 78 f., 83, 85,
   89, 165 ff.
Scattered light, in monochromators,
   54 f., 73
   quantitative analysis, 159 f., 162 f.
Scattering by crystalline particles,
   135 ff.
Schroedinger equation, 15
Schwartzchild microscope, 235 f.
Secular equation, 259 ff.
Selection rules, dipole moment change,
   18 f.
   harmonic oscillator, 20 f.
   rotation, 299, 302, 304 ff.

Selection rules, symmetry, 18 f., 291 ff.
Sensitivity limits, compensated spectra,
   216 ff.
   quantitative analysis, 170 ff., 187 ff.,
   202 f., 219 ff.
Servo system, 75 ff., 85, 89 f., 205 ff.
   damping, 81
   dead, 79 ff., 85, 105 ff., 205, 208 ff.
   drift, 81 f., 85
   energy, 76 f., 79 ff., 85, 90, 205 f., 208 ff.
   hunting (oscillation), 76, 80, 85, 209 ff.
   loop, 70, 71, 76
   motor, 67 f., 75 f., 78, 89
   overshoot, 80 f., 85
   programming (compensated spectra),
   90, 205 f., 208 ff.
   response, 76 f., 79 ff., 85, 90, 205 f.,
   208 ff.
Signal-to-noise ratio, 77 ff., 172 ff., 203,
   224 f.
   difference spectra, 224 f.
   quantitative analysis, 172 ff., 203,
   224 f.
Silver chloride, polarizer, 247 f.
   sample films, 131, 134
   windows, 11, 112 f., 131, 134
Single-beam spectrometer, 64 ff., 88,
   161 ff., 243 f.
   "cell-in-cell-out" method, 161 ff.
   compared to double-beam spectrometer, 65 f., 69 f., 164 ff.
   limitations and uses, 65 f., 69 f., 161 ff.
   principle, 64 ff.
   quantitative analysis, 161 ff.
Single-double-beam interchange, 88
Slit, 35 f., 46 ff., 49 ff., 52 ff.
   cam, 53
   curvature, 36
   function in monochromator, 35 f.
   height, aberrations of, 36, 51
   ratio to focal length, 51
   program for blackbody distribution,
   52 ff.
Slit function (Gaussian), 177 ff.
Slit-limiting term (resolving power),
   46 f., 50
Slit width (see also Spectral slit width),
   Beer's law failure, 177 ff.
   compensated spectra, 205 f., 208 ff.
   automatic programming, 90, 213 ff.

Slit width (*see also* Spectral slit width), effect on band shape, 177 ff.
monochromator energy, 49 ff.
noise, 77 f., 83, 172 ff., 203, 205 f., 208 ff., 219 ff.
quantitative analysis, 163, 172 ff., 203, 219 ff.
resolution, 46 ff., 77 f., 83 f., 177 ff., 203, 205 f., 208 ff.
servo energy, 77, 79 ff., 90, 172 ff., 205 f., 208 ff.
Sodium chloride prism, 10, 40 f.
Sodium chloride windows, 10
preparation, 107 ff.
Solid angle, 49
Solid state, *see* Crystalline solids
Solubility (in infrared transmitting solvents), 94, 96, 97, 99 ff.
Solution technique, 92 ff.
advantages, 93 ff.
CCl_4-CS_2, 94 ff.
cells, 107 ff.
solvents, 94 ff.
Solvent, absorption by, 94 ff.
infrared transmitting, 94 ff.
polymers, 133 f.
relation to cell length and concentration, 94 ff.
Solvent compensation, 105 ff., 208 ff
Source, 29 ff.
Globar, 30 f.
mirror, 32
Nernst glower, 31
nichrome wire, 31
optics, 32
Special cells, *see* Cells
Special techniques, 204 ff.
Spectral slitwidth, 47, 177 ff.
Beer's law, 177 ff.
effect on band shape, 177 ff.
Gaussian function, 177 ff.
Spectrometer (*see also* specific uses, as Quantitative analysis, Compensated spectra), construction, 29 ff., 63 ff., 75 ff.
operation, 75 ff.
optics, 29 ff.
testing, 84 ff.
types, 63 ff.

Speed of light (relation to frequency and wavelength), 3
Speed suppression, 89
Spherical aberration, 32
Spherical mirror, 32
Square-wave signal, 59 f., 63
Standard spectrum, quantitative analysis, 161 ff., 181, 184, 186, 192 f., 200 ff., 222 f.
spectrometer testing, 86 f.
"Symmetric top," 303 ff.
Symmetry, assignment of normal modes, 287 ff., 301 ff.
band contours, 301 ff.
character tables, 281 ff.
group theory, 276 ff.
point groups, 277 ff.
reduction, 293 ff.
representation, 280 ff.
secular equation factoring, 272 f
selection rules, 19, 291 ff.

$\% \ T \ = \ I/I_0$, *see* Transmission
Temperature-measuring cells, 248 ff.
Testing spectrometers, 84 ff.
Theory, detector, 61 ff.
energy limited spectrometer, 46 ff., 61 ff.
group theory, 276 ff.
harmonic oscillator, 12 ff., 261 ff.
infrared spectra of polyatomic molecules, 24 ff., 258 ff.
molecular vibrations, diatomic, 17
polyatomic, 24 ff., 258 ff.
quantum, 14 ff.
rotation-vibration bands, 297 ff.
Thermocouple detector, 57
Time constant, 62, 76, 78 f., 83, 173, 205, 209, 218 f.
band pass, 62, 76, 78 f.
noise, 62, 76, 78 f., 83, 172 f., 205, 209
recording time, 78 f., 83, 89, 205, 209, 218 f.
Trace analysis, compensated spectra, 215 f.
micro samples, 230 ff.
Transmission, 100%, *see* I_0
0%, *see* Zero
and absorbance, 158 ff., 171 ff., 224 ff.
Beer's law, 156 ff.

Transmission, compensated spectra, 105 ff., 204 ff.
crystalline particles, 135 ff.
cutoff, 10, 40 f.
measurement, double-beam spectrometer, 67 ff., 165 ff.
single-beam spectrometer, 65 f., 161 ff.
monochromator, 49 ff.
optimum value in quantitative analysis, 171 f., 224 f.
photometry, 65 ff., 161 ff., 165 ff.
quantitative analysis, 156 ff., 161 ff., 165 ff., 171 ff., 219 ff.
sample, 161 ff., 165 ff., 205 ff., 208 ff.
solvents, 94 ff., 208 ff.
windows, 10 f.

Ultraviolet radiation, 6
Units in spectroscopy, 5
Urey-Bradley force field, 274 f.

Vacuum systems, 128 f.
Valence coordinates, 263 ff.
Vapor phase, 122 ff.
cells, 127 ff., 230 f., 238
complications in spectrum, 122 ff.
rotation-vibration bands, 122 ff., 297 ff.
sample preparation, 127 ff.
Variable-length cells, 215
Velocity of light (relation to frequency and wavelength), 3
Vibration, anharmonic, 22 ff., 25 f.
classical, 12 ff.
diatomic molecules, 17
energy levels, 14, 15 ff., 20 f., 23, 25
harmonic, 12 ff., 15 ff.
polyatomic molecules, 24 ff., 259 ff.
quantization, 15 f.
Visible radiation, 1, 6
Voltage sensitivity (detectors), 61 f.

Volts-per-unit-attenuator-displacement, 76, 77, 79 ff., 85, 90, 205 f., 208 ff.
compensated spectra, 105 ff., 205 f., 208 ff.

Water, cutoff, 226
transmission, 226 f.
vapor in spectrometer, 65 f., 69, 80
Water solutions, 225 ff.
analytical applications, 228 ff.
biological applications, 228 f.
cells, 226
Wavelength (see also Frequency), 2 ff., 5
cam, 36 f.
grating orders, 42 ff.
interference, see Fringes
radiation (and relation to other properties), 2 ff.
resolution, 46 ff., 51 ff., 78, 124, 177 ff.
Wave nature of light, 1, 4
Wave number (waves per centimeter), 5
Wien displacement law, 9, 52
Windows, 10 f., 107 ff., 226, 243 f.
cleaning, 107 ff., 115
cleaving, 107 f., 112
cutoff, 10 f.
flatness, 111 f.
grinding, 108
material, 10 f.
polishing, 108 ff.
transmission, 10 f.

Zero-point energy, 16
Zero % transmission, definition, 81 f., 86, 162, 252
measurement, 86, 162
quantitative analysis, 162
scattered light, 54, 86, 162
spectrometer, 81 f., 86